# OVERVIEW

# OVERVIEW

## A Life-Long Adventure in Aerial Photography

Brigadier General George W. Goddard,
USAF (Ret.)
*with*
DeWitt S. Copp

DOUBLEDAY & COMPANY, INC., GARDEN CITY, NEW YORK
1969

# CONTENTS

To the military and civilian personnel
who gave me their support over the years
and
to my wife Elizabeth and daughter Diane

# INTRODUCTION

No one can say how much mankind came to owe to the technological art of aerial photography in the explosive autumn of 1962. Certainly it can be said that without the aerial camera, history would read differently today, or perhaps not at all. Political chicanery on the part of the Soviets; preconceived beliefs on the part of our top leaders, supported by an inaccurate intelligence evaluation, set the stage for the hair-trigger confrontation.

On September 4, 1962 the Soviet Ambassador, Anatoliy Dobrynin, assured the U. S. Attorney General, Robert F. Kennedy, that his country had no intention of placing ground to ground missiles or offensive weapons in Cuba.

While President Kennedy issued a public statement, warning that we would not tolerate any kind of offensive weapons in Cuba, neither he nor anyone close to him in his administration believed the Russians would make such a move. As Robert Kennedy was to write: "No official with the Government had ever suggested to President Kennedy that the Russian build up in Cuba would include missiles."[1]

Further, between September 4 and October 14 the Soviets officially, through the written and spoken word, continued to give the most solemn assurances that they were not up to any nuclear hanky-panky. The CIA's Board of National Intelligence Estimates confirmed these assurances.[2]

[1] Robert Kennedy, "The Thirteen Days of Crises," *The Washington Post,* p. B1.
[2] Stewart Alsop, *The Center.* (New York: Harper & Row, Inc.), p. 216.

On the other hand, a growing volume of "raw" intelligence information, coming out of Cuba gave strong indications that the missiles were there. Senator Kenneth B. Keating of New York was one of a handful of Congressmen who cried alarm. But his information, like all the rest, was based primarily on reports from agents and eyewitness accounts. And so, although the type of evidence normally associated with intelligence gathering piled up in and out of the Administration, neither the President nor his top advisers were about to buy it.

Thanks to aerial photography, proof of the real Soviet intent was finally obtained, however, on October 14, 1962, and it was due to two factors. First, the CIA, despite its NIE evaluations, had been puzzled over the motivation for the large Soviet military build-up in Cuba and was therefore anxious to overfly the island and keep a photographic eye on it. Second, once this had been done, CIA photointerpreters were able to establish at once what the Soviets were up to although others could not. When the first batch of photographs taken by the U-2 were shown to the President and his staff, they had to take the word of Arthur C. Lundahl, the country's foremost photointerpreter, that the missiles were really there. President Kennedy studied the pictures with a big magnifying glass and could see nothing provocative in them. But on the strength of Lundahl's expertise he gave orders for all of Cuba to be photographed on a crash basis.

From a strategic point of view, John A. McCone, then Director of CIA, was to say later: "War over Cuba was avoided because every weapons system was correctly indentified in time to give the President and his policy advisers time to think, to make a rational estimate of the situation and to devise means of dealing with it with a maximum chance of success and a minimum risk of global war."[3]

In the tense and dramatic days that followed the President's public announcement of October 22, 1962, it was aerial photographic proof of the missiles that convinced the whole world that

[3] *Ibid.,* p. 207.

the Soviets, using a smoke-screen of lies, were attempting to establish a nuclear foothold in Cuba.

No other proof could have been more irrefutable, and no other proof would have been acceptable to many among ourselves, our allies, and, of course, those unsympathetic to us. The UN could not debate away the iron reality of the aerial photographs, nor could the world.

The aerial camera, having found the missiles, then supplied additional proof of their dismantling, crating, transporting from site to ship, loading, and voyage back to the Soviet Union. Involved in these hazardous missions besides U-2 pilots, one of whom was shot down and killed, were low-flying reconnaissance pilots of the Air Force and Navy.[4]

Although at the time of the crisis, Brigadier General George W. Goddard had been retired from the Air Force for nearly ten years, he had never been retired from the art of aerial photography. Thus when the Staff of the Air Force found that it was having trouble with clarity of its low-level photographs, it was natural for General Curtis LeMay, Chief of Staff of the Air Force, to turn to General Goddard for help and to request that he act as a consultant for the duration of the ordeal.

A meeting at the Pentagon swiftly followed. Attending besides LeMay were Under Secretary of the Air Force Joseph V. Charyk, General Gabriel P. Disosway, on the air staff, scientists from Secretary Robert S. McNamara's office, and a number of other officers. General Goddard examined the photographs laid out on a board table, and then quickly informed the assembled what was wrong.

"It's all in the camera you're using. You can't use a shutter camera for this kind of low-level mission, you'll get distortion and blur every time. You've got to use the stereo continuous strip camera. It stops motion no matter how fast you fly, and you'll be able to view the results three dimensionally."

The General not only informed the troubled group of officials

[4] Major Robert Anderson was shot down over Cuba by a SAM missile on October 24, 1962.

how to get sharp, low level photographs, he told them where models of the particular camera could be found gathering dust, and how to go about installing one in an F-101 Voodoo reconnaissance aircraft. And if he'd thought there was any chance of getting approval he would have volunteered to fly the mission himself. Since he had pioneered in the development of the stereo-strip camera and knew it to be at the time the most efficient of all low-level high-speed reconnaissance cameras, he was understandably disturbed that it had not been put into use over Cuba at the outset.

When President Kennedy saw the results of the three dimensional stereo photographs taken by the strip camera he didn't have to take any expert's word for what he was looking at. Now he could see with his own eyes stereoscopically what actually lay between the leaves of the trees. He was so impressed that he asked that the film be run a second time. Of the more than 125 miles of photographic footage recorded over Cuba during the crisis, the President expressed particular interest in the one picture showing the missiles in great detail on their launching sites. The jacket of this book is taken from that same film.

General Goddard's 1962 assist to the missile crisis is but a fragment of his total contribution. That he was called on by men in power for assistance in a moment of peril is a measure of how highly his knowledge is regarded.

In November 1968, the General, a guest, and three of his former subordinates met for lunch at the Army-Navy Club in Washington, D.C. One of the three he had recruited off an Illinois farm in the early thirties to attend the Aerial Photographic School then at Chanute Field. The second he had talked into leaving the Fairchild Company to enter Air Corps reconnaissance, and the third, a West Point graduate, had worked under him at the Wright Field Photographic Laboratory and later at NATO. The three were representative of literally hundreds who either worked for or with the General, or at some point had come within his canny touch.

By pure coincidence at the top of the luncheon menu was a daily historical citation reading:

FIRST SUCCESSFUL NIGHT PHOTOGRAPHY BY AIRPLANE ACCOMPLISHED BY LT. GEORGE W. GODDARD USA OVER ROCHESTER NEW YORK USING 50 LB MAGNESIUM FLARES DROPPED FROM ARMY MARTIN BOMBER. 1925

When it came time to order, the General cracked he thought he might have the 50-pound bomb on the rocks. From there the conversation swirled around the table in a kaleidoscope of reminiscence, mostly laughable. But following the luncheon, after the General had departed, a more serious question was raised:

"Would there be any way to sum up the General's career and his contributions to aerial photography through a single event or episode?"

The answer was immediate and unanimous: "Yes, the Cuban missile crisis."

*It was George Goddard who pioneered long range high altitude photography from the early twenties on. It was George Goddard, who pushed aerial camera development high, low, daylight and dark when no one could have cared less. It was George who fought for the development of the strip camera at the risk of his career and his neck. The cameras in the U-2s, the cameras in the low runs, the clarity, the resolution, the works. There isn't a thing you can say about the missile crisis photographically that isn't traceable in part to his efforts. And even more than that there isn't much you can say about aerial photography looking at the earth or into space that isn't in someway connected to his name.*

Brigadier General George W. Goddard, USAF (Ret.) pioneer inventor, innovator, a leader whose spirit and enthusiasm inspired many, and whose ideas contributed to the peace and to the knowledge of mankind . . . This is his story.

D.S.C.

# PART I

---◆---

## *The Mitchell Era*

# 1

It has often been said that women and whiskey make a potent mixture. I confess that in my own case this stimulating combination actually supplied the fuel that launched my career in aviation. The woman in the picture was Ruth Law, who in the summer of 1916 was billed as America's most daring female flier. One bright July day she came to Chicago's Grand Park on a Liberty Bond drive to thrill us groundlings with an exhibition of stunt flying.

I attended the event with friends from the nearby Art Institute plus thousands of other Chicagoans, and for most of us this was the first time we had seen an aviator of either sex or a flying machine up close. On her head Ruth Law wore a dome-shaped helmet that looked something like a beehive, and although it was a warm day, she was buttoned up in heavy leather coat and gloves. It was hard to tell whether she was pretty or not in those togs. But pretty or not, she certainly knew how to fly her early model Curtiss Pusher. This was not the first Curtiss I had seen, however, for some years earlier as a student at Keuka Institute in Penn Yan, New York, my fellow classmates and I had had the privilege of watching Glenn Curtiss making test runs up and down Keuka Lake. Our professor, I recall, was not amused by the advent of aviation since every time Curtiss flew by, we'd rise en masse and rush to the windows, and the professor was powerless to control us until the daring Mr. Curtiss had made his turn and headed back up the lake to Hammondsport.

My interest in aviation had been tweaked at the time, but now watching Ruth Law put her plane through its paces, diving on the crowd, zooming up into tight turns, executing graceful eights and then dropping down in tight spirals, I was really grabbed. I had two reactions that day: *Hell, if a woman can do that so can I!* and *Where can I learn to fly?*

The answer came little more than a year later, shortly after we entered World War I. At the time I was a staff artist for the Coke and Iron industries, *Coke and Iron Monthly*. The industry magazine was a prestigious publication whose underlying purpose was to get more work out of the many thousand workers. My major assignment was to do safety-first sketches, workmen's sport events, and patriotic cartoons. It was a good job and paid me around $3000 a year, which for a twenty-six-year-old bachelor made life sweet and enjoyable. But there was a war on and when a recruiter from the Corps of Engineers arrived in Chicago, he talked me and some of my artist pals into exchanging the pleasures of civilian life for three months training and first lieutenancies in the Army. So it was in the fall of 1917 that I and about ten others bid farewell to Chicago and boarded a train for New York where our training was to take place.

It was well on in the evening when I entered the club car for a nightcap. For me the car was suddenly empty of all but the slight sandy-haired officer wearing captain's bars and aviator's wings on his breast. I went directly to the seat next to his.

He looked me over and, with a slight smile and soft southern accent, said: "What'll you have?"

"Scotch and soda, thanks, if I get the next round."

"That seems reasonable." He placed the order and looked at me again. "Where are you bound?"

"I'm on my way to New York to join the Corps of Engineers . . . I'm an artist by trade."

"What are you going to do as an artist?" He made the idea sound slightly asinine.

I explained how after three months of training at the New Amsterdam Theatre I'd be an expert in camouflaging and a first lieutenant.

He continued to study me as though there must be something

radically wrong and then taking a gulp of his drink, planked down his glass and said: "I don't see a helluva lot of future in that. Why don't you get into aviation like me?"

"Aviation!"

"Sure, boy, aviation is the coming thing!" He launched into an enthusiastic sales pitch of the wondrous future that lay ahead for the art of powered flight and those who joined the fun. And time, I must say, has proved his predictions anything but fanciful. He concluded his oration with the admission, "When I see a young buck as healthy as you, I get interested. Here, finish that thing so we can have another. Of course, I can't offer you a first lieutenant's commission right off. You'll have to be a second lieutenant first, but you'll take your ground school training at Cornell University, and you'll never have to worry about KP."

A short time later I was positive I could have flown the club car without any assistance from Captain John Gordon, recruiter for the Signal Corps' Aviation Section. In the interim he had convinced me that I must get off the train when it reached Harrisburg, Pennsylvania, and catch another train for Washington. There I was to make contact with a Captain Herbert Jacobi, a key administrative officer in the Aviation Section. Since Gordon had given me his card to present to Jacobi with the notation on the back, *"a good prospect,"* everything would follow in order. Finally as a kind of encore, Gordon produced some excellent, if now slightly blurry, photographs of fighting planes and flying schools. Thus he had me landed cleanly and happily. As the train thundered through the night-darkened Ohio countryside, its whistle cheering me on, I announced to the captain and the world at large, "By God, I am interested in flying and have been ever since I saw Ruth Law!"

Between the time Captain Gordon bade me bon voyage at 6 A.M. the next morning in Harrisburg and my arrival at Cornell University in Ithaca, New York, lay a two week *snafu* (a word unknown in those days) which all but terminated my dreams of flight. On the presentation of Captain Gordon's card to Captain Jacobi, I was assured of being assigned to the U. S. Signal Corps'

School of Military Aeronautics at Cornell. There was, of course, the small formality of enlistment, which took place painlessly enough that very day. But then I was informed that as Private Goddard I would first have to go through a few days' course of military indoctrination at the big Army Reception Center at Fort Slocum, New York. And as Private Goddard I learned very swiftly that sergeants are not inclined to give ear to the eminently reasonable complaints of the lower ranks. Two weeks later, lost in a welter of pots and pans, well experienced in the digging and cleaning of latrines (punishment for having dared to wash my mess kit in the men's washroom rather than follow orders to wash it in a communal kettle of filthy water), I decided I was doomed for the duration unless I took direct action. I might add that the decision to take such action was a kind of solo flight in circumventing a fog bank of Army Regulations and that it was a kind of flying at which when the occasion required, I became singularly adept.

In this particular case, I merely executed a swift disappearing act from the world of pots and pans and got myself to a telephone in New Rochelle where I put in a long-distance call to Captain Jacobi. Jacobi, a lawyer in private life, saw the grave injustice of my plight and got to the nub of the matter at once. As a result, early the next morning, with joy once again in my heart, I journeyed northward to Ithaca and Cornell.

The change was wonderful—no more mess kits, good food, comfortable sleeping quarters—and Ithaca was practically home to me. I had gone to preparatory school in Syracuse and later had left Keuka Institute to become a free-lance illustrator in Rochester. But again there was a hitch or two—one a matter of regulations and the other, a major turning point in my life.

At the time I was not an American citizen, having been born in Tunbridge Wells, Kent, about thirty miles south of London, England. My father George W. Goddard, Sr. was an agent of the Prudential Life Insurance Company and my mother Ellen Le Strange was of French extraction. I was one of eight children, boasting five brothers and two sisters. In 1904 when my father decided to come to America to visit the St. Louis Fair, he asked me if I'd like to come along. On the way we stopped in Syracuse to visit an uncle and aunt. I was fourteen at the time and was having so much fun with my two female cousins and their boy friends that when the day came to go west to St. Louis, I asked if I could remain. Not only did I remain for the summer, but when my father returned to take me back to England, I did some fast talking and the result was that I did not see the land of my birth again for another twenty years.

Of course, once in the U. S. Army, it was necessary for me to become a U.S. citizen, something I had long wanted to do. In filling out the various applications that went with becoming a flying cadet and a citizen, I had listed photography as a hobby.

My artistic talent had developed by natural means. As a freelance, among my clients were a number of Rochester newspapers, commercial firms and the noted Elbert Hubbard of the Roycrofters Press in East Aurora. Hubbard put out a Who's Who in Rochester. In all this work I had found a camera to be a valuable asset. I had an old speed Graflex, and when the need was there, I'd snap the picture. It was the click of that shutter that changed my fortune and once again put an obstacle in the way of my becoming a pilot.

The adjutant of cadets, a major, broke the news to me: "Cadet Goddard, you're a photographer."

"Well, not really, sir. I'm an artist."

"But you take pictures. You own a camera."

"I suppose so, sir." I had no idea what path the major was leading me down, but I sensed it was someplace other than where I wanted to go.

"We're establishing an officer's training school for aerial photographers. We need the right kind of people in it." His glance said I was that kind of people. "It's a vitally new important field in fighting a war. The training course is three months, and you'll be a commissioned officer before most of your fellow cadets finish their pilot training."

"Well, that's fine, sir, but I joined the air service to be an aviator."

"And I promise you you will be . . . some day. But right now we need aerial photographers more than we need pilots."

And so, at that moment with a vast emptiness in my stomach and a reluctance that must have added a foot to my face, I was temporarily grounded.

The adjutant was not exaggerating when he said I was to be a member of the first officer's school to train commanders of aerial photographic sections. It was so much a first that the forty of us who made up the class had to build it. As soon as our British and French instructors arrived on the campus we went to work with hammers and saws and in famous Schoellkopf Hall, we erected and installed sinks, tables, and partitions for laboratory, dark room, and class work. The purpose of the course was to qualify officer graduates for staff duty and command of aerial photographic sections urgently needed in France.

This was the late fall of 1917 and after three years of war, despite the conflict's largely static quality, both sides had come to recognize the value of aerial photography as a new means of reconnaissance to find out what the other fellow was up to. Every two weeks during the course large shipments of current aerial photographs taken by the French, British and American aerial photographic units were shipped to the school at Cornell to be used by the aerial photographic interpretation class of instruction.

An up-to-date map of the entire battlefront from the English Channel to the Swiss border was located on a long, high wall in the classroom. The map showed in great detail the first, second, and third German trench systems, no-man's land and the first, second, and third English, American and French trench systems. Each day the students would interpret the various pictures with the assistance of the French and British instructors who were familiar with the particular areas along the battle lines. The students would then revise the map and bring it up-to-date.

There were two of our ten instructors who were outstanding

not only for their abilities but also their differences. Sergeant Major Haslett of the RAF was a tough little banty rooster, all spit and polish, who had served over the lines in France as an aerial photographer. He knew his business but he was highly critical of what he considered our deplorable lack of discipline and slovenly unmilitary dress. On the other hand, Lieutenant Callier of the French Air Force, equally as experienced as the sergeant, was physically and mentally his opposite. The only thing that was important to the lieutenant was getting the photograph, spit and polish be damned! The two would get into roaring arguments over their respective approaches which always became a battle between the relative merits of British and French photographic methods and achievements over enemy territory. Naturally, we ate up their debates and while Callier's relaxed, slightly disheveled philosophy appealed to us, we admired Haslett's gruff expertise.

Although aerial photography prior to World War I was about as primitive as the aircraft, there had been considerable research and development in the field, particularly with regard to aerial mapping.

In 1906 Captain Theodore Scheimpflug of the Austrian Army invented the first mapping camera. It actually produced photographs using nine lenses and offering eight oblique shots which when combined offered 140 degrees of visual angle. Despite this advance, when war came, none of the European armies had what they considered was a workable aerial camera. The Germans found Scheimpflug's too heavy and complicated. However, they had learned to heat their cameras with electricity which aided performance at high altitudes. And it was not long after the war started that they instituted the practice of photographing the entire Western front every two weeks. In 1917, the Zeiss Corporation brought out a single-lens camera, which first saw use during the critical battle of the Somme. By the end of the war, the Germans were taking about four thousand aerial photographs a day.

The British and the French were not far behind. The British had had some prior experience making aerial maps of Egypt and the Suez Canal zone. Soon after hostilities began, they were turning out a thousand exposures and prints daily. The French were actually the first to try out aerial photography and use the results for military purposes. Cameras designed and engineered in France were later produced in the U.S.

Our entry into the war did not find us totally inexperienced for two reasons—General John J. Pershing's punitive expedition into Mexico in 1916 and the dedication of a man named James Bagley.

When Pershing went south of the border after Pancho Villa, the First Aero Squadron, under the command of Major Benjamin D. Foulois, went along, too, with about fifteen Curtiss Jennys. This was the first time we had used aircraft in any military venture and during it reconnaissance and photographic missions covered some 19,000 miles. But it was due to James Bagley that we entered the war with an aerial mapping camera comparable to that of our allies and the Central powers.

Bagley had been keeping a close watch on German and Austrian photographic developments, and as soon as the U.S. entered the war he went to work as a major with the Engineers of the U. S. Geological Survey team. The result was that he produced a three-lens camera that could not only duplicate the job the Austrian camera would do, plus overlapping photographs in a simple manner, but also the film could be processed and printed swiftly. The major arrived in France about the time we were attending school and his camera was put to immediate use there.

Although studying, interpreting and piecing together aerial photographs demanded a careful eye and quick mind it nevertheless struck some of us as a pretty tame business. We were extremely eager to find out what it was like to be airborne, camera in hand.

Camera in hand was literally it, for the equipment available, a Folmer-Schwing, was hand held, by a pistol grip and weighed from eight to ten pounds. It took four-by-five-inch photos and there were twelve shots in the magazine. The photographer stood in the rear cockpit belted in by a leather strap hooked to the inside cowl. In taking his pictures, he looked through a view finder with cross hairs and fired away at the prescribed area. Optimum altitude ranged from 12,000 to 15,000 feet, and, of course, there was no such thing as an oxygen mask should it be necessary to go higher. When the picture had been taken and the aircraft was back on the ground, the men in the laboratory field units raced against time to get the photos developed. Ten minutes was considered fast work.

That long-sought golden day of first flight did not come for me until after I had graduated in March 1918 and was impatiently waiting overseas assignment and my second lieutenant's commission. In the interim, I had been made an instructor at the school in aerial photointerpretation. This I liked, but flying was what I really wanted.

When the opportunity came it was not really a golden day at all. It was windy and overcast and the pilot who had flown his 80-horsepower Curtiss Jenny down from Baker Field near Rochester was singularly uncommunicative. To him it was old stuff, taking budding aerial photographers on their first hop. To me bundled in a flying suit, wearing helmet and goggles, it was a moment of supreme anticipation and I climbed into the rear cockpit, feeling like young Lancelot off to the wars.

The feeling was of brief duration, and what I remember most about that flight was trying to remain in the cockpit, belt or no belt. I had no idea the air could be so rough and unpleasant. But, I hung on camera and all, the Jenny's OX5 engine racketing in the heavy rush of the slipstream, the plane rising and falling sharply, above the gray underbelly of the clouds, and below me, the pastoral quilt of the ripe summer land sliding away unevenly.

I indicated the assigned area I was to photograph by tapping the pilot on the shoulder and hand-signaling directions. Despite the roughness of the air, I took the required photographs and then, all too soon, we were coming in for a landing and the flight was ended.

That night I wrote to Captain Jacobi again, reminding him that I had joined the Air Service to be a pilot and now that I had graduated from photographer's school, I should like to take flight training. Instead, shortly thereafter on August 8, 1918, I received my commission (five months late) as a second lieutenant in the Army Reserve and was ordered to Langley Field, Virginia. There I was to take a one-month course in the operation of aerial cameras, plus the field operation of photographic trucks and laboratory trailers . . . also, I hoped, some flight training.

Anyone old enough will recall that early Hollywood movies about flying usually opened up with the brash young hero arriving at a flying field, supposedly a novice in the art. There he was strapped into the rear cockpit of a plane whose pilot took him skyward and then put the aircraft through every maneuver in the book and a few that weren't. If after that joy ride the hero had not been violently ill or lost his nerve, or both, he was welcomed into the noble fraternity of airmen.

I was no brash young hero when I arrived at Langley. As recounted, I had only been airborne once. Still, I made it known I wanted to learn to fly. So what followed was standard operating procedure, and no doubt, because it was such common practice, Hollywood later picked up the idea or variations of it. Of course, I didn't know that. I only knew that some of my new officer friends had fixed it up so I could get some real flying time.

The pilot, naturally, was the "hottest" on the field, and once in the air he put the Standard biplane through its wild paces—rolls, spins, Immelmanns, verticle reverses, hammerhead stalls, the works!

We had no parachutes in case he pulled the wings off, which I was sure he was going to do. The brace wires screamed, the earth spun. The earth was above, the sky had fallen. An unseen force was trying to push me through the bottom of the cockpit. I was hanging in the breeze free of the cockpit, and the world was really out of joint. Nothing was as it should be, and everything was better than it could be. At one point the demon at the controls looked back at me and grinned like a wolf. I returned the compliment and he swung around to his work, the smile gone. That was the day I really entered the Air Service. When we got back on the ground, which still was spinning a bit, the pilot pushed up his goggles in the ear-ringing silence and said: "Goddam, boy, I was beginning to feel sick myself! You're gonna make a good aviator."

Kinder words were never spoken.

Between my month's duty at Langley and orders to report to Taliaferro Field near Fort Worth, Texas, my budding career was nearly extinguished. On the way to Texas, where I was to organize and equip three photographic sections, preparatory to taking them to France, I came down with a severe case of flu. This was September 1918 and a serious epidemic was raging throughout the country. Proof of its severity were the coffins lining the Fort Worth railroad platform. Their sight did nothing for my 104 degree temperature, nor did the room given me at the base hospital. It afforded a grandstand view of the morgue where the flow of traffic was constant and heavy. However, I kept my eyes shut as much as I could and in a few days all was right with the world.

In fact, my luck went up the same way my temperature had. The three photo sections I was to organize were located at three different fields—Taliaferro, Carruthers, and Barron. I was provided a Jenny and two pilots, Lieutenants Harvey Montague and Harry Brants. Harvey was for weekdays and Harry was for weekends; this so that I could visit the fields daily. The Jenny had dual controls, and I quickly put both my pilots to work teaching me to fly. In no time I was making pinpoint landings, doing acrobatics, and navigating my way from place to place. Harry Brants was also a gunnery instructor. Under his able tutelage I took that up as well and from the rear cockpit made life hell for prairie dogs.

Naturally, we happy few had to have our earthly diversions and Saturday night in Fort Worth was a beacon of hope and a place of comfort to all us homesick tent dwellers who had been living the long week in a land of Texas black gumbo mud. There were dances and parties and Judge J. H. Barwise, Jr., a well-known lawyer, held open house every weekend. At one such function I met La Rue Sweatman, a real Texas sweetheart and, in the course of the evening, she invited Harry and me to fly over to her home in Ennis for Sunday dinner. She assured us we'd have no trouble landing as there was a good flat field near the ranchhouse, and she'd put a sheet in it as a marker. Harry and I thought it was an excellent idea. In fact, I was sorry he had to come along, and I knew he must have the same idea about me. But we had to make it look legal, so the next morning I called the flight officer on duty and reported we were headed off on a photo reconnaissance mission, which was true enough. Ennis just happened to be on our course.

What we didn't know was that it had rained Saturday night in Ennis. Harry outdid himself on the landing, a beautiful job, just a bit tail high into the appointed field . . . of Texas gumbo mud. All at once I was looking at the mud from an inverted position and it was very close to my face. I did not linger long in my examination as there was always the chance of fire.

La Rue was wonderfully concerned for our safety, and I was rather proud of the fact that I had experienced my first crack-up. The Jenny looked sad upside down in the mud, but aside from a broken prop it appeared to have acquired only a few minor contusions and abrasions. However, because of its plight, instead of staying just for dinner, Harry and I stayed on for three very enjoyable days, La Rue's family practically adopting us. Our delightful sojourn was the result of having to wait for a new propeller and an Accident Board to arrive on the scene.

Since crack-ups, many of them serious, were an everyday occurrence, the three investigators on the Board were not overly investigatory. They were pilots as well as good joes, and if a fellow pilot had had a forced landing because of poor navigation, and he just happened to come down in a pretty girl's sticky backyard and was able to walk away from the crate safely, more power to him . . . or in this case, us.

Harry and I finally bid a reluctant farewell to La Rue and her entire family, including sisters, brothers, uncles, and aunts. New prop spinning, off we went again in a clatter of sound and a cloud of Texas dust.

Wickedness will out. On our return flight, almost in sight of the field, we had a genuine forced landing. When the mechanics had checked the plane over, they failed to spot a crack in the engine sump, acquired no doubt when we'd flipped. As a result, while in flight all the oil had leaked out and the engine bearings had seized. Old Harry, nothing daunted, put us down in a cow pasture right side up this time. It had been quite a date, but we both agreed that La Rue was worth it.

As noted, crack-ups were nothing unusual. The state of the art and the planes we flew had a long way to go and a lot of developing to do. But quite suddenly we began to experience an ugly rash of fatalities and always in the same manner. The Jenny would shed her wings in acrobatic flight.

Anyone who has flown and experienced the loss of a fellow pilot in any kind of crash knows the sickening feeling that bores into you. It's much worse if it's the kind of crash in which the pilot has no chance, and you are witness to the results. This was the way it was until, unannounced, a team of investigators arrived.

Usually when the Jennys crashed they'd burst into flames, and there was no way of telling what had caused the accident. But one did not burn upon impact, and I learned about the investigation when I was sworn to secrecy and the evidence was brought for me to photograph.

The crashes had not been accidents, and this was the first I'd ever heard of sabotage. It was being carried out by two German agents who were employed as mechanics. They had entered the country via Canada, using false identification and in 1917 had enlisted in the Army.

The wings of the Jenny were held to the fuselage in the same manner a door is held to a door jamb by a pair of steel hinge pins. Only in this case, the Germans had been substituting wooden facsimiles. The investigators found a whole foot locker full of them, carefully polished to look like metal. They were strong enough to hold the wings on in normal flight, but under the stress of acrobatics, they snapped.

I photographed the evidence and the two saboteurs were taken into custody. I never heard what happened to them and, so far as I know, this incident has never been reported before, nor are there any records of it in the Archives. A bad business, but it ended well for our pilots.

On November 7, 1918, I received orders to transfer my three photo sections to Hempstead, Long Island, there to prepare for embarkation overseas. I was elated, and four days later the Armistice took me by surprise. One cannot mourn the end of a ghastly war, but after all the training and preparation and anticipation, I couldn't help being disappointed when my orders were canceled.

Fort Worth on Armistice Night reflected the general attitude of public and military alike. It was a real wingdinger of a never-to-be-forgotten celebration with thousands upon thousands of soldiers and civilians whooping and shooting it up in the hopes of a brighter tomorrow.

With regard to my own tomorrow, I had a decision to make. The next morning I reported to the CO, a Major Macauley. I told him I'd gone into the Air Service expecting to become a pilot but "while I can fly anything on this field, sir, officially I'm not a pilot. I don't have my wings."

"Well, dammit, Lieutenant, you've worked hard enough around here so I don't see any problem," replied the major. "Just stay in. With so many wanting to get out, you can pretty well name your own game. You'll have to take written exams for a regular commission, but we'll give you plenty of time to bone up."

During training at Cornell, I had been offered a $5000-a-year job similar to the one I'd held as Art Director on *The Coke and Iron Monthly* in Chicago. This time with the Hog Island Shipbuilding Administration in Delaware. The offer would have gotten me an immediate release from the Air Service, but then I'd had no trouble in rejecting it because I knew at that time I wanted to become a pilot.

My reasons then were basic enough. I'd been bitten by the flying bug, and anyone who has been so bitten knows that it is a passionate, if one-sided, love affair. Further, anyone who has flown an open cockpit plane knows that such flying offers a special kind of magic, a freedom unique unto itself and like no other. And in those days all flying was open cockpit.

At war's end, I wanted to become a rated pilot for the same reasons, but other reasons had been added. I had come to believe that Captain Gordon's predictions about the future of aviation, delivered in that fateful club car, were true, and literally, the sky was the limit. The thought of returning to the life of a commercial artist, no matter how well paid, left me cold. The salary of a second lieutenant wasn't worth talking about, but where else could I get to fly every day at no cost, with Uncle Sam providing the gas and the airplane? To acquire such experience outside the Air Service I would have had to be independently wealthy.

As for my newfound specialty, aerial photography, I was not a scientist, not even particularly mechanical, but ideas crowded my mind and enthusiasm was afire in me. I knew, too, that what I lacked in scientific knowledge, I could gain through study and observation. Just as I could visualize in some measure what lay ahead for powered flight, I could perceive how to make improvements in the primitive art of aerial photography. In short, I had my eye fixed on the sky.

## 2

The Signal Corps' Air Service had entered World War I with a handful of pilots and fewer than 250 planes, none of which could be considered of combat quality. At war's end, the Air Service was two hundred thousand strong and had on order 13,000 planes and 20,000 engines. The orders were swiftly canceled and, in reverting to peacetime strength, the number of officers and men dropped to about 10,000.

In January 1919 plans to establish a postwar Air Service strength of 24,000 officers and men had to be canceled because Congress would only appropriate approximately a third of the required funds. In so doing the legislators declared not a penny was available to buy new aircraft. This approach all but destroyed the country's budding aircraft industry.

Even though the understandable, if not enlightened, parsimony of Congress cut military aviation to the bone at the time, there was another factor that whittled us down and this was the desire on the part of most pilots in the service to return to civilian life. Few could see anything but a very hazardous future in flying. Most of the officers were professional men wishing to return to their professions. Many were married and their wives wanted them on the ground, safe and sound. As for the injection of new blood, there were very few cadets graduating from West Point who looked upon flying as a chosen specialty; the Corps of Engineers was the crème de la crème and the cavalry and infantry followed close behind.

The Air Service showed its need by writing us all letters, selling the glories of a flying career. Since I'd already made up my mind such letters were unnecessary but they made little mileage with most, nor did the efforts of various base COs who did everything they could to stimulate continued interest in aviation. This worked in my favor, too, for a part of Major Macauley's sales campaign was to assign me to fly around West Texas, photographing likely locations for landing fields. Thus I added to my rear-seat flying time and launched my own campaign of selling the Air Service to the press.

Several weeks after the Armistice, orders came for me to report to Carlstrom Field in Arcadia, Florida. Since Carlstrom was a pilot training school, I thought my lucky day had finally arrived.

Upon reporting at Carlstrom, I was assigned as commanding officer of the photographic section, which didn't consist of much more than a dark room, a specially equipped photographic Jenny, and a pilot. My job was much the same as it had been at Taliaferro—to fly around Florida photographing possible landing sites, as well as making a few mosaics of principal cities throughout the state.

About this time we began receiving more advanced aircraft than Jennys and Thomas Morse single seaters. One of these was the Le Père, a two-seater biplane.

Unlike the DH-4, which had the gas tank between the pilot and observer, the Le Père had its in front of the pilot. Unfortunately, there were only about a dozen Le Pères off the production line at the Armistice and so to fly one was a rarity. As to the DH-4s, there were several thousand on hand and, for a number of years after the war, one could crack up a DH-4 and, if he walked away from the wreck, simply call the supply depot and order a new one.

While I was gaining flying experience in all these aircraft, I was also at work examining ways to make improvements in existing aerial photographic equipment. Early in March 1919 I had begun putting together a special camera mount to be used in the installation of my modification of a K-1 Folmer Schwing camera in a Thomas Morse scout. Within the mount I had utilized four tennis balls which practically eliminated vibration and made it shockproof. My modification of the camera made it possible for the pilot to see his target through a special view finder positioned in the cockpit so that he could automatically photograph the target by pressing a button on the control stick.

On a day whose memory will never fade, I had, with the assistance of two mechanics, just placed the camera on the plane's undercarriage and climbed into the cockpit. I was bent over and out of sight when I heard a voice ask, "Are you Lieutenant Goddard?"

Something about that voice made my head come up fast. There standing along side of the fuselage was the first general I had ever seen in the flesh. He was snappily dressed, wearing the high uncomfortable military collar of the day. But in this case, it was not the uniform that made the man. The intense, very direct, brown eyes that appraised me were set in a lean handsome face, mature but youthful and full of energy.

Even before I gulped, "Yes, sir," I knew who he was.

"What are you doing there? I'm General Mitchell."

The name and fame of Brigadier General "Billy" Mitchell were already legion in the Air Service, and in about no time at all I understood why. He was genuinely interested in what I was doing, and as I explained my efforts, his interest and enthusiasm grew. He asked the questions in a rather high-pitched slightly twangy voice, and I supplied the answers, climbing out of the cockpit, crawling under the plane with him.

In his company were the CO, a Major Duncan, and Lieutenant Colonel Edward Steichen. Steichen, then on Mitchell's staff and in charge of all aerial photographic activities, was a long gaunt man with a manner that for some reason reminded me of Abraham Lincoln. With his photographic knowledge, plus what he had seen in France, he was, of course, a prime booster of aerial photography and was later to become recognized as one of the world's great photographers. But then, unknown to me at the time, Billy Mitchell was also a booster of aerial photography. As far back as 1904 he had conducted experiments with cameras attached to kites.

After I finished my explanation he said, "I'd heard about you, Goddard. You don't belong here. You belong at McCook—the idea factory where this sort of work goes on."

Steichen grinned, quickly seconding the motion, and right then and there the decision was made to ship me to McCook Field in Dayton, Ohio, where I would be assigned as Director of Aerial Photographic Research and Development.

Billy Mitchell, as Assistant Chief of the Air Service, was never a man to delay action once he'd made a decision. In those days whatever he wanted he pretty well got, and it was very unusual if anyone talked him out of a chosen course of action. That he saw and grasped the vital necessity of aerial reconnaissance was simply a measure of his total visionary ability to see and grasp all the facets embodied in the use of aircraft, both military and civilian.

However, aside from himself and a handful of subordinates like Steichen, no one in the Air Service gave a tin nickel for the advancement of aerial photography. The young eagles who had come back from France were veteran fighter and bomber pilots and could only think in terms of better fighters and better bombers. Furthermore, neither the infantry nor the cavalry understood the value of photography. The cavalry thought reconnaissance was its job and the science of photoreconnaissance was something too highfalutin and alien for the man on horseback to accept. In fact, it's safe to say that while the U. S. Army cared about reconnaissance, it cared very little about reconnaissance from the air, particularly since the war was over. In any age few men are gifted with the ability to project the new and relatively untried over techniques and methods that have been found usable for centuries. Billy Mitchell was one of these few.

My reaction to the sudden promotion in title, if not in rank, was mixed. Here I was just about ready to begin ground school and become an officially rated pilot, and once more the chance to get my wings was eluding me. That evening I nearly went through the routine of making a call to Captain Jacobi, but fortunately, over a beer or two, Major Duncan and some of my fellow officers prevailed upon me to keep my feet on the ground even if my head was stuck in the clouds.

They pointed out, quite rightly, that for me to decline the honor to go to McCook—and it was an honor—would not be very intelligent. Billy Mitchell was the voice of authority in the Air Service even though he was subordinate to its Chief, Major General Charles T. Menoher—former commander of the 42nd (Rainbow) Division in France—an infantryman who had never flown. Since I was determined to push the advancement of aerial photography, what better sponsor could I have behind me than General Mitchell? It suddenly dawned on me that my luck was running well, and instead of drowning my sorrows, I ordered another round and we celebrated the event.

McCook Field was located between the Miami and Mad rivers almost in the geographic center of Dayton, Ohio, where on hot summer days main street often became the extension of the north-south sod runway. Established in October 1917, it was originally known as North Field, its name changed in memory of the "Fighting McCooks," all of whom were Civil War heroes. McCook Field's purpose was to design and test aircraft, aircraft engines, and aircraft ordnance. Despite the Field's affinity for low lying winter fog, its site was chosen because of the general proximity to the major automotive industries whose job it would be to manufacture the Liberty engine.

The man most responsible for the establishing of McCook was Colonel Jesse Vincent, who had been chief engineer of the Packard Company.

In early 1917, a French and British mission came to the U.S. to see what we could provide in the way of aircraft engines. Both missions had more than thirty different models for which they wished to be supplied, and Vincent realized that unless the effort was organized and directed from a central point, things would get out of control. He proposed the creation of a "mammoth engineering division" and given the authority to do so, set up shop on October 14, 1917.

Sadly enough the testing of the first Liberty engine at South Field, Dayton, in May 1918, ended in a crash in which both pilots were killed. It was not the fault of the engine. The pilots, Major Oscar Brindley and Lieutenant Colonel Henry J. Damm, had removed its spark plugs and replaced them with new plugs, forgetfully leaving the old ones on the wing. In flight, one of the plugs slid down and got caught between the aileron and the trailing edge of the wing. When Brindley, who was flying, made a turn preparatory to landing he was unable to roll out because of the jammed aileron and the crash resulted.

It was Reuben Fleet, the noted aircraft designer and later founder of Consolidated Aircraft, who was given the job the next day of testing the second Liberty engine at nearby Wilbur Wright Field. Fleet, then a major and in charge of flight training for the Air Service, was not very happy about the assignment.

As he put it, "I'd never flown anything over two hundred horsepower, and when I warmed the Liberty up it scared the living tar out of me 'cause it made so much noise. I took off, flew at twenty feet the length of the field and then took it up to about four thousand feet and made a few gentle turns. Eventually I took it up to six thousand and threw it into a spin. Every time I tried to get it out of the spin it just spun all the more. Finally I held her square at the ground with the stick forward until I reached eight hundred feet, then I pulled the stick back and gave her solid rudder as much as I could . . . and she pulled out."

Reuben Fleet's test flight of the second Liberty engine when translated for the layman means he, too, came very close to a fatal crash.

When I arrived at McCook, less than a year later in March 1919, the volume of work had been reduced to a trickle. Still, its mission, as outlined by Colonel Vincent, was the same and thus the inventiveness of its personnel, military and civilian, supplied the faint pulse that kept our young but economically starved Air Service alive.

The Commanding Officer was Colonel Thurman H. Bane, a West Pointer with a flair for engineering who had been an early advocate of air power. He was a meticulous officer with a skeptical show-me attitude, just the kind of CO needed for a field where everyone was busy chasing the future. Tall, bushy-haired with a long strong face and a dab of a mustache, he liked people who were doers, providing they had thought things out.

When I reported to him he looked me over and then said, "Lieutenant, according to my instructions from General Mitchell, I'm making you director of our photographic laboratory. Your assignment is to improve the state of the art."

No one could ask for more all encompassing orders and I was elated, but very shortly I discovered that, while my job and title were imposing, I had mighty little to direct. My staff consisted of five technicians assigned to the equipment section of the Engineering Division and, of course, there was no money.

One reason for this last was that research, development, and the testing of cameras and related material had been conducted by Eastman Kodak scientific personnel and at the photographic school at Langley, Virginia.

Now that the work was to be terminated at Rochester, it was my job to pick up where Eastman Kodak left off, but in order to do so I had to get some financial support from the Engineering Division. This last was the real stinger, for the devaluation of aerial photography permeated the Engineering Division as thoroughly as it did the rest of the Army. The top priorities were focused on the development of engines and their many accessories, new types of fighters and bombers, the refurbishing of existing aircraft, the DH-4 in particular. Fire prevention equipment and parachutes came way ahead of aerial photography. In fact, just about everything did.

Late in the war the U.S. K-1 Folmer Schwing film camera went into production. It carried a roll of film 9 inches wide, which took seventy-five pictures and, thanks to Dr. Kenneth

Mees of Eastman Kodak, the film was the best in the world. Directly after I arrived at McCook, I flew to Rochester to meet Dr. Mees to thank him for his efforts and to ask his advice on a number of problems. I found him to be a middle-aged professorial Englishman, kindly and extremely helpful. As the world's greatest authority on photographic sciences, he was responsible for the development of panchromatic plates and film, which gave great impetus to the Eastman Kodak Company. The only way George Eastman could get Dr. Mees to go to work for him in the U.S. was to buy the Wratten & Wainwright Company where Mees was employed in England and transfer him to the U.S.

As for the K-1 it could be mounted on the gun scarf behind the observer and swung obliquely as required. But despite the fine quality of its film, under cold conditions the film had the nasty habit of developing static streaks. I gave top priority to the elimination of these streaks. Also I wished to improve the K-1 by shortening its focal length and, in so doing, install a wide angle lens to cover a larger picture area.

Up until this time I had known nothing about the three lens Bagley camera because the Corps of Engineers, who had been utilizing it in France, had not bothered to acquaint the Signal Corps with its development and use. However, because McCook not only had models of all the aircraft that had come out of the war, it also had all the cameras. I found the Bagley camera in the laboratory and recognized its unique design. It took its pictures like three cameras operating at once, one shot vertically and with left and right obliques. In the laboratory we could rectify the obliques, but the camera had a serious defect because of a shutter that only worked sporadically. I set up a program with my miniscule staff to correct this deficiency and to engineer an improved camera mount for it on the rear cockpit.

Aside from working to improve the existing cameras, I developed a new view finder through which the observer could look and see objects on the ground. When the objects moved into the finder's cross hairs, the observer made his next exposure. This gave the film a 60 percent overlap, making possible the viewing of pictures in stereo. We also engineered a better stereo machine. Strictly, in the laboratory we had new kinds of emulsions and printing equipment from Kodak with which to experiment. And, despite a lean and hungry purse, experiment we did, aiming in every aspect to improve the state of the art.

Always in the back of my mind there was an area of research and development that once successful, I believed, would bring the aerial camera the attention it so richly deserved. I had first got the idea when at Cornell. As Sergeant Major Haslett had so aptly put it, "once the bloomin' sun goes down and it gets dark, armies are blind as bats. Neither one knows what the other's up to till the blinkin' light's turned on again."

But suppose the blinkin' light could be turned on in the middle of the night? Suppose you had aerial photography at night?

It was an idea I slept on a great deal, but aside from the fact there was no money to push it beyond my dreams, at the time I was busy far into the wee hours on the aforementioned projects.

As the days went by there was one lack I felt above all others. My morale took a beating over the fact that I still did not have my pilot's rating. Finally, I decided to stop feeling sad and do something about it. I went and made myself known to McCook's chief test pilot, Major R. W. (Shorty) Schroeder.

Shorty was tall and thin, thus his nickname. With his high cheekbones, gaunt face and prominent brown eyes, he reminded me of an Indian. He was always dressed in coveralls, and if you didn't find him in a plane, you found him close to one. He was more than chief test pilot and practical engineer, he was a pioneer, the kind of man whom a century before you would have found at the farthest frontier.

He heard me out silently as I unfolded my tale of woe. "I've been damn near two years trying to get my rating," I concluded, "and between Taliaferro and Carlstrom I've got over two hundred hours of rear-seat time. That includes all the acrobatics and landings in the book."

"Hmm," he gave his long chin a thoughtful stroke and looked

away as though concentrating on a DH-4 that had made a bouncing landing. "Tell you what, shavetail"—he brought his gaze back to bear on me—"you meet me at Operations tomorrow morning at seven. If you fly as good as you talk, I'll give you a chance to solo."

As far as I was concerned seven o'clock the next morning took a grievous long time in arriving, but when it finally did, it was a beautiful spring day, the sky fresh and clear, waiting for me to come do my stuff. Up we rose, the Jenny's Hispano-Suiza engine tugging like a hound on a leash. Flying from the rear cockpit, I followed Schroeder's hand directions and proved to him I knew the alchemy of loops and spins and rolls. After a while, he pointed to the ground, and when I had landed he had me taxi to the end of the field. Once uncoiled from the cockpit, he stood on the wing for a moment, his back to the prop blast. Over its sound, he leaned down and said, "All right, shavetail, let's see you do it by yourself."

No pilot ever forgets his first solo flight. He usually makes it with a great gaggle of unseen wings flapping around in his stomach. In my case there were only the wings of the Jenny and a wonderful feeling of elation and release that rode on them. I came back to earth anxious to be airborne again.

Schroeder waved me toward him as he ambled across the field. I fully expected his congratulations. Instead he hunched his back to the idling propeller and said, "Tell you what, you go on over to Fairfield, gas up and spend the rest of the morning practicing landings and take-offs from the front seat. You survive that, I'll check with you later."

His instructions were better than kind words of praise. I headed for Fairfield and was I a happy man!

Early next morning, I went hunting for my new mentor and found him hard at work on the flight line. "Well, I survived," I greeted him.

He nodded and said, "Yup . . . seems like."

"And now what?"

"You've got a JN-4 assigned for photographic flying, don't

you?" He turned, resuming his work with screw driver and wrench.

"Yes. We've got a Jenny."

"Well, as far as I'm concerned, shavetail, you're free to fly it . . . you're pilot enough."

I nearly pounded him on the back and took off right there without benefit of aircraft. But under his coveralls, Shorty was a major, and so I restrained myself. Only momentarily, however, for in the next week or so I managed to flight test every camera at McCook. And every time I met Shorty he'd give me that look and say, "Well, shavetail, I see you're still alive."

There is a well-known saying among fliers: "There are old pilots and there are bold pilots, but there are few old bold pilots." One learns the truism of the saying through the watchfulness of Divine Providence or just plain good luck.

During the latter part of May, I had to visit the Burke and James Company in Chicago. Working with their engineers to try and debug our version of the DeRamm camera was high on my list of priorities. Naturally, I didn't want to take the train, and again it was Shorty Schroeder who came to my assistance by approving my cross country flight with instructions to land at Grant Park, the airmail's regular landing site.

My plan was to fly to Chicago, stay overnight and leave early the next morning for Dayton.

I invited Private Benny Thomas, my aerial photographer, to accompany me. Benny was Polish and had taken the name Thomas in place of something unpronounceable. Squat and powerful, he was an indefatigable worker, but because of his accent I could seldom understand what he was talking about although he could understand me, and somehow our relationship worked out fine. I wanted Benny with me to help in the refueling which was quite a chore.

The gas was contained in 50-gallon drums which were tipped on end slightly and pumped with a small hand pump we carried for the purpose, through a chamois fitted over the end of a large funnel to strain out the water and scum. We would leave a gallon or so of gas in the steel drum with the waste material. It was a time-consuming job and generally required an hour or so, depending on how clean the gas was in the drum.

When we took off, I figured I could make it all the way through without refueling. However, the northwest wind was much stronger than I had anticipated and, when we were almost to Valparaiso, Indiana, I decided I'd better land and refuel. Down below we spotted a large pasture with a number of horses at the far end.

I figured with the wind I could stop short of the horses, so in I went slow and low over the fence and landed the Jenny in the pasture. Apparently the horses were high-strung, for when they heard and saw our strange contraption bearing down on them, they bolted and did some taking off themselves, going over the fence and charging away in all directions, kicking up a screen of dust.

I had no more than switched off the engine and climbed out of the cockpit to join Benny when we saw a model-T Ford barreling toward us.

Driving it was the farmer who owned the now absent cavalry. He was not a happy man: "You gawdamn soldiers!" he greeted us, almost forgetting to stop his car before jumping out. "What in tarnation hell you mean stampedin' my horses all over the countryside!"

"I'm sorry," I tried to placate him. "We're nearly out of gas, and we had to come down."

"Is that so!" he snapped, hands on hips, his Adam's apple bobbing angrily as he fought for words and breath, "Any man who'd get in one of them things is a damn fool, and any man who'd fly in one without gas is an idjit!" He glared at us both, to show that we were equally "idjits."

Benny said something which fortunately neither of us could understand, but I could tell it was not exactly polite.

"Maybe we can help you get the horses back," I interjected quickly.

"You bet your boots you're gonna help me get 'em back," the

farmer thrust out a long bony finger, "that or I'll have you arrested for trespassin' and attempted horse stealin'!"

For the next few hours Benny and I became cowboys, bouncing around with the farmer in his model-T, rounding up the nags. As the job went on the farmer calmed down and by the time we'd finished, he'd forgotten about being angry. In fact, he'd admitted to being an aviation enthusiast. When he took us home to meet his wife and family and have some lunch, he telephoned the oil company in Valparaiso and instructed them to bring out sufficient gas and oil.

When we finally took off the whole family and most of their neighbors were on hand to wave us on our way.

Some hours later as we approached the north end of Grant Park, I couldn't help feel it was in the nature of a homecoming. This was where less than four years past I had watched Ruth Law put on her exhibition and now here I was about to land at the very same place. Or was I? I spotted plenty of people below, but they were watching a baseball game! Orders were orders, and I began to put on an exhibition of my own, diving at the crowd to get them to move so I could set the plane down. Every time I pulled up they would swarm back on the field again. After the fourth go round, I started a slow glide for a landing, and when the crowd realized I was coming in they formed two narrow lines, giving me just enough room to make it. Although by the enthusiastic reception we received it appeared that we had just circled the earth nonstop, I was not feeling overly confident. The landing had been a near thing with so many people swarming about. The swift arrival of the police on the scene clarified matters but did not improve them. We were informed that we had broken the law by landing, that the field was officially closed. I pled ignorance and was told that airmail planes were now landing at a field alongside the federal Haines Hospital at Maywood.

"How do I get there?" I asked.

"Just take off," the police captain gestured, "go down the

park to the Illinois railroad station and follow 12th Street west. You can't miss the hospital."

Once again we took off, but it wasn't easy to follow the captain's direction, for it was late afternoon and the farther west we flew, the hazier it got. Soon I had only vertical visibility. The loss of the horizon and any forward sight put a cold fist in my stomach. It came to me that I wasn't such a hot pilot after all. If I didn't find the field or some place to land before dark, I was going to be in serious trouble.

It was Benny who spotted the bulk of the hospital, looming out of the twilight haze. Beside it on the south side, I saw what I thought was the field. Down we went and I pancaked the plane into a mess of grass and weeds four or five feet high. Luckily, we didn't roll far, for dead ahead we discovered what would have been a devastating reception—railroad ties scattered all over.

Of course, I'd picked the wrong field. The right one was just across the road. As the fact dawned on me, I realized how weary I was and grateful to be on the ground in one piece.

In one day's flight I had misjudged the strength of the wind, stampeded a herd of horses, broken up a ball game, broken the law, gotten lost, and landed in the wrong place. The final ignominy was having to take the wings off the Jenny and, with the aid of the airmail boys, *truck* the plane across the road to the proper field. Now I recalled a word of caution Shorty Schroeder had offered and which I had ignored.

"Don't be too cocky, shavetail."

I understood what he meant.

## 3

While I was working to improve the state of aerial photography, military and civilian aeronautical engineers at McCook were engaged in improving the various components of powered flight. In one laboratory there were engineers testing and developing new types of aircraft power plants. Congressional legislation did provide a small amount of money to build prototypes even if they could not be put into production. Mostly, however, the division worked at debugging the Liberty engine which at that time was like a dog with fleas.

In the forefront of this work was George Hallett. A small quiet man, George could always be found deep in the parts of a dissembled engine, or one about to be assembled. Whenever there was a problem, George was in demand. This was almost constantly. Further, a rigid Air Service regulation required that all Liberty engines had to undergo major overhaul after every seventy-five hours of flight.

George Hallett's aviation career had begun with Glenn Curtiss when he had joined him in 1911 as a mechanic in San Diego, California, where Curtiss made the first flight off water.

In 1912 Curtiss sent George and pilot George Whitman to Europe to demonstrate the Curtiss flying boat. While on this tour Curtiss had produced a new aircraft which he sent to Paris with instructions to test it on the River Seine.

As was the practice with the Curtiss Company in those days, they forwarded the plane without completing the necessary flight tests and no drawings accompanied the craft, just a few sketches. On the first flight, as soon as they became airborne, George and

Whitman discovered the flying boat was so tail-heavy they couldn't take the chance of landing it until they had worked a solution to the problem. Whitman had George climb out over the nose of the boat and hang onto the cowling to provide the necessary weight to counterbalance the tail section. In this manner they splashed down before they came to the next bridge over the Seine. The following day Hallett started to work, cutting off part of the trailing edge of the center section of the boat and moving the engine ahead seven inches, which corrected the tail-heavy situation and expedited their sales program.

At McCook Field, George was responsible for many contributions that eventually turned the Liberty engines into reliable old work horses.

One all important improvement of the Liberty was engineered with the aid of our photographic section. To test what happened to a DH-4 on impact, a steep ramp was built with a concrete barrier at the end of the incline. DH-4s minus wings, with throttle wide open, were sent down the ramp one at a time. In most cases, when they hit, they immediately caught fire. Using high-speed cameras it was possible to observe the cause. The long exhaust stack and the gasoline tank would rupture on impact. Gas would hit the red hot stack and that would be that.

As a result of these tests, the Liberty engine was redesigned with six short stacks on each side in place of the single long one, and the gas tank was positioned ahead of the pilot and behind the engine. These modifications saved the lives of many pilots.

Although it wasn't realized at the time, the turbosupercharge was among the most important developments of the power plant section. Here was a device that took thirty years to perfect and, in World War II, gave our reconnaissance bombers and fighters the required superior high altitude performance they sought. The early test work on the supercharger, which rams more air into the combustion area of the engine at extremely high altitudes, was done at Pike's Peak by General Electric. Just about the time G.E. planned to give up the project, the Air Service transferred it, together with the inventor Dr. Sanford A. Moss, to McCook Field.

Aided by many of the power plant engineers there, one of the units was developed and installed on a Le Père. It was Shorty Schroeder who conducted a test in it that broke the world's record but nearly broke his neck, too.

In October 1919 he took the Le Père up to 33,113 feet. His air supply, unlike today's dependable systems, was compressed oxygen feeding through a small tube about the size of a match, and the inside of the tube was not much bigger than a medium-size needle. By the time he reached 33,113 feet his goggles had fogged up, making it difficult to see. As he was trying to remove the frozen moisture from inside the goggles, he must have shifted his face mask, for at that moment a tiny drop of moisture froze in his oxygen tube. The last time he got a glimpse of his instrument panel he saw that he was at 30,000 feet, his engine running full throttle, and he was not getting any oxygen. He didn't remember anything after that.

Apparently his plane went into an almost vertical dive with the engine continuing to run wide open. The intense cold froze Shorty's eyeballs, and the lack of oxygen made his heart enlarge until it was almost the size of a man's hat. As the airplane got into denser air he regained consciousness long enough to land and then passed out again. The high-speed dive sent him so suddenly into the denser lower atmosphere that it crushed all the nearly empty fuel and oil tanks, together with the metal floats in the carburetors of the engine. Luckily Shorty's eyes recovered in a couple of weeks, and he went back up in the blue to do his daily test chores.

Major Howard Davidson was supply officer at McCook and, as a result of Shorty's experience, he searched all around the country to obtain oxygen that did not have any moisture in it, a very difficult assignment. Aviators in those days never went high enough to need oxygen, or so we believed. There were many times when I was testing aerial cameras in my DH-4 at 19,000 feet that an oxygen supply would have made for a much more comfortable situation. Davidson finally located a company that was willing to try to produce moisture free oxygen. In the process of

My parents—George William and Ellen Le Strange Goddard.

I discovered America at age fourteen in ~~1914~~.

1904

Ruth Law—the girl who made me want to fly. *Mitchell Collection, Library of Congress.*

Private Goddard goes to Cornell University, December 1917.

Photo-interpretation class at Cornell using aerial photos of Allied and German trench systems, 1917. *U.S. Army Air Service*

Aerial photographic processing laboratory in the field, World War I, 1918. *U.S. Army Air Service*

La Rue Sweatman and the Airman who came to dinner. *Lt. Harry Brandt*

manufacturing it, however, something went wrong and a compressor and a tank exploded and actually blew the shoes off the operator's feet. Naturally, Davidson was concerned because he could see a big law suit against the Air Service. Much to his surprise, all the operator wanted was a new pair of shoes.

Because so much that was going on at McCook was in the realm of experimentation, there were some real squeakers. Practically all the early important progress on propellers took place at McCook under the supervision of Frank Caldwell, an internationally known propeller expert. However, in 1919 one of his engineers, Julian Hart, came up with a variable pitch propeller that looked promising. Unfortunately, it was tested on a Curtiss JN with an 80-horsepower engine which was too underpowered to illustrate the propeller's real potential. But it was a test flight by Lieutenant Muir Fairchild that literally put the experiment in the drink. Coming in for a landing and trying to adjust the propeller at the same time, he accidentally reversed its pitch. Momentarily this created the unusual sight of a plane backing up in the air. It then stalled and fell about fifty feet into the Miami River. Fairchild with a broken arm and several broken ribs made it to shore mad as hell that he'd ruined the test.

Billy Mitchell was intensely aware of everything that was going on at McCook, but the armament laboratory was of special interest to him. On one of his frequent visits he came to witness the test firing of a new recoilless cannon, later to be fitted into the nose of a twin-engine Martin bomber, of which there were only about twelve in existence at the time.

The nonrecoil feature of the cannon was accomplished by firing bullets or shells out of the muzzle and a big load of buckshot out the opposite end. The test engineer in his excitement forgot to take into account where the buckshot would go. When he pulled the trigger he hit the bull's-eye all right in both directions, for the buckshot went through a hangar chewing up airplanes and creating havoc. General Mitchell's only remark was, "Let's try and be a little more careful around here."

While major testing of what we produced at McCook usually

took place at Langley Field, Virginia, a great deal of preliminary testing was done at home base, particularly of parachutes. At the time, a good many pilots thought wearing a parachute was sissified; others thought it was a sure way to die. Until April 29, 1919, drops had been made with dummies. On that date John J. Irving, a parachute maker from Buffalo, New York, got credit for the first live jump at McCook. Irving bailed out of a Jenny at 1700 feet and floated down with the greatest of ease. That is until he landed and then in chasing his billowing canopy, he tripped and broke his ankle.

My own introduction to parachute jumping had somewhat different results. Major Ed Hoffman, the man in charge, had dummies filled with buckshot to simulate actual jumps, and they were dropped from all types of aircraft. Every day the major's "leather men" would come raining down on the field, and once in a while they would have to be fished out of the Miami River or nearby streets. It got so dangerous around the field that the major was ordered to take his tests elsewhere away from air traffic.

It was during this time that we were called on to photograph in slow motion a "live" drop. An English firm had come forth with what it called the "Guardian Angel" parachute. It was to be demonstrated at McCook, and one of the demonstrators was an extremely pretty twenty year old lass named Sylvia Boyden. She came replete with chaperon. One of her jumping companions was Lieutenant Robert A. Caldwell, a Canadian, who had distinguished himself in the RAF during the war, shooting down ten German planes.

"This parachute is going to make you boys sit up and take notice," he announced repeatedly as chute and ship were readied for take-off.

The chute was packed into a little canvas bag made fast to the belly of the aircraft beneath the observer's cockpit. A rope ran from the chute up the side of the plane and was fastened to a belt around the jumper's waist.

Masked in helmet and goggles, Lieutenant Caldwell waved a confident farewell to the assembled watchers who included Colonel Bane, Major Hoffman and Sylvia Boyden. Then with a civilian pilot named Eversole at the controls, off they went.

I followed close behind, leveling off at about 1500 feet. Sergeant Lewis Hagemeyer stood in the observer's cockpit, camera ready. The Canadian was also standing and when the pilot had the plane in position directly over the field, Caldwell saluted us broadly and went over the side. As he jumped, he slipped on the cowling and the rope attached to the chute did not drop clear but snagged between the elevator horn and the fuselage. In open mouthed horror I saw the line snap under his weight and down he plummeted, *sans* parachute.

It was a dreadful experience; the first so called *live* parachute jump I'd witnessed. As for Miss Boyden and the large crowd watching from the ground, it was even worse. When I landed I found her shocked and sobbing, but she insisted that she be given the chance to demonstrate the "Guardian Angel," for there was nothing wrong with the chute and English planes did not have any kind of projection on their fuselages.

Colonel Bane, tough as he could be, simply couldn't refuse her, and so a short time later Hagey and I were airborne again, ready to photograph the jump. It would be safe to say that neither of us nor anyone who watched that girl go head first over the side of the cockpit was relaxed or calm. Frankly, I was sore as hell at the "old man" for giving her permission to make the jump. There was a sour taste in my mouth, the July sky had lost its warmth, and my hand hurt from gripping the stick so tightly. But this time, pretty as a picture, thank God! the chute opened smoothly enough. However, the wind had suddenly changed and Sylvia Boyden, instead of coming down on the field, landed in the Miami River, where she was swiftly rescued. I was extremely sorry I wasn't on hand to do the rescuing myself.

Later I heard that the Canadian's last jump was not really necessary, for the U. S. Government had agreed to buy the rights to the patent after three successful jumps, and the jumps had already been made elsewhere. However, Major Hoffman continued work on his back and seat-type chutes and finally was able to gain acceptance for them.

Few of us considered wearing them at first, that is, until Lieutenant Harold Harris, a top test pilot at McCook, saved his life with one. Harold weighed about 220 pounds and stood 6'2". He was testing a new plane by dogfighting with Muir Fairchild. Everything was going fine until an aileron came off. For a few minutes Harold tried to get up on the cockpit to avoid the control stick which was beating the devil out of him. Finally, he was forced to jump. He landed in a grape arbor not far from McCook. Calmly he rolled up the chute and hiked back to the field. It was about noontime when hundreds of people were on their way to the mess hall. Lunch turned into a large celebration, and both Harold and Major Hoffman were beaming guests of honor. The major knew that parachutes were "here to stay." As for Harold, with great aplomb he accepted the plaudits of the assembled and went nervelessly about his business until late in the afternoon. Then the closing whistle blew and he must have thought it was Gabriel's horn because he stood up, turned a brilliant white, and fell on his face in a dead faint—the shock having finally overtaken him.

If Harold was the first man to save his life using a chute one of his fellow test pilots, Lieutenant Harry Sutton, had the distinction of bailing out twice from the same plane. He was testing a DH-4 that had bad spinning characteristics. He proved the point all right by not being able to get out of a spin so he "hit the silk." Before he could open the chute, the plane's wing came around and he landed on it and then had to jump off again.

One of the most outrageous parachute exhibitions in the annals of McCook was put on by Lieutenants Jimmy Doolittle and Louis Meissner. Both were test pilots and Meissner had been a well-known ace in World War I. They were also great practical jokers. They threw a picnic to end all picnics with Meissner wearing a derby hat and smoking a big cigar. The *pièce de résistance* was to be three live parachute jumps. Actually, the jumpers were "leather men" whom Doolittle and Meissner had named Hart, Schaffner, and Marx. The picnickers weren't aware of that, however. The show started with Hart making a dandy jump, followed by Schaffner. He, too, had his chute billow out nicely, but when Marx came down, he came down like a rock. Women fainted, strong men paled, but when they learned it was all a joke their anger soared and the two test pilots had to make themselves scarce.

Despite such fun and games it wasn't long before every pilot at the field was wearing a parachute, and it took the supply a long time to catch up with the demand. A sign was posted in the operations office which read: PUT YOUR TRUST IN GOD BUT BE SURE YOUR PARACHUTE IS FOLDED RIGHT.

Major Hoffman, having proved his point, went on to develop many other useful aviation accessories.

Certainly the evolution of the parachute supplied plenty of drama. But, so too did the creative aeronautical firsts racked up at McCook, many of them prophetic.

William Kettering, working in great secrecy, brought forth the Kettering "flying bomb." It was radio controlled and was loaded with a hefty charge of dynamite, so far as is known, the first guided missile.

The concept of the dragon ships used in low-level attack missions in Vietnam was born at McCook when engineer John M. Larson designed the JL-12. It was an all metal aircraft, boasting a main battery of twenty-eight Thompson machine guns. Smaller than the Vietnam war's C-47 dragon ships, it had a range of 400 miles and was very swift and maneuverable.

Russian designer, Dr. George Debothezat, worked to construct a flyable helicopter. Aided by aeronautical engineer John Roche, he came out with the great granddaddy of today's "chopper." To get off the ground it required shock absorbers and a catapult, but off it got up to an altitude of about a hundred feet.

Roche went on to design the XB-1-A. It was patterned after a Bristol SE-5 and was the first plane with a *monocoque* fuselage. Muir Fairchild had the misfortune to crack it up. When Roche rushed out on the field and found Fairchild extricating himself from the wreckage unhurt, he excitedly congratulated him.

Fairchild shook his head disgustedly, and said, "Mister Roche, this is hardly a time for congratulations. I'm sorry as hell I busted your airplane!"

There were other talented aeronautical designers at McCook such as Fred Verville and Theophile Deport. They had come from France during the war and had stayed on. Among Verville's many accomplishments was the first monoplane sanctioned by the government. Deport came up with a small fast scout plane, whose mission was to carry messages from the ground to a dirigible or between dirigibles.

Of course, not everything that came out of McCook was a screaming success. In such an environment of experimentation no one expected it to be, and with every failure, valuable lessons were learned. The GAX bomber was a good case in point. The GAX was a completely armor-plated craft, boasting a cannon and other heavy armament. Its purpose was for low-level attack. While it was being constructed, some of the boys warned the project engineer, Mac Laddon, that the landing gear wasn't going to stand up under the weight. They predicted it would collapse and someone would get hurt. They were half right because the gear did collapse right in the hangar, but fortunately no one got flattened by it. Mac redesigned the gear and that old tub of tin actually flew, but much too slow for any practical use—a kind of early day TFX. However, some of Mac Laddon's ideas of crew protection by armor plate are found in today's fighters.

The men who flight tested everything that came out of McCook—new, remodeled, old, and rebuilt—were a small select breed of the sort that we Americans produce in every generation. Pilots like Schroeder, Niedemeyer, Doolittle, Harris, Meissner, Fairchild, Barksdale, Moseley, Aldrin—to name a few—find their counterparts today in our astronauts and other young men who dare to try the new and unknown.

The breed specializes in a quality of nonchalance and wry humor in the face of danger. Louis Meissner possessed such a quality. On his noon hour he'd climb into his single-seater Thomas Morse Scout and up he'd go and, for his own amusement and ours, put on a wild display of acrobatics. One day, as some of us were watching him, we observed him go into a spin from which he didn't recover. Helplessly we saw the twisting plane fall down the pale blue sky and disappear behind the trees. Motionless we awaited the sickening *whummp!* and the telltale pyre of black smoke arising. But there was nothing. In a mad race we joined the field fire engines and ambulance. When we arrived upon the scene, there was Lou perched in the top of a big elm tree, his plane splattered all about in adjoining trees. He paid us little heed and seemed to be searching for something in the branches.

A ladder was put up and finally down came Lou, protesting bitterly, "I've lost my damn goggles. Help me look for them. They must be in the bushes around here."

Everybody joined the hunt, Lou refusing to get in the ambulance until they were found. We never did find them, but Meissner was back on the job that afternoon, sporting a new pair though still muttering over the loss.

To Lieutenant J. Parker Van Zandt, more than any pilot I know, must go the credit for pioneering the highly dangerous realm of "blind flying." A bug on navigation, with World War I and subsequent Naval aeronautical training, he constructed his "cloud flying" instrument panel at McCook and installed it in the cockpit of his plane. The instruments consisted of a rudimentary turn and bank indicator, a rate of climb indicator, plus air speed and altimeter calibrators. With his "cloud flying" panel to guide him, Van Zandt made the first cross-country flights on instruments, proving that regular flight schedules could be maintained despite adverse weather.

One foul day, Billy Mitchell was weathered in at McCook, as we all were. A racing gray mass of clouds was practically sitting on the hangar tops and Billy was restlessly pacing the flight line trying to order them away. Suddenly, above the wind and rain, he heard a plane approaching the field.

"Who in the devil is flying in that stuff?" he asked Colonel Bane.

"Oh that must be Van Zandt," Bane said nonchalantly. "He goes looking for bad weather so he can try out his navigational equipment."

"Wonder he doesn't break his neck. Does he ever get lost?"

"No, he always brings his ship back."

"Good! Excellent!" Mitchell chortled, "That's the kind of man we want around here."

Behind everything that went on at McCook was the presence of Billy Mitchell. That isn't to say that men like Thurman Bane, who oversaw and initiated much of what came out of McCook, were not important. Or that others such as Hap Arnold and Benny Foulois did not play decisive roles in keeping the Air Service going. But it was Mitchell, externally enlisting the support of his high-level contacts in government, and internally through his charismatic and inspiring personality, who gave motivation and impetus to everything we did.

Often, unannounced, he would show up flying his DH-4, the *Osprey*. If there was a new plane to be tested, he'd be the second man to fly it. If it was a plane that carried two, he'd be one of them. In this way he learned to fly a glider. He also reversed a negative opinion concerning the value of superchargers by flying a plane, equipped with one, that had easily outclimbed his own plane. He was everywhere, probing, asking, stimulating. At one impromptu mess hall meeting discussing new model aircraft, he drew on the blackboard a design of what looked like the B-17 flying fortress. "This is the kind of bomber we should be building," he told the assembled. At another meeting on power plants, he pooh-hooed plans for a new engine and described the type of engine he envisioned—a jet engine.

On his regular planned visits, after holding all-day meetings with Colonel Bane and members of the staff, the General would invite a group of engineers to join him for an evening meeting at his hotel suite in town. This was before air conditioners were ready for hotel use. As each guest—mostly airplane designers and government engineers—would arrive, the General would meet them at the door in his undershirt and, to make them comfortable and ready for some hot discussions, insist they remove their coats and shirts. These planning meetings, generally running into the wee hours of the morning, laid the groundwork for many new ideas in aircraft and equipment.

At one such session which I attended, I took advantage of the opportunity to get the General aside for some judicious needling in regard to centralizing at McCook all the aerial photographic research and development work being done elsewhere. Colonel Bane and the chief engineer had repeatedly petitioned HQ in Washington for action but got none. After the General returned to Washington we were instructed to set up a new department of photography in the Equipment Section. Also, I heard that the R&D being done at Langley Field Aerial Photographic School, and at the experimental field in Rochester, was to be transferred to our photographic department at McCook.

This was just the kind of reorganization I had hoped for. It was Billy Mitchell who had taken me away from flight training and sent me to McCook. It was Billy Mitchell who had responded to my suggestion of reorganization, and now it was Billy Mitchell who sent me on my way again, only this time there was no grief.

I was sitting in my JN-4 photographic plane one fine day talking to Shorty Schroeder when the General suddenly appeared out of nowhere.

"What's he doing flying an airplane? He hasn't qualified for a pilot's rating," he said.

"Well, sir," Shorty replied, picking his words with care, "maybe he hasn't qualified *formally*, but *informally* he's not half bad."

"Well, it won't do," the General snapped. "You see that he gets orders to go to Carlstrom Field immediately. I want all my pilots *formally* qualified."

I restrained myself from yelping for joy.

## 4

Just as my first solo flight was in the nature of an anticlimax so, too, was my return to Carlstrom Field to get my official rating as an RMA—Regular Military Aviator. Certainly attaining my RMA was good cause for celebration, and my fellow pilots saw that we honored the occasion thunderously. After all, it had taken me more than two years to sprout my wings.

Now that they were properly attached, I was anxious to return to McCook. My aim was to place there all aerial photographic research, development and testing under one roof and one command.

As previously mentioned, during the First World War, the Corps of Engineers, which had always figured military mapping of any sort was its business, had, through Major Bagley and his T-1 camera, been engaged in aerial photography, utilizing Air Service pilots and observers. The Air Service, of course, had also been so engaged, but it didn't end there, for the Signal Corps had given over-all supervision of the development of photographic equipment to its Science and Research Division, which had offices in Washington, D.C., Langley Field, Virginia, and Rochester, New York. Added to that the Ordnance Department had been put in charge of the development of optics.

At war's end each of these services continued to hold on to its part of the aerial photographic cake and failed to share it with any other. Thus it was that I had known nothing about the Bagley camera until I went to McCook and found one in my laboratory. Even more incredible, while I spent much time in the office of Mr. Folmer, of Folmer-Schwing, discussing how to improve the K-1 camera, I was never aware that he was working with the Science and Research Division of the Signal Corps to carry out such improvements. It was departmentalization with a vengeance!

We kept hearing at McCook that the Corps of Engineers was going to take over all aspects of aerial mapping and we would simply become their flying chauffeurs. The Corps' position was that only engineers knew how to map from the air. With our nine photographic sections located throughout the U.S. and its territories, we had already proved quite differently.

Each section had a complement of two aircraft, a single officer, and twenty enlisted men. Under the direction of General Mitchell, they worked with county, state and federal survey agencies who requested aerial photographs for map revisions of rivers, harbors, highways and the like. The Corps of Engineers using the Bagley T-1 camera made considerable use of our services as well, but I worried that they were out to dominate and eventually control aerial mapping, and I decided to voice my fears in Washington where they would count the most.

Today, it would be highly presumptuous for a second lieutenant to ignore the prescribed labyrinth of military channels and, in so doing, request that reason overcome an entrenched resistance to change wrapped in the iron-clad cocoon of vested authority. But, at the time, we enjoyed a somewhat unmilitary flexibility in the Air Service. Most of us by nature had not been cast in the military mold, and we were not awed by rank alone. Further, I had the tacit support of Colonel Bane, if not his written authorization, and from the beginning of my military career I had adopted a philosophy of need—when the need arose I would carry out the spirit of Army regulations if not the letter.

On the train to Washington that night, I joined Orville Wright in the smoker. I had met him before, and when I told him my plan he replied, "If you have as hard a time selling your ideas as I had selling the Army airplanes, you've got a big job ahead of you!"

I did, but I had a supporter on my side the Wright brothers had lacked—Billy Mitchell.

There was never a time when I was in Billy Mitchell's presence that his magnetism didn't strike sparks. As to his mood, you always knew it by the expression he wore. From it, you knew when to ask and when to keep silent, but whatever his mood he made me feel that our struggling, ill-financed, militarily downgraded Air Service was the most important creation in the world, bar none.

When I arrived at his office on the second floor of the Munitions Building, I had already planned my opening, and when I was ushered in, I completed my salute by pointing to my newly received wings.

He rose from behind his cluttered desk with a grin, thrusting out his hand. "Congratulations, George. Now you're one of us—officially. It's a wonder you didn't kill yourself. How did you know I wanted to see you?"

"Well, sir . . . maybe because it's mutual."

From that point on not only did I have little say, but for the time being my purpose for coming to Washington was all but forgotten. My plan had been to inform the General that his approval for aerial photographic centralization was getting nowhere and to ask him to suggest what I might do about it. My hope was that he would pick up the phone and have a talk with his boss, Major General Charles T. Menoher, Chief of the Air Service, and from that point some orders would be issued. Instead he completely scattered my thoughts by saying, "George, you're not to discuss outside this office what I'm about to tell you. I don't want you to breathe a word of it."

And then he told me. Since his return to the States from France and Germany in February 1919, he had been contemplating putting on a demonstration that would show all the doubters in the military and the government the true nature of air power. As part of the Armistice agreement, Germany had been directed to turn over a portion of its fleet to the United States. Our Navy wished to use these ships for gunnery practice. Mitchell wanted to illustrate his point and the vulnerability of battleships to air attack by bombing them.

The Navy was dead set against his plan, he told me. "Daniels[1]

[1] Josephus Daniels, Secretary of the Navy.

is giving us a helluva hard time, but we've got our friends, too, and it looks like we're going to win out."

The friends he referred to were powerful Senators and Representatives, such as Congressman Roy G. Fitzgerald of Ohio and Senator William E. Borah of Idaho.

"If things go right," he said, "we'll conduct the tests off Cape Hatteras in about a year's time, maybe earlier. But I want you to come into this office, George, and manage all the photographic work in connection with the operation. I want you to see to the proper equipping of all photographic sections. I want this to be the most thoroughly photographed event in world history."

I had, of course, heard rumors of the General's plan. Once, when he had dropped by my laboratory at McCook, he had made passing reference to the possibility of bombing battleships. But there in his office what he described, and the excitement with which he described it, excited me too.

Here was a challenge—a chance to prove that we were not an "upstart service," a bunch of undisciplined odd balls led by a flamboyant publicity seeking dreamer. Here was the opportunity to prove that our military value must be recognized if the United States was to remain secure from attack and be reckoned a strong military power. The public and many in government had been sold on the belief that we had fought a war to end all wars. But if the lesson of history taught anything, it was that peace depended on strength and strength depended on those who looked and planned ahead.

I returned to McCook all fired up over the role aerial photography was alerted to play in the tests Billy Mitchell was fighting to stage. Centralization would come, he assured me, and in being transferred to the office of the Chief of the Air Service, I would be in a better position to work toward that end, but in the interim between the transfer and the tests, I would have much to do.

I knew it was not just our camera equipment that required improvement to photograph the bombings, but our photographic aircraft as well. Directly after my trip to Washington, I had a personal experience that emphasized the point.

In doing our mapping missions, we operated our DH-4s from take-off to operational altitude, which ranged from 16,000 to 18,000 feet, at full throttle. The climb required at least an hour and, once we'd leveled off, it was necessary to maintain altitude by continuing to use nearly maximum power. This was tough on the Liberty engine.

I had made the flight in question to an altitude of 18,000 feet, and as I took up position the engine went dead, the gearing having been stripped on the Liberty's camshaft. This was my initiation into the commonplace, but never comfortable, realm of dead-stick landings. In the course of my descent, I observed that there is nothing very soothing in hearing the wind whistling through the wing braces while an immovable slab of propeller stares you in the face. Fortunately, I was able to set down at Fairfield near McCook and upon returning to home base I made a call on George Hallett.

We discussed the problem on the basis of heavily loaded photographic planes having to make forced landings over rough terrain and in remote areas, but my immediate concern was the possibility of their having to do so over the water far from shore during the bombing runs.

The Liberty engine had been mass produced during the war by Buick, Marmon, Packard, Ford, and others. By way of some rugged experiences, we knew that the Ford was the best of the lot, and I had seen that all our photographic planes were so powered. Now with the aid of George Hallett and his mechanics, efforts were made to remove defective camshafts, replace faulty gears and water jackets, and to improve the ignition system.

These improvements took time and, with the lack of money, we had to improvise and make-do with what we could scrounge. It was necessary for me to go to the Engineering Division to get approval—which meant funds—for all technological advances. Until my trip to Washington, I had been met with plenty of sympathy but little else, so upon my return I began to make judicious use of Billy Mitchell's name.

I'd shake my head woefully on rejection and say, "But General

Mitchell insists we get it done." Or, "This is the way General Mitchell outlined it when I spoke to him in Washington."

The best I got out of my efforts was a small increase in my staff, but it was a most welcome and necessary increase. The proposed budget for the Air Service for the fiscal year 1920 had been $83,-000,000, and Congress had approved $25,000,000. We simply had to operate with what was on hand, and the hand was almost empty. Without Billy Mitchell we would have been doing it on even less, or not at all. He did not endear himself to the brass of other Army services, such as the Corps of Engineers or the Cavalry, by getting his friends to raid their projects. Someone would have to forego his pet plan for a drainage canal or a better row of stables because the funds for same were siphoned to the Air Service. He infuriated the Navy by exposing its intention to dissolve naval aviation and, in all the many congressional hearings at which he testified, he belittled the concept of sea power via the battle ship, maintaining that everything on land or sea was vulnerable to aerial attack.

The war had made flying popular with the public. The hero was the daring ace of the skies and Mitchell, with his color and dash, kept the image alive. He was no cardboard image, sporting a handsome face and an unorthodox be-ribboned uniform, he was exactly as he appeared. He was playing no part, but he was willing to capitalize in every way that he could to gain what he considered was the proper recognition and utilization of air power, and his reasons were based on a faith and a vision not on personal aggrandizement.

There were many kinds of innovations in which we all participated to keep public interest in aviation at a high level. One of these was the aerial meet. In August 1920 it was announced that "the world's first competitive aerial gunnery match" would take place at Camp Perry, Ohio. Military contestants from all over the U.S. were invited to participate, and my job—or so I thought—was to handle the aerial photographic details together with the production of photographs for publicity purposes. Naturally, the underlying purpose of the event was to impress on the public the value of air power in national defense.

The meet was a huge success, thousands coming to look over the ground displays of planes, the latest aerial bombs, and assorted equipments, and then to watch the exciting aerial activities . . . some of which were unexpected.

Major William Ocker, commanding officer of the Air Service group that was competing, thrilled the crowd with a fine display of acrobatics in his English SE-5 pursuit ship. Then he proved his marksmanship by diving on targets and, with machine guns stuttering, scored some spectacular bull's-eyes. When he finished his classy demonstration, he lined up for a landing heading toward the gun butts. It was a nice landing, but in the still air a mite too fast. Alas, the advent of brakes on aircraft lay in the future, and the major finished the day by scoring a perfect bull's-eye with his plane! Not only was the SE-5 damaged, but so was the major's sunny disposition.

The following day aerial gunnery over Lake Erie was the big event. I was prevailed upon to take part in this sport, but not as one of the hunters. Instead, I was to fly a Jenny up to 3000 feet accompanied by my photographer, Benny Thomas. On a given signal, Benny was not to throw the camera over the side but a five-gallon tin of gasoline. The falling tin would pull a parachute out of a box under the fuselage, and as the tin drifted away on the chute, the fighter planes would dive on it and, using incendiary bullets, hopefully set it on fire. The first demonstration worked just fine, but on the second run some trigger-happy eagle got carried away and started shooting too soon. Suddenly Benny and I knew what it was to be under attack. With a tail full of holes, I departed the scene in a screaming dive, and from that point on, despite all kinds of entreaties, I stuck strictly to my photographic assignment.

Despite my firm stand I was tremendously popular for a while because the pilots had learned that I was using pure grain alcohol to quick dry my film and prints in the laboratory trailer we had brought along. This was during prohibition, and the boys had learned to mix grain alcohol with Virginia Dare, which was a fairly good drink. I had brought along fifty gallons of the former, and by the third day the barrel ran dry. After that, interest in our photographic contributions died swiftly. Even so, from every aspect the Camp Perry competition was a great success pleasing public and press alike.

On my return to McCook, I learned that Colonel Bane had grown increasingly annoyed by the lack of action in Washington. He had written a letter to the office of the Air Service Chief, General Menoher, complaining further about the lack of progress not only in photographic consolidation but also in acquiring the funds to support it. He wished me to follow up his letter by returning to Washington to press for action. So back I went, only to see that none of the officers on the staff wanted to do much about it. There were, in their minds, so many more important plans such as laying out new airways, and developing navigational and radio aids.

Again it was General Mitchell who offered at least a partial solution. He would no longer delay my transfer, and he would see to it that I was assigned to the Operations and Plans Division in the office of the Chief of the Air Service. There it was thought I would spend part of my efforts on the consolidation problem and part in preparing for the aerial photographic coverage of the battleship bombing program which at the time was part dream, part secret, part boast of Billy Mitchell.

During my transitional period at McCook and Carlstrom, I had been pursuing a separate but important course of action. In March, 1919, shortly after I arrived at McCook, Colonel Bane had informed me that the War Department was interested in giving regular Army commissions to Air Service Reserve officers who could meet the educational and professional requirements. I told him my educational and professional efforts had been projected toward a career in commercial art, and he said that did not matter because all Reserve officers would be given a year and a half or so to bone up on certain subjects.

I was sent to Washington where a special board decided I would have to pass written examinations in math, English composition and two other subjects to meet the requirements for a regular Army commission.

When I first went to McCook, I had made the acquaintance of a young aeronautical engineer, René LeMere, and we roomed together in the Dayton YMCA. René was a sharp mathematician and had taught the subject in a school in the Middle West. For over a year in the evenings he helped me with my calculus and logarithms, and I was able to find enough time during the day, particularly on weekends, to master the other subjects. On many of my overnight cross-country trips, I took my textbooks along and found a few hours to devote to them. Sometimes on long flights, adverse weather conditions grounded me and I was able to get in two or three days of study in my hotel room.

Late in the summer of 1920 I took the two days of written examinations at McCook under the supervision of the local examining board. The board was composed of early-bird senior officer pilots, three West Point majors, Herbert A. Dargue, Lawrence W. MacIntosh, and Alfred H. Hobley. A week or so later I received the good news that I had passed the examination and received a second lieutenant commission in the Regular Army. Shortly thereafter, I was upped in rank to first lieutenant, due to my length of service as a shavetail.

This did not end my off-hours studies, for I was now definitely embarked on a career in aerial photography. In order to obtain assignments directing research and development, field operations and in administration, I had to study optics, photographic chemistry, electronics, mechanical engineering, map making and other related subjects. This habit of study continued throughout my career.

Before my departure for Washington, General Mitchell had called me and asked that I select someone to take my place at McCook. The officer I chose was Captain Albert Stevens. We had not met at the time, but I had heard plenty about him.

Steve, as he was called, was strictly a Westerner in size and attitude. Nothing phased him. Six foot three, over two hundred pounds, he had a wide open face with jug-handle ears and a bushy mustache that made him look like an old-time law man. He had studied mining and when he joined the Air Service in 1917, he was working as a civil engineer.

Awarded a captain's commission and given a short course at Cornell, he went off to France and there, perched in the basket of an observation balloon, he got plenty of experience photographing enemy lines. The hazard that went with the experience he took as a matter of course. When the war ended, he remained with the Army of Occupation, continuing his photographic endeavors in the rear cockpit of a Samson. Upon his return to the States in 1920, he was put in charge of taking aerial publicity pictures for the Air Service. In such capacity he made the first aerial mosaic of Rochester, New York. Steve had also been on the board responsible for sending a detachment of engineers to McCook, abetting my plan for centralization.

In making my selection, I was not aware of how close I had come to losing Steve even before I met him. About the time I was finishing up my flight training at Carlstrom, Steve and Lieutenant Shorty MacSpadden took off one morning in their DH-4 from Mitchel Field, Hempstead, Long Island. There was a flag pole in front of the headquarters building which they somehow managed to hit. They had sufficient flying speed to miss the building, full of personnel at the time. Instead, they crashed through the roof of the commanding officer's living quarters. The nose of the plane landed on the COs bed an instant after his wife had left the room. Both men were knocked unconscious and were rushed to the field hospital where it was discovered that the pilot was not seriously injured and Steve didn't have a scratch on his body.

They put both men to bed in separate rooms for observation, with a nurse in charge. During the night Steve got restless, hopped out of bed, dressed and took off for New York City in a car he borrowed from a friend. Shorty MacSpadden suffered some internal injuries and was hospitalized for several weeks. It was lucky that the plane cracked into one of the frail wooden temporary buildings, for the roof and the bed provided quite a cushioning effect, and the plane did not fracture the main fuel tank and catch fire.

Steve was relaxed about everything but his work. Many stories grew up around his eccentric activities, most of them true. It came to be clearly understood that every afternoon, rain or shine, Steve would don his running suit and sneakers and canter for two or three miles "just to keep in trim." This daily exercise took precedence over everything else and it was generally followed by a snooze, either on the floor, bench, or table.

Shortly after Steve took over my job at McCook, Major Davidson invited him to dinner. Apparently on the evening in question, he was taking his nap and forgot all about the dinner engagement. When he didn't show up the Davidsons telephoned him. In a few minutes they saw his car drive up and stop in front of the house. They waited and waited, and finally they looked out to see Steve struggling to change from coveralls to black tie in the back of the model-T.

When I left for duty in Washington, I issued orders, making Steve chief of the photographic branch at McCook. The deal, approved by Colonel Bane and General Mitchell, was that Steve would take my job for four years, but at the end of that time I would return.

Steve and I shook on it and, on October 4, 1920, I headed east to take up the position of Photographic Officer, Training and Operations, Air Service Headquarters, Washington, D.C.

## 5

Although it was not until February of 1921 that the Navy finally accepted Billy Mitchell's bombing challenge, upon my arrival in Washington I worked with the knowledge that at some juncture in the not too distant future the tests would take place. Therefore, with myself at the focal point, I had to see to it that photograph crews were thoroughly trained and their aircraft and camera equipment were in unparalleled condition.

The crews were to be drawn from our seven photo sections within the U.S., and from the photographic training school at Langley Field. As noted, better aircraft performance already had a top priority. With the degree of skill we had at hand, we knew that men and planes could be brought to peak efficiency. This was particularly true under the inspiration of a Billy Mitchell who, in that brief time, instilled within us all an unspoken esprit de corps. However, the quality of our cameras and photographic equipment was another matter, a matter that spirit alone could not improve.

At McCook, I had labored to bring about needed refinements in the K-1 Folmer-Schwing, but when I arrived in Washington, it was still *the* principal aerial reconnaissance camera of the day. As such, it took only vertical pictures and was too heavy and unwieldy to be held over the side of an airplane. There was a serious spacing problem between each exposure which restricted the number of pictures per mission. It had a 20-inch lens which prevented our getting the kind of sharp detail required when flying at higher altitudes or through haze. Its focal length was such that when we got down low, we could only photograph a limited area.

There was also a static effect which often caused marked exposures.

As I saw it, what we needed for the bombing tests and reconnaissance in general was a camera that could be hand held, would take both vertical and oblique pictures, and with a focal length that would permit high- and low-level photography offering wide angle photos with maximum definition. To go with it, we needed better quality film and better developing and printing machines.

Before my transfer, some progress had been made toward these ends, but now there was an urgency that had been lacking heretofore and with it, for once, enough money to help accomplish them. The key factor was time, for until the problems of the K-1 were licked, the Air Service was certainly not going to sign a contract for a new model of it. Yet, in my mind for the first time the aerial camera was going to be called on not so much to prove its own merit as that of the Air Service in a contest that might well determine the future of air power in the United States. To me whatever tests took place, the public and the government should be able to evaluate them through the eye of the camera. No words would convey the results of the coming confrontation between sea and air power as would an aerial photo or film, and if the cameras that took the pictures did not measure up to the men and the planes who flew the bombing missions, the public and the administration might fail to judge the vital results correctly. The issue had become acrimonious. We in the Air Service believed that those standing against us would go to almost any length to protect and preserve their own vested interests.

At least that is how all my fellow pilots and I saw it. Even so I could not devote my full time to it, for as Chief Photographic Officer it was necessary that I also take a leading role in the major peace time photographic job of the Air Service—aerial map making. In this regard, having been made a member of the Federal Board of Surveys and Maps as the Air Service Representative, it was my job to raise the standard of the work being done by our photographic sections.

It was agreed that photographic mapping pilotage was the most difficult and precise type of flying to be had. Complaints were beginning to come in from pilots and observers who were required to fly long missions at 16,500 feet doing aerial mapping. The oxygen starvation plus the breathing of the engine's carbon monoxide exhaust caused a dulling of judgment and intellect and a very uncomfortable sensation in general. Those effects were compounded by the constant roar from the 12-cylinder Liberty engine less than six feet away from the open cockpit. The only cure was plenty of sleep after a mission. My attempts to get the medical department at McCook to equip our aircraft with oxygen met with nothing but debate for a number of years, for the test pilots at McCook considered us a bunch of sissies. They felt that any pilot worth his wings didn't need oxygen under 20,000 feet. Like the bumblebee who doesn't know he's aerodynamically too heavy to fly, we accepted their verdict and got on with it as best we could.

Many times I took off and going up to 18,000 feet flew straight and level flight lines. To maintain a constant altitude on flights of two or three hours required a close watch of the altimeter. At the same time it was necessary to check the compass and land marks on the ground so that at the end of each strip, when I made my 180-degree turn, the adjoining strip in the opposite direction would make it possible for the cameraman to make his pictures with a 25 percent overlap of photographs on each strip. In the line of flight each picture would overlap the next picture 60 percent to provide the stereoscopic feature. The pilot, in turning from one strip to another, had to follow the various lines drawn on a map and pass exactly over the terrain detail indicated. The photographic plane had to be held in a level position at all times during the mission, and cross-winds had to be determined so that the plane could be headed a few degrees into the wind and thus not drift off the straight line course. Compensating for drift, the cameraman would be required to rotate the camera in the camera suspension in order to make a straight line of pictures over the flight line. Sometimes while flying flight lines in strong cross-winds, the plane would be headed in what we call the "crab" angle as much as 15 to 20 degrees.

The test pilot boys might call us softies, but one had only to fly such a mission once before he knew what precision really meant under tough conditions.

With all that I had to accomplish, it was necessary that I do a great deal of flying. At Bolling Field, not far from Washington, we had two special photographically modified DH-4s, and I was always in need of one of them. The planes were kept in good condition and ready to go on a moment's notice. However, the Bolling Field operations officer did not take our efforts seriously and on several occasions when I showed up to fly somewhere in a hurry, one or both of the planes would be missing.

We had some impolite words over this matter which reached a climax when he dispatched one of our planes to take part in a burial service at Arlington Cemetery. The plane was one of three designated to drop flowers over the grave site of a fellow officer killed in a crash. This was a standard practice, and unfortunately a frequent one, but just as our bird came over Arlington, its engine quit. The pilot chose as his landing field an area of experimental fruit trees grown by the Agriculture Department. With considerable expertise but questionable motivation, he managed to glide into the top of a big apple tree. The engine took off in one direction while much of the fuselage and the tail went in the other. The flower-dropper lay on the ground bedecked with garlands of red and white carnations, and the pilot sat entwined in the branches above picking the bark out of his teeth. In all a rather splendid and colorful descent with neither man hurt, but I was furious at the loss of the plane.

I went to see General Mitchell, and the result was that from then on, until December 1941, all our photographic planes bore the yellow lettering—*FOR PHOTOGRAPHIC USE ONLY*. My move did not endear me to the operations officer and his buddies, but it assured me a plane when I needed it.

On one memorable flight I made what can only be described as a red hot landing. Unfortunately, it was a part of *me* that was fired up. I had flown the DH-4 with its Liberty engine for so many hours with the throttle wide open that I was beginning to lose hearing in my left ear. With the throttle on the left, it was natural to lean to that side of the cockpit. The engine was only a few feet ahead and its short exhaust stacks made a helliferocious racket. To cut out some of the noise I always flew with a big wad of cotton batting tucked in over my left ear under my helmet.

On the flight in question, I was coming in for a landing and as I throttled back, leaning to the left and leveling off, an unusual amount of hot carbon sprayed back from the exhaust stacks and started a fire in the batting. I did not stop to consider that I might be taken for a flying dragon, but let go throttle and stick and with all my strength tore the helmet from my head and got it and the burning cotton over the side. The landing was perhaps the first no-hands event of its kind. I walked away from it still smoldering, and for the next week sported a very sore ear. After that I used sponge rubber in place of batting.

Because of so much flying, my office paper work was being neglected and I was asked to do something about it. This gave me an excuse to add another officer to our Bolling Field unit, which consisted of four enlisted men, two pilots, a shack for a dark room, and a one-room office.

I flew down to Langley and interviewed several students due to graduate from the photographic school. My selection was Lieutenant Howard K. Ramey, a former acrobatic pilot. Howard had a game eye, the result of a flight training dare taken during the war. The idea was to see who could spin closest to the ground and still pull out. Howard misjudged and luckily lived to tell about it, but ever after with a squinting eye. Several years my junior, he spoke with a quiet southern drawl that somehow went with his introspective manner. We became fast friends.

Shortly after Howard joined me, we did a big mapping job in which we made mosaics of the Massachusetts Agricultural College, plus the cities of Boston and Portland, Maine. Because there were no landing facilities at Portland, we used the beach at Old Orchard. The finished prints were exhibited at the Federal Board of Surveys and Maps. The exhibit, in turn, stirred up further interest and brought numerous requests to the Air Service from various government bureaus for similar operations.

Interlarded among these regular duties there were special missions, many of which reflected Billy Mitchell's determination to further the cause of aviation, military and civilian. We photographed possible landing fields along America's first two airways from Washington, D.C. to Dayton, Ohio, and from Chicago to New York. The opening up of such airways had been Mitchell's idea from the first.

Following this project, I was assigned by the General to supervise aerial reconnaissance work urgently requested by the Governor of West Virginia. I was to fly Sergeant Andy Matos, my trusty cameraman at Bolling, to the Mingo, West Virginia, coal district and take aerial pictures of the strike riots.

While Benny Thomas, my trusty cameraman at McCook, had been short and barrel chested and Polish, Andy was short and barrel chested and Greek. Our mission was to photograph roving mobs of miners armed with shotguns. Everything looked very warlike and President Warren G. Harding had called out the National Guard.

Before we could begin our work, it was necessary for us to fly to McCook to obtain a supply of photographic film and paper. We took off from Bolling intending to fly non-stop. We had so much equipment in the rear cockpit we had to put some of it on the wings tied to the struts in order for Andy to sit down and be comfortable. Then the plane with its extra large gasoline supply was so heavy that we used all the field before it would leave the ground.

As we were flying over Moundsville, West Virginia, the normal halfway stopping point for Army planes enroute to Dayton, I noticed an airplane which had cracked up on the edge of the flying field.[1] Believing that help might be needed, I spiraled down

[1] Cross country flight necessitated an itinerary that included stops in Moundsville, West Virginia; Dayton; Bellwood, Illinois—generally an overnight—Muskegee, Oklahoma; Dallas and San Antonio. The next overnight was Del Rio, Texas, and, after a couple of additional touchdowns, El Paso. Of course, this had to be an overnight halt because it was in the days of prohibition and, also, the boys surely liked that Mexican

and landed. To my great surprise I discovered it was a McCook Field photographic plane which had stopped for gas on its way to Washington and a mapping mission in New Hampshire. The pilot was Lieutenant Leigh Wade, and the photographer was none other than Steve. Leigh, coming in for a landing, had leveled off and the tail of the aircraft simply kept on going down. After that the wheels splayed out and retracted through the wings while all sorts of parts and appendages including the propeller came unstuck.

I taxied up to the line and then walked out to the little group of mechanics surveying the wreckage with Leigh. Steve, dressed in a heavy leather flying suit, was sitting on the ground nursing a sore head and staring off at the great beyond.

To my query: "What happened?" Leigh, short and wiry and on the dry side said, "Take a look in the back end."

I did so. It looked like a junk shop. There were cameras, film magazines, chemical containers, even a foot locker, plus assorted tools and other heavy items. The biggest puzzle was how Steve had managed to fit himself in the cockpit at all.

I went over to him and said, "Steve, why did you leave it out?"

He looked up, one eye puffed and swollen, "What out?" he mumbled rubbing his numb shoulder.

"The hotel kitchen sink."

Steve did not see the humor of it; he was dazed and banged up.

Leigh chuckled and said, "I'll tell you one thing, big boy, from now on when I fly you anywhere I'll inspect the rear cockpit first."

A test pilot at McCook, this had been Leigh's first assignment on an aerial mapping mission. He had an excellent record and

---

food and the senoritas. All the way from Washington generally required some major maintenance work, too.

The next stop was generally at Tucson, Arizona, although if there was a strong west wind it was necessary to land at Lordsburg, New Mexico. From Tucson the next point was Yuma, Arizona, and from there you could make San Diego or Los Angeles. Counting stops for maintenance and that extra day in El Paso, it was generally four to six days from Washington to Los Angeles.

was later selected as one of the four pilots to circle the globe in 1924.

While I had been talking to Leigh and Steve, the field mechanics had loaded my big extra size gas and oil tanks, and the question now arose—should I attempt to take off?

There was little wind. The field was short and poorly placed in a valley and, further, it was unseasonably warm and there was little lift in the air. All were good reasons for delaying until conditions improved, but grit overbalancing brain power, I determined to try it.

Halfway down the field I knew it was going to be close. With our added weight we were bouncing and, although the air speed was building and I had the tail up, the bouncing was cutting down on our lift. Somehow I managed to stagger the plane off the ground and then just as I thought we'd make it, the engine quit. I had time to cut the switches and then we crashed into a corn field, landing upside down.

The next thing I knew I was in an inverted position with gasoline spraying all over me. I struggled frantically to get free, the horror of fire filling me, but I couldn't get the seat belt unfastened and I began shouting for help.

The first men to arrive were two or three naked swimmers fresh from the Ohio River. To me they looked like something out of the River Styx, and there wasn't much they could do but dance around and tell me that Andy, who for some reason had forgotten to fasten his safety belt, had been thrown far ahead of the wreck and was unconscious. Then suddenly Steve, Leigh, and mechanics from the field arrived and they literally tore me loose from the cockpit with crowbar and wire cutters.

I had spent so much time trapped in the wreck that gasoline had burned my skin, particularly in certain sensitive areas. It was a small price to pay for what could have been a fiery departure. Andy was unhurt, and the doctor who arrived on the scene supplied me with skin oil. At a nearby house, I was able to take a bath and borrow a shirt and some underwear.

And so it was the following morning that Leigh, Steve, Andy

Matos, and I sat aboard a B&O train enroute to Dayton to get two more DH-4s out of the Fairfield depot supply. After completing the lengthy Air Service crash reports, we hurriedly modified another plane for our photographic work. Then Andy and I returned to Moundsville and photographed the coal strike riots, which covered a large area of the surrounding country. Other planes were also operating out of Moundsville on visual observation missions and several returned with bullet holes through their wings.

Our job was to locate the rioters so that the military ground forces could take them into custody. This gave us some good training in quick-work photography, for we had set up a shed at the end of the airfield and we were able to drop finished photographs to the ground forces in less than an hour from the time the pictures were taken.

During that same period of time, I had another memorable landing in connection with the beginning of a memorable U.S. event. The Board of Surveys and Maps decided to see how useful aerial photography could be to the Engineers on a big general survey of the Tennessee River Basin. A power and water conservation project was in mind which later became familiarly known as the TVA.

After one such mapping mission, Howard Ramey and I, flying back from Chattanooga, got caught in soupy weather and couldn't find a landing field in Asheville, North Carolina. Extremely low on gas, we spotted the Vanderbilt estate at Biltmore, a suburb of the city, and decided it would be a dandy place to land. We went right down the center of a nice flat, green fairway, our tail skid with its V-shaped blade cutting a neat deep furrow.

In no time at all we were descended upon by Mrs. Vanderbilt, the gardener, rake in hand, and assorted members of the household. They had no words of cheer and greeting.

"How dare you land that—that thing here! You've ruined the lawn! Look at it, look at it!"

We looked and apologized.

"I shall report you to the Secretary of War!" declared the great lady and the gardener shook his rake.

We tried to explain.

"Madam, we regret having had to land, but we're very low on gas."

"We do not supply gas here, young man, and there's a perfectly good landing field at Asheville!"

" 'Fraid we missed it, mam," Howard piped up, "awfully dark up there," he raised his eyes to the low scudding clouds.

A survey of the overcast by all assembled seemed to mollify our unexpecting hostess momentarily. Further, a great crowd was beginning to trickle in from the surrounding countryside, and it appeared that if she didn't give us some assistance soon, she'd have a real trespassing problem on her hands. A gas truck was duly summoned from the city. But, by the time we had refueled, the field was so crowded with curious spectators that Mrs. V. had stalked away in high dudgeon, and I wondered, as we finally took off, if she were on the phone to the President.

It was not the President but the Secretary of War, for orders were issued very swiftly thereafter to all Air Service stations banning landings on the Vanderbilt estate. However, before the orders could be properly assimilated, another lucky pilot landed on the same fairway and cut a furrow next to ours. If he got out of the cockpit, we figured they may have had him for dinner. At any rate, shortly thereafter, the Vanderbilts had a bunker installed halfway down the fairway and the problem was forever resolved.

When I was in my office for any length of time, I always tried to drive my model-T Ford to Bolling around noontime to get some exercise. One noon I was late leaving the office and was speeding along through town and over the Anacostia Bridge. As I approached Bolling, I was stopped by a motorcycle cop and told to follow him to the Anacostia police station. The charge was that I was speeding at 22 miles an hour—the regulation speed limit being 15. Also, I had failed to stop for a stop sign.

I was forced to put up $25 collateral and told to report to the

District Court on a certain date. About a month before I had been stopped for speeding along Pennsylvania Avenue by a cop on a bicycle. He said I was going 18 miles per hour, three miles faster than the legal speed limit. It was noted on my driver's license and I was afraid this second go-round might mean the loss of my license, so I had to think fast.

The following day the judge asked what my excuse was, and I told him I was hurrying to Bolling Field to supervise the development of some aerial films I had made at 10,000 feet over Washington for use by the District in city planning work. The old judge became extremely interested in my photo work and for the next fifteen minutes or so, much to the curiosity of the packed courtroom, we talked about aerial cameras, lenses, films, and the mosaics being made for the Corps of Engineers and other federal agencies. I told him I was making a mosaic map of the city which would be delivered to the Commissioners in due course and that, in my excitement in wanting to supervise the development of the film, I went a few miles over the regular speed limit.

To my surprise the judge exclaimed, "Lieutenant, you are doing valuable work in the service, and maybe in your haste you did forget about the city regulations. I am going to give you back your twenty-five dollars and please, in the future, keep your eyes on your speedometer."

Three or four days later, General Menoher was attending a civic function in the city and met the judge, who told him what a wonderful job I was doing for the District of Columbia. The General tactfully replied, "That's news to me. I've never okayed such a project. The lieutenant must have been spoofing you."

The following day the General called me in for an explanation, and I told him Sergeant Matos and I had been making some training test flight trips over Washington and that some day we would assemble them into a mosaic and, with his permission, give them to the Army city engineer. This, of course, took me off the hook and since the General seemed to like the idea, I naturally assumed he would explain to the judge.

A few days later, a Lieutenant Van Vecton, located at Bolling Field, got picked up for speeding and asked me for a little advice in appearing before the same judge. I suggested he get him interested in some of his Air Service flying duties. Van appeared in court the next day, all spruced up in his service uniform, and as he was about to do a little explaining, the judge shot out, "You don't need to say a word. That will cost you fifty dollars!" Then he continued, "You're one of Goddard's Bolling buddies," and related the cock-and-bull story I'd given him.

General Menoher also heard about this exchange and sent me down to square things, which I did, but it wasn't easy.

February 1921 was a milestone month for me for two reasons. First, the Navy took up the gauntlet and publicly accepted Billy Mitchell's long-sought challenge to permit aerial bombing tests on four ex-German warships—and, secondly, I met Sherman Fairchild.

Sherman's father, Congressman George W. Fairchild of Oneonta, New York, brought him to my office in the Munitions Building. The Congressman, a portly authoritative gentleman, who had been an extremely successful business man before entering politics, came directly to the point.

"Lieutenant, I brought Sherman down to meet you because I've been told by General Mitchell that you know more about aerial cameras than anyone around this town, and Sherman has designed a new one he wants to show you."

What the very boyish, soft-spoken young man had to show me was a design the like of which I might have dreamed about but had never seen. The camera was electrically driven, not hand wound; it had a between-the-lens shutter which meant sharper definition without distortion to the objects photographed. It had an intervalometer, an indicator you could pre-set to take pictures at whatever intervals you chose. In addition, the magazine had been designed to eliminate the old bugaboo of unequal spacing. It was, in fact, in every respect a masterful piece of designing and I had no reluctance in saying so, wishing vainly that we had such a camera for the bombing tests.

The fact that Sherman Fairchild and I had not met previously was another stunning example of why my cry for consolidation made awfully good sense. He had been working with Dr. Herbert Ives, then in charge of the Signal Corps Science and Research Division for the development of new aerial cameras. The Division was as closely associated with Eastman Kodak as I had been. Yet I'd never heard of Sherman.

In 1919 he had volunteered his services to Dr. Ives, whom I knew only slightly, and unbeknownst to me—in fact, for many years—Sherman contributed much to the development of the K-1. In my capacity at McCook, I had been laboring to bring about *improvements* in the K-1 and consequently I had little to do with Dr. Ives. Now, by a stroke of luck, I had met a young photographic genius, whose mother had actually been disappointed when he refused to give up his interest in cameras and become "a society man."

In a few moments we had all but forgotten his father and my excitement soared as we discussed his new design in particular and aerial photography in general.

The result was that I took father and son to see General Mitchell right then and there, and he, in turn, became so enthusiastic that he gave me approval to buy an experimental model of the camera at a cost of approximately $2000.[2]

While Sherman Fairchild's camera was a product of the future, I, of course, was directly concerned with fulfilling our immediate needs, particularly now that the bombing tests were officially on

[2] Within two years of the date of the first Fairchild contract in the spring of 1921, the K-3 became a standard aerial camera in the Army and Navy Air Services and it marked a milestone in the development of aerial cameras for military, governmental agencies, and civilian aerial photographic surveying companies in the United States, Canada, and countries around the world. Thousands of these cameras, both for military reconnaissance and civilian aerial mapping, have been procured through the years and are in use in the Vietnam military operations. Of course, many refinements have been made, but it is remarkable how much of the old basic Fairchild design has endured. Little did I realize in the '20s when I used to fly Sherman and his engineers around on tests of the first K-3, that it represented the beginning of a company that was to dominate the industry for many years and wind up with a backlog of some forty million dollars worth of business at the end of World War II.

and we were all operating at full throttle in preparation. I had been riding the Folmer-Schwing division of Eastman Kodak pretty hard to come forth with the modifications we had so long been seeking and, lo and behold, a month or so after my meeting with Sherman they did just that, producing three test models of the modified K-1 which we simply dubbed the K-2.

A tremendous weight was lifted from my mind after Howard Ramey and I flight tested the K-2. It had all the improvements I had felt were essential, and I knew then the bombing tests were going to be photographed to suit Billy Mitchell's pleasure.

I was, of course, most anxious to show him what we finally had, but I wanted to pick the right moment. Since he was then almost constantly on the move, and I knew he often flew into Bolling, I waited until such time when I was sure he was due to land there, and then I waylaid him in the pilot's dressing room as he was climbing out of his flying suit.

Without protest, the General came with me to the shack we called a laboratory and there, with Howard and Andy Matos, I unveiled the K-2 for him. He had a sure grasp of the mechanical, and after we had dissembled the camera he was able to understand its inner workings.

"George, it's excellent!" he finally said, clapping me on the shoulder. "I knew I was right in bringing you here. We'll really show them what a picture's worth."

## 6

Throughout the first half of 1921, even before the bombing tests had been confirmed, General Mitchell seemed to be everywhere at once, appearing before congressional committees, flying to cities around the country giving lectures about the money being wasted on building battleships and coastal defenses, and the great possibilities of military and civilian aviation.

When he was not selling his wares to Congress or the public, the General was dashing out to McCook for pep talks with Colonel Bane and his engineers. At one such meeting, a classic exchange took place between the two.

The colonel, a graduate of West Point, liked everything neat and plain. When you did something wrong, you were required to write an explanation of it in longhand, but nothing fancy, it had to be in the colonel's lexicon, "vertical."

On the occasion in question, Billy was being blunt and derogatory. "Don't show me all this stone age stuff, Colonel, show me something new!" he complained. To which the colonel replied flatly, "General, if you've got any complaints to make of this division, you just put it in vertical."

For once Billy Mitchell had no response.

The General's continual lecturing on the superiority of the airplane over the battleship caused quite a ruckus in the top echelons of the Navy and Secretary of the Navy, Josephus Daniels, requested an immediate reprimand of the General. The naval aviation officers and men were, naturally, in Mitchell's corner and that further irritated the Secretary. The General had so many friends (even in President Harding) that there was not much the Secretaries of the Navy and Army could do.

Realizing this, the Honorable Mr. Daniels started to ridicule the General's battleship bombing plans. He announced that he would be willing to sit on the deck of a naval vessel while it was being bombed. The press had such a field day over the statement the Secretary wished he'd kept his mouth shut.

The General could not help making a great many enemies, for as he put it to a congressional committee: "We do not like to see things destroyed that we have been brought up to revere and protect: that is human nature and it is nobody's fault. The battleship is looked on all over the world by all the navies as being the thing that must be glorified. We think we can destroy it; it is our business to attack it, and it is up to you to judge whether we can do it or not."[1]

A short time before the bombing tests took place his opponents put on a last minute drive to have him removed from his job as Assistant Chief of the Air Service, and with a lesser man they might have sccceeded. The attack followed the country's worst air disaster.

There had been a bombing test near Langley Field for Captain de Lavergne, the French Air Attaché. Also on hand was a large newly developed Curtiss-Eagle aircraft, designed as an ambulance plane. At the conclusion of the test, it had flown into a terrific thunderstorm and, with five Air Service officers and two prominent civilians on board, it had crashed near Indian Head, Maryland, killing all.

Many other pilots, including Billy Mitchell and Eddie Rickenbacker, were caught in the storm and narrowly escaped crashing. The winds were estimated at 100 miles per hour, and I had a strong taste of them myself, for I, too, was aloft, returning with Andy Matos from Langley to Bolling. I attempted to go west around the edge of the storm but got caught in the wind shift line. The turbulence was so violent that I thought the wings

[1] Isaac Dan Levine, *Mitchell, Pioneer of Air Power,* Duell Sloane and Pearce, 1943, 1958, p. 219.

were going to come unstuck, and I quickly gave it up and headed back to Langley.

The crash caused great controversy and the press, backed by Mitchell's enemies, called for an official inquiry. But Billy went on the attack. He laid blame for the crash on the fact that the Army had not supported the air arm with funds and facilities for the development of radio service to fliers, weather bulletins to airplanes and improved navigational equipment. It actually turned out to be quite a victory because the whole country was demanding that there should be a complete reorganization of the Air Service to guard against future airplane accidents and loss of life and that it should be commanded by a flyer with General Mitchell's qualifications.

One of Billy Mitchell's staunch supporters was Congressman Roy G. Fitzgerald, whose home town was Dayton, Ohio. A big heavy-set man, gruff and outspoken in Congress and out, the Congressman was a friend of Orville Wright and an aviation enthusiast from the outset.

As a result, one evening the General called on me at my boardinghouse, which today has been replaced by the west half of Blair House just across from the White House.

"George," he greeted me, "Congressman Fitzgerald has to be in Dayton tomorrow about two o'clock for a speech and picnic. The pilot scheduled to fly him is reported ill. Can you take him? You can get off at seven, be there in plenty of time."

The next morning I met the Congressman at Bolling at the appointed hour. The weather in Dayton was reported flyable, and after bundling my jowly passenger in a flying suit and into the rear cockpit, off we went.

A short time later, I noticed Fitzgerald was busily at work writing his speech. I also noticed that the weather was beginning to look not so flyable. As we proceeded over the mountain ridges, a gray overcast lowered and it began to rain. When I had passed Cumberland on my right, I tried to work my way through the gap toward McConnellsburg, Pennsylvania, but it was no good, for the ceiling had come down to the treetops. Reluctantly, I executed the sanest maneuver in aviation, the 180-degree turn, and headed back for Bolling.

As we headed back I turned around and the Congressman smiled and went on writing. When we passed very close to the Washington Monument the smile was replaced by expressions of disbelief, consternation, and then downright anger.

After we landed and were taxiing up to the flight line in front of the operations office, I could hear the Congressman behind me, the sound and fury mounting over the sound of the engine.

I cut the switches.

"Lieutenant, will you tell me what in the name of hell we are doing back here! Why aren't we in Dayton where we belong!" He had a powerful voice and it carried well.

"I'm sorry, sir," I said, standing up in the cockpit and pulling off my helmet, "the weather got too bad."

"But I've got to go to Dayton! I'm expected! I have to be there!"

"You don't want to break your neck, do you, Congressman? I know I don't want to break mine. I wouldn't have turned back if I hadn't known that's what would have happened."

"But I've got to *be* there! I've got to get there!" He waved the pages of his speech, and as I climbed out of the plane, he followed me, ranting all the way. His outcry had attracted considerable notice and as we walked into the flight clearance office, one of McCook's crack test pilots was waiting to greet us.

"I'm going to Dayton, Congressman," he said, "I'll be glad to take you."

Congressman Fitzgerald let out a great sigh of relief and beamed upon the test pilot as though he had been presented as a gift from the voters.

A few minutes later I watched him become airborne again, not at all pleased with the situation. Weather reports were few and far between and, at best, not very dependable. I had brought back what the weather was enroute, but the test pilot had chosen to ignore it. Concerned as I was, I made it a point to call flight operations at intervals during the day. Sure enough about three o'clock I was told that the plane had cracked up near Keyser, West Virginia, but the Congressman and the pilot, aside from a few bumps and bruises, were uninjured. It was time for my sigh of relief.

The following day I was pleasantly surprised to receive a phone call from Congressman Fitzgerald. He told me of his accident and how he had phoned his speech to Dayton to a secretary who gave the talk on schedule. After apologizing for his behavior, he said: "George, from now on I'll fly with you any place, any time."

He really meant it because I later flew him to Dayton on several occasions. He worked hard for the cause of military aviation and the establishment of the extensive Air Service facilities at Dayton can be credited, in a large measure, to his untiring efforts in the halls of Congress.

As for Congress, once it had approved the bombing tests, Billy Mitchell and his aides went furiously to work organizing and setting up training for the First Provisional Air Brigade at Langley Field. Mitchell summoned all the pros in the service on whom he could lay hands—pilots, bombardiers, and mechanics alike, one thousand strong, to man and attend 150 pursuit planes and bombers.

Preparations went forward on an around-the-clock basis, and morale soared. Lieutenant Clayton Bissell, one of Mitchell's aides who had won the British Distinguished Flying Cross in the war, established a tactical school and with Lieutenant Tom Milling and a handful of other instructors, began teaching gunnery and dive bombing.

The major brunt of the bombing attack was to be carried out by twin engine Martin bombers. The conditions under which the tests were to take place had been laid down by the Navy and they were as tough as could be expected. The bombing area was fixed some 70 miles off the Cape Charles Light Ship, and nearly a hundred miles from Langley. Such distance was extreme in that day and permitted only a limited time for our aircraft to remain in the target area.

The Brigade's photo section had its work cut out as well, and I saw to it that by drawing on our other sections its complement of planes was increased from two to nine. In fact, soon after they arrived at Langley, Mitchell landed and, stepping out of his SE-5, saw them all lined up.

"What are you doing with those DH's?" he said to Major "Jam" Johnson, who was acting CO. "We're going to bomb with Martins, not DH's."

"I know," Johnson replied, "that damn Goddard ordered them in here to take pictures."

Mitchell laughed. "That's great. You give him everything he wants."

In getting everything I wanted, our planes were equipped with the new K-2 and we had a plentiful supply of motion picture cameras. I flew up to Aberdeen, Maryland, and talked the Ordnance people into lending us one of their class "D" dirigibles, so that Louis Hagemeyer would have a stable platform to take films of the bombings for motion picture newsreels and engineering studies at McCook.

Complete responsibility for the actual picture taking of the tests was in the hands of the Langley Photo Section, and the four officers in charge, Lieutenants George C. MacDonald, Jimmy Hodges, Jasper K. McDuffie, and Bill Boyd, were all old pros at the game.

The big day finally arrived on June 21, 1921, and Billy Mitchell was right where the action was throughout. His DH-4, was plainly marked with a long red and blue streamer attached to the tail. During the course of the tests, his rear cockpit was occupied by one of his aides, Captain Billy "Wingborne" Streett. Mitchell's only worries concerned the weather and the reliability of his bombs, which had been developed by the Army Ordnance Corps.

To sink a modern non-sinkable battleship seemed almost beyond the present development of bombs, bomb sights and, in par-

ticular, the bomb shackle release mechanism. Throughout World
War I, bombs generally weighed around 100 pounds and were
dropped by single-engine aircraft. These tests were to require the
release of 1000- to 2000-pound bombs, and from November 1918
to June 1921 there had been little done to ensure the dependability
of this equipment. The Ordnance Corps, under the able guidance
of Major William Borden and his group, worked around the
clock to help Mitchell prove his claims. They were just as enthusiastic as the Air Service to make the tests a success.

The U. S. Navy made the transport *Henderson* available to
carry Congressional leaders, Navy, Army, and Air Service officials, the press and members of the diplomatic corps to the scene
of the bombings. With so many skeptics and proponents aboard,
it was not difficult to start an argument.

The first exercise involved the sinking of a German submarine
and was strictly a Naval aerial gunnery and bombing test. The
Navy planes struck and sank the sub so swiftly many of those
on board the *Henderson,* and the great flotilla of observing Naval
ships, hardly had time to register the results of the attack before it was over. However, we in our photographic planes had
caught the whole sequence and we raced back to Langley to get
the films developed and before the public that same day.

The second bombing tests did not occur until three weeks
later on July 13. This was to be strictly our show and it involved
the bombing of a German destroyer, the *G-102.* If our bombers
failed to sink it, there was an agreement that the Navy would
bomb it with their airplanes and if they too were unsuccessful,
then the Navy would use standard naval guns. Those gunners
did a lot of praying during the bombing and a lot of money
changed hands between our boys and theirs.

The bombers were led by the Air Service's number-one bom-
bardier, Captain W. R. "Tiny" Lawson. Four minutes after the
first bomb was dropped, two direct hits struck. The destroyer
began sinking at the stern immediately and, after a few more
hits she almost rolled over and, with her bow high in the air,
sank beneath the waves. It had required forty-four bombs

dropped within nineteen minutes to send the destroyer to Davy Jones's locker. Those who witnessed the sinking from the *Henderson* reported terrific scenes of both joy and disappointment, particularly when Billy Mitchell began doing acrobatics over the Naval transport.

The next attack, of the light cruiser *Frankfurt,* was scheduled for July 18 and, as a result of the previous successful bombing, the entire country was intensely interested. It was quite a boon to the radio business at a time when people were building their own sets.

The *Frankfurt,* built in 1915, and painted red, white and blue, was considered a fairly modern ship. The program called for a series of Army and Navy bombing attacks. Lightweight 200- to 300-pound bombs were to be dropped in the first six runs, then 600 pounders would be allowed in the remaining four runs by the Martin bombers.

The proceedings started at about 9:30 A.M. The light bombs were accurately dropped but, unfortunately, most of them were duds.

Between each attack, official observers on the S.S. *Shawmut* boarded the *Frankfurt* to evaluate the damage done on each phase of the bombing. This took a great deal of unnecessary time, and Billy Mitchell's hour didn't arrive until four in the afternoon when the brass on the *Shawmut* radioed PREPARE TO ATTACK.

The Martin bombers and camera planes took up formation in column and at intervals dropped their bombs. The ex-German cruiser received a well-placed hit and immediately started to sink by the bow. Ten minutes after the last 600-pounder in this attack was dropped, the stern lifted and then disappeared and Mitchell was back over the *Henderson* giving the victory salute with his banner flying triumphantly.

A short time later at Langley, our field photo laboratory was a great center of attraction. Pilots and bombardiers were milling in and out of the darkrooms, trying to get a first peak at the bombing results. There were also civilian newsreel men anxious for us to fly their films to Bolling and then to relay them to New York City. The place had a carnival air about it.

I had flown that day to Langley in one of our Bolling photographic planes, and I was anxious to carry all the processed film I could back to Bolling so that it could be delivered to the press and motion picture theaters. Together with the film, I had packed assorted camera equipment and tripods so that the rear cockpit was completely loaded. In fact, so loaded that I had had to strap one heavy tripod on the right wing near the fuselage.

I had just revved up the engine and was ready to take off when the general drove alongside and signaled me to cut the switches.

He climbed on to the wing beside the front cockpit and said, "George, I want you to take a bag of oysters to Bolling for Senator Borah."

I told him I didn't have room for them and, besides, I felt the plane was overloaded already. He looked in the back cockpit, turned to me and said, "There's plenty of room for the bag on your left wing," and he had his driver and the mechanic tie them on the wing close to the fuselage, back of some crosswires. He thought it would balance up with the camera tripod on the right wing. As nice as he had always been to me it was the least I could do for him, so the engine was started and away I went, headed north.

Flying at about 3000 feet, and a short distance past the Rappahannock River, the old Liberty engine quit without warning. As the plane was gliding down, I was able to read with great clarity the "Hartzell of Piqua, Ohio" trademark on the motionless propeller in front of me. Luckily, I was in a section of Virginia where the country was fairly flat, and I immediately decided to land through two or three small fields, for I was well lined up with them into the northwest wind. Going through the fields I knocked down one or two fences. There was a ditch on the far side of the last fence and over the plane went, bursting open the bag of oysters and scattering them all over the ground.

Soon a big crowd gathered around and they ate Borah's oysters. I went to a small village nearby and called General Mitchell at Langley. He did not worry so much about the oysters as he did about getting the newsreel films to the movie people waiting for me at Bolling. He told me to make a deal with a farmer to drive me to Bolling and he would reimburse me.

The auto trip to Bolling in a beat-up model-T Ford took five or six hours, but the films were delivered and the mission completed.

The following day the Bolling Field mechanics reported that my forced landing was caused by a blocked gas line. Other damage was minor, except for the installation of a new propeller. The plane was flown back to Bolling in time for my return to Langley and the final most crucial bombing test.

At Langley there was great excitement preparing for the test of the "non-sinkable" German battleship, the *Ostfriesland*. This was like an evening of boxing with the main event coming up last to decide who was the champion, Mitchell or the battleship boys.

Many Naval advocates still had faith in capital ships and they felt that a ship like the *Ostfriesland*, so modern, with so many watertight compartments, would withstand anything that Billy Mitchell and his tribe could rain upon it. To date nothing more than 600-pound bombs had been used on previous tests and under the rules the General was authorized to use his "big daddy" 2000-pounders—the largest ever produced up to that time by the Ordnance Corps. Actually, the Navy's conviction that battleships were here to stay, regardless of the size of the bombs, was so strong that they were preparing the main battery of 14-inch guns on the battleship *Pennsylvania* to sink the *Ostfriesland* when the Air Service failed. The *Pennsylvania* was to do the firing from not less than 18,000 yards.

Even so, some people in high places actually believed that neither the Air Service nor the Navy, with the *Pennsylvania*, could sink the *Ostfriesland*, and they were planning to use depth charges carried by the battleship *North Dakota*. This feeling prevailed because it was known that the *Ostfriesland* had once been the flagship of the Kaiser's fleet and had struck a mine during the Battle of Jutland. She did not suffer serious damage and made port without much difficulty. The German captain who piloted the battleship to the United States after the Armistice declared in the Washington *Post* that it was constructed especially for Admiral Alfred von Tirpitz to be as near unsinkable as possible. She had four skins to protect her against mines, torpedoes, and heavy bombs. She was also divided into many watertight compartments by bulkheads, so that no matter how many big holes were made in her hull she would still get back to port.

The big day, Wednesday, July 20, was windy, with overcast skies, low clouds and a choppy sea, not at all to the liking of the Air Service. The exercises were scheduled to start at 8:30 A.M. and end of 3:00 P.M., with the Army and Navy bombers alternating. The Navy conducted numerous tests all morning with various types of armor-piercing projectiles and different kinds of American and foreign fuses.

The Army Air Service was scheduled to drop its first bombs at one o'clock in the afternoon. All through the day Naval observers boarded and reboarded the *Ostfriesland* and poor Billy was having a hemorrhage waiting to get his licks in and sink that battleship. He had waited many years for this moment and the *Osprey* darted around the skies impatiently.

During the early afternoon there was quite a hassle on between Captain Johnson, the skipper on the *Shawmut,* and the Air Service. Apparently the captain held up calling Mitchell to send in his bombers pending the inspections on the *Ostfriesland* by the board of officers. Mitchell was so mad he ordered his bombers out anyway, but when they arrived over the battleship they could not drop their bombs because the inspecting teams were still operating aboard, looking over the minor damage to the superstructure. Mitchell was sure the Navy was conducting stalling tactics and that it was being done on orders from the Navy staff officers.

The bombers hovered around the *Ostfriesland* for fifty-seven minutes until they received a warning in Morse code from Langley Field to return immediately to avoid a terrific thunderstorm raging on shore and headed on its way out to sea. Just before the bombers turned around they received orders from the *Shawmut* that all was clear to drop their 600-pound bombs. There were two direct hits which tore big holes through the upper deck, causing a slight list astern.

The storm was moving out to sea swiftly, so all ships and planes scurried toward land. A fast destroyer made port in time for the press to announce to the nation and the world that Mitchell had failed. One morning newspaper headlined the news: FLYERS FAIL TO SINK TEUTON BATTLESHIP.

I was a photographer on that last flight over the *Ostfriesland* and Lieutenant Clarence Crumrine was my pilot. We were on a free-lance look-and-see mission and there was not much action to photograph. However, we had a rough time, along with all the other planes, getting back to Langley Field. We were headed west and directly in front, for as far as we could see north and south, the sky was black, with streaks of lightning to make things worse. Like others, we changed our course to the southwest to try to get around the storm. This did give us a chance to get to shore and we were close to the North Carolina border where we made a landing and obtained three or four five-gallon cans of gasoline. We waited a few more minutes until the storm had abated and finally worked our way back to Langley Field.

Flying along the shore we saw many of the planes that had been out on the bombing exercises that afternoon and only a few of them had cracked up.

General Mitchell and his aide, Captain Bill Streett, had had a forced landing on a narrow neck of land in Currituck Sound. There was another airplane there and it turned out to be a First Brigade photographic section aircraft flown by one of our most experienced photographic pilots, Lieutenant Bill Boyd. In the darkness Mitchell landed his plane nearby and ran into a shallow ditch which he could not see for the high weeds. Sheltered by the wings of the plane they waited out the storm and Streett was able to get a farmer with a team of horses to get them out of the ditch and off they flew to Langley Field.

When Crumrine and I landed at Langley the entire field looked like a big lake except for a few high strips of ground just long enough to land on. When we taxied up to the flight line, dozens of anxious wives were wringing their hands waiting for their husbands to arrive. Many pilots did not make it back that night and were scattered around the area. Captain Tiny Lawson, the top dog of the bombing tests, got mixed up in the storm and landed his Martin bomber near Norfolk, and didn't come flying into Langley until one in the morning.

No one got much sleep that night, but the man who got the least was Louie Hagemeyer. What happened to him and his fellow argonauts had all the earmarks of a scene from *Around the World in 80 Days*.

When warning of the approaching storm headed us all away from the bombing area, Clarence Crumrine and I had passed the slow-going dirigible as though it were standing still, and I felt distinctly sorry for Hagey and his lighter than air comrades. I had taken a ride in the thing at Aberdeen, and I hadn't liked its flying speed then.

The dirigible puttered along as best it could, its motors wide open when the storm hit. With nose headed west, the ship began backing up in an easterly direction, and due to a dwindling fuel supply there was understandable concern as to how far the occupants felt they might be blown out to sea.

Darkness descended rapidly and, with the drop in temperature and the fact that a lot of water had accumulated on the bag, they began losing altitude. About ten o'clock that night the gondola gently hit the water and in no time, those aboard were up to their waists in it. Although they were bouncing around on the waves, the partial buoyancy of the gondola in the water took weight off the bag, which remained above them. And through the night they took turns bailing, which was the only thing that kept them from sinking.

When morning finally dawned they were still bobbing up and

down, drifting around. As the sun rose it evaporated some of the moisture from the bag and warmed the cool gases within sufficiently to provide the lift needed to raise the gondola above the water. Amazingly they became airborne and managed to get the two engines started again. About that time a big wave hit the gondola and bounced them high enough to enable them to rev up the engines and head for the coast, which they finally identified as being south of Virginia Beach. When, at long last, they reached Langley Field, Hagey, strictly a heavier-than-air man, bemoaned the fact that there was still another bombing mission to photograph.

Personally, I don't think Billy Mitchell slept much that night either, for I am sure his blood was still boiling when he turned in. But the morning of all mornings in his life had arrived. It was July 21, a perfect day, with the skies clear and a light breeze blowing. All the pilots and crews, together with their planes loaded with bombs, were ready.

At about 7 A.M., with Mitchell's *Osprey* in the lead, a formation of eight Martin bombers took off, each carrying 1000-pound bombs. The photographic and observer dirigibles had left a short time before while the special photographic airplanes took off with the first bomber formations. A second element of eight Martin bombers stood ready on the flight line, loaded with the 2000-pound bombs. The Ordnance Corps specialists, Captains Stribling and Roberts, had stayed up all night making certain that the fuses, sights and other details of the bombs were ready. These two were also responsible for their proper loading, which was a pretty ticklish job. To attest to the careful work of the Ordnance Corps, no serious accidents occurred throughout the entire series of tests.

As usual, the photographic airplanes flew alongside the bombers with their cameras mounted on the machine-gun scarf in the rear cockpits. Their K-2 cameras were loaded with rolls of film sufficient to take one hundred $7 \times 9$-inch photographs per plane. The General had been more than pleased with the photographic results obtained to date. We and civilian motion picture men had

At Bolling Field, October 1922, DH-4 and I ready to fly. *U.S. Army Air Service*

Dr. George Debothezat, with beard, poses before his helicopter at McCook Field. Colonel Thurman Bane in the center. On the right is engineer John Roche. *U.S. Army Air Service*

It flies! Colonel Bane at the controls. *U.S. Army Air Service*

The William Kettering "flying bomb" radio controlled, loaded with dynamite. Our first guided missile. Dayton, Ohio, 1920. *U.S. Army Air Service*

Sergeant Lewis "Hagey" Hagemeyer in U. S. Army dirigible ready to photograph the famous Billy Mitchell bombing tests (below). *U.S. Army Air Service*

The unsinkable *Ostfriesland* gets sunk by Billy Mitchell's bombers, July 21, 1921. *U.S. Army Air Service*

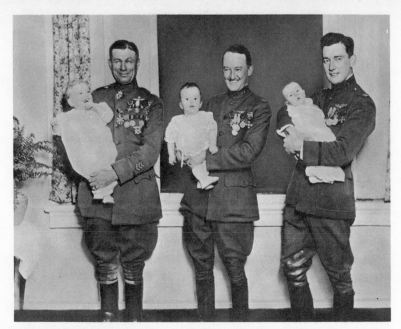

Three proud papas pose with their sons at a triple christening in 1921. From the left, General Billy Mitchell, Captain Harold Hartney, Captain Burdette Wright. *Harris Ewing*

Ready to cast off for the great balloon ascent, my back to the camera. *U.S. Army Air Service*

made thousands of feet of dramatic movie films for Pathé, Fox-Movietone News, Paramount, and others. The American people were naturally for the underdog in this hot contest and they flocked to the movie theaters in droves.

Soon after eight o'clock, the eight bombers arrived in the target area, and orders were given to begin the attack. The first plane over, at 2000 feet, made a direct hit on the *Ostfriesland,* and immediately the stop-bombing signal was given from the *Shawmut.* The signal was not observed, and four more planes dropped bombs, racking up a total of three hits, which was one in excess of that authorized under the rules. This started another hassle. Captain Johnson, on the *Shawmut,* ordered Lieutenant Bissell's squadron back to Langley. This caused sad disappointment to the crews, who had been practicing bombing all summer on dummy targets near Langley. Practically the entire Atlantic fleet was in the bombing area observing the exercises, and as Bissell's planes were swinging around they dropped the rest of the 1000-pounders—in some instances a little too close for comfort —demonstrating their displeasure at the questionable handling of the exercises.

Back at Langley, Mitchell and his men were straining at the bit to proceed to the target with the three 2000-pound bombs. It had been agreed with the Navy in writing that the Army bombers, using a maximum of three 2000-pound bombs, would be authorized to obtain two direct hits on the deck of the *Ostfriesland* and no more. Mitchell was not afraid of this restriction, for he had learned from a young White Russian pilot and aeronautical designer Alexander de Seversky that a bomb dropped close to the side of a ship's hull can have a far more damaging result than a direct hit. This is due to the so-called "water hammer" effect which Seversky had observed as a bomber pilot during World War I.

Mitchell sent a message to the controller on the *Shawmut* stating that a formation of bombers with 2000-pound bombs had taken off from Langley Field and were on the way to attack the *Ostfriesland*—IF TWO HITS ARE NOT OBTAINED, he radioed,

BOMBING WILL CONTINUE UNTIL THE ARMY ACCOMPLISHES THE
TWO HITS AUTHORIZED.

A few minutes after noon, Captain Lawson and his bombers
arrived in the area. Flying in a column formation they passed
alongside Mitchell and Streett in the *Osprey.*

Then at 2500 feet the lead plane released its giant 2000-
pound bomb. It hit 200 feet off the bow of the *Ostfriesland,*
and exploded under water with the desired hammer effect. It
also dumped thousands of tons of water on the deck of the
warship. A couple of minutes later another 2000-pounder followed. It struck the side of the bow and exploded beneath the
deck, actually lifting the warship out of the water. The bomb had
torn a large hole in the starboard side and there was a tremendous burst of fire and smoke. Three more drops followed using
the same technique of near misses and it was quite apparent that
the ship was taking a terrible beating.

Regardless of this, there were still many skeptics aboard the
*Henderson* and other craft carrying observers. Bomb number six,
however, carried the knock-out punch. It landed off the starboard
side the desired distance away from the hull. The explosion lifted
the 540-foot warship stern high and it settled back, starting to
list to port. The bow began to rise, disclosing a large hole in
the hull. The stern was now under water and sinking fast, finally coming to rest on the ocean floor 300 feet below. This left
the beat-up bow of the battleship standing straight up for a
short time and then, at 12:40, twenty-one minutes from the start
of the bombing, the *Ostfriesland* vanished beneath the waves!

Everything, as far as the bombing was concerned, was finished,
signed and sealed. The only detail remaining was the Mitchell
victory salute. According to Bill Streett, the General put on his
best show of acrobatics and came near pulling the wings off.
Those below knew how he felt and on his last passby he dipped
his wings in passing salute on his triumphant flight back to Langley Field.

There was a great celebration at Langley that night. Very few
photographers participated, though, for we were busy processing

the films and making the hundreds of prints required for publicity and for the official reports. In the early evening I left for Bolling Field with some of the motion picture film and the aerial pictures for the morning newspapers.

Mitchell was not resting on his laurels, for now he had the people with him and he wanted to fan this interest with more demonstrations of the great possibilities of air power.

At noon on July 29, 1921, he led his big Langley Field bomber armada, supported by other Air Service units in the East, over New York City to simulate an aerial attack on that city. Thousands of people flocked out into the streets to watch the largest battle formation of aircraft seen to date. The afternoon and morning newspapers carried startling headlines on what would have happened to the city if the planes in formation had dropped the 2000-pound "German battleship-killer bombs." The U. S. Fleet in New York harbor would have been wiped out, the skyscrapers in ruins, electric power plants, water works and surface transportation knocked out, and millions fleeing to the country.

The General took care to stress that this peacetime maneuver was being conducted in the interest of our national defense. After what he had demonstrated on the battleship bombing tests, he claimed it was quite possible for a country with a much larger air service to bomb and invade our country. To guard against such an eventuality, he recommended a separate air force and greater recognition of air power with larger appropriations for men and material.

Billy Mitchell had proved his point, but it was not enough to bring about what he envisioned. However, on a lower level, but of primary importance to me, he did slowly bring about the miracle of consolidating aerial photographic research and development having it placed under the Engineering Division Air Service command at McCook Field. As far as my future was concerned, it was a great victory.

## 7

Although we did not know it at the time, the long summer and early fall of 1921 marked the apogee of Billy Mitchell's dramatic and illustrious career. It was at any rate the pinnacle of the six stormy years—three of them still lying ahead—in which as an Army officer he gave his all to put military air power on a sound basis in the United States.

It was August 20 of that summer that a joint Army-Navy board issued a report on the bombing tests. The report upheld the supremacy of the battleship over aircraft, and it was signed by General John J. Pershing. Billy Mitchell had written his own report, understandably reaching exactly opposite conclusions. He submitted it to his chief, General Menoher. Menoher, an old line War Department type, buried it in a convenient file, but on September 13, Mitchell's report somehow appeared in the press. Its public release raised such a ruckus that General Menoher, who had never understood what flying was all about and consequently had been at odds with Mitchell from the outset, declared to Secretary of War John W. Weeks that either his uncontrollable subordinate be disciplined or he would resign as Chief of the Air Service. The Secretary, wisely taking into account Mitchell's great public popularity and Menoher's inability to handle the matter, accepted the General's resignation.

Several weeks thereafter, the First Provisional Air Brigade really put the bung in the Navy's barrel by repeating its bombing performance on the old battleship *Alabama,* sinking it in thirty seconds with one 2000-pound bomb. The public, spurred on by much of the press, clamored for Billy Mitchell's promotion to

Chief of the Air Service. It was this moment that marked the high-water point to which I refer.

Naturally, most of us who served Billy Mitchell wanted his promotion, but we knew full well that he was not in favor with the War Department. Further, what most of us didn't know at the time was that he had submitted his own resignation and it had been very nearly accepted. So, at the end of September, it was not Billy Mitchell but Major General Mason M. Patrick, Chief of the Air Service during World War I, who was assigned to take the coveted post.

General Patrick and Billy Mitchell were long-time friends and, although the General at the time was not a pilot (he later became one at the age of sixty-two), he was a dedicated advocate of air power. Later, in my long association under his command, I came to believe he had been an excellent choice for a most difficult job. While he and Billy Mitchell locked horns almost immediately over who was really boss, once General Patrick established that he was, they worked well enough together. One reason could have been that Mason Patrick understood people as well as he understood what Billy Mitchell was shouting about. He not only looked more diplomat than soldier, mustached with firm straight features, he also acted it, but firmly.

While Billy Mitchell stirred us with his magnetism and made his cause our own, Mason Patrick did what he could quietly, using reason and patience and intelligence, and always with a soft spot in his heart for his men. When you came to see him about something, he had the habit of throwing his arm around your shoulder and saying, "Well, what can I do for you, son?"

The first time he asked me that in the late fall of 1921, I was quick to reply, "Sir, there's been a persistent rumor around that the Corps of Engineers is going to be put in command of all aerial mapping."

The General smiled wryly and said, "Seems I've heard the rumor, too, Lieutenant. I've even heard the Department of Interior has designs on aerial mapping."

"I sure hope we can keep our hands on it, sir. We've been doing a lot of good work. We've got some well-trained people."

"I know we have, son. I've seen some of the things you and your boys have turned out. First rate." Then he smiled. "As a former Engineer," he emphasized former, "I think you can stop listening to the rumors. The Air Service will keep what's its own."

Shortly thereafter, the rumors faded away and it became apparent that our new chief had laid them to rest once and for all. In the months that followed the pace of my activities naturally quickened. Increasing recognition of the value of aerial mapping by military, governmental, and civilian agencies had stimulated our industry of course.[1] But the bigger, more diverse work load was also due to the fact that there were so few of us available to handle it.

The new year began with twin tragedies, one in which aerial photography became involved, and the other in which aerial photography was to have played a role.

The first occurred on the night of January 28, 1922, when, following a 24-hour snowstorm, the roof of the Knickerbocker Theater in Washington, D.C., collapsed from the weight of the snow. Nearly one hundred persons were killed and many others injured.

The next morning General Patrick sent me to see the District Engineer who asked if I would take some close-up aerial shots of the theater for use by a Congressionally appointed investigating board. In the clean whiteness of the snow, the shattered theater had the appearance of a bombed-out building, and the

---

[1] Like most everything else in this country of ours, the aerial photographic industry started on a shoestring, backed by an idea and the grit to make it go. After World War I, an enterprising fellow could buy a Jenny for very little, pick up a surplus aerial camera, and go into business. He couldn't make mosaics at first because he didn't know how, or else he didn't have the proper equipment. But he could take shots from the air of a factory, a golf club, or an estate, and if he did a halfway decent job he could sell his photos for a pretty fair price. As time went on, he could improve his equipment, maybe even start designing cameras himself.

In this way, or variations of it, a number of the best known aerial photographic concerns in the country today got started, and as time went on, we began to look to them for new and better cameras. Sherman Fairchild's K-3 was the first of the lot.

photographs we took close above it made a graphic display of the tragedy.

Several weeks later General Patrick gave me what appeared to be a much more pleasurable assignment. I was to fly to Langley Field and there take charge of the newsreel cameramen who were going on a test flight of the semi-rigid airship, *Roma,* which the Air Service had had built in Italy.

On the *Roma*'s maiden flight some months earlier, it was discovered that her six Italian Ansaldo engines were underpowered, and so they had been replaced with improved four hundred horsepower Liberty engines. This was to be the first test with the new engines, and I was to be on board with the cameramen and many top military and civilian engineers.

On the morning of the flight, just as Andy Matos and I were climbing into my DH-4 at Bolling, an enlisted man came dashing out of Operations to tell me General Patrick wanted me on the phone. I had a feeling it wasn't going to be good news, and as I went to take the call, I was wishing we'd gotten off just a few minutes earlier.

Sure enough the General ordered me to cancel my flight to Langley and to call there and have a local photo officer take over. I was to report on the double to the Chief of Engineers regarding a new river and harbor mapping project. My mind was full of unkind thoughts as I reluctantly moved to obey.

That afternoon, February 21, 1922, the *Roma* crashed killing all the personnel in the camera compartment. Thirty-four officers and civilians perished, and eleven survived. All the survivors were in the airship's control cabin up forward beneath the keel. Just prior to the accident, the *Roma* had appeared to be operating normally. Then it suddenly plunged to earth, crashing through high tension wires, exploding as it hit the ground. Many authorities felt that had there been a master switch in the control cabin, the six engines could have been shut off and the crash would have been avoided.

For a time thereafter I looked upon General Patrick as my guardian angel, and went about my appointed affairs quietly with the personal view that such near misses work wonders to make believers out of the wickedest of us.

In the outcry that followed the *Roma* crash, there were those who maintained that if the thirty-four who died had been wearing parachutes, they would have survived.

A Chicago *Tribune* article stated: "Thirty percent of the aviators who have met death in crashes had an opportunity to jump free from their planes, and would not have been killed had they worn parachutes."

This statement started a storm of controversy and one of the strong anti-chute men, Major Follett Bradley, a graduate of the U. S. Naval Academy, a pilot and officer in charge of flying at Fort Sill, sent a scorching letter to the Chief of Air Service, which read:

"I do not know what the attitude of your office is with regard to the wearing of parachutes, but I should like to submit my own personal viewpoint on the matter. This viewpoint is concurred in by the majority, if not all, of the older pilots at the station.

It is our opinion that a pilot who leaves his ship by means of a parachute, except under the following circumstances, is guilty of gross misconduct. So doing he does not endeavor to save an extremely valuable piece of government property. We think that if pilots are required to wear parachutes, and are encouragd to use them, it will lead to many crashes that could have been perfect landings, and will encourage faintheartedness. The occasions upon which we consider it is justifiable to use a parachute are practically all covered by the following: A—fire, B—collapse of the airplane or of some essential portion of it, such as a wing, loss of control surface, breaking of control wire, C—collision."[2]

From McCook Field, Major Hoffman, who had done so much to develop the parachute, answered Major Bradley thus:

"In addition to the circumstances mentioned, which are certainly sufficient to justify the use of parachutes, it may sometimes be advisable to use a parachute:

[2] Monthly *Air Service News Letters,* 1922.

"A—when engine failure occurs while flying at night over rough thunderstorms when ceiling is low, occasionally when in fog near the ground, perhaps out of control. No doubt there are other emergencies which have been overlooked. Any aviator's life is worth more than any airplane, and it is not proper to leave the impression that any pilot should save an airplane at the cost of his life. It usually turns out that both aviator and airplane are lost.

"Suffice it to say that Major Bradley's deductions that 'If pilots are required to wear parachutes, etc., it will lead to many crashes, etc., and will encourage faintheartedness,' is not borne out by experience either here or abroad. Most all pilots at McCook Field wear parachutes and have for the past year or more, and they are considered mandatory."[3]

I don't know whether Major Bradley ever came to regret his hard pants approach to survival, but I do know the seat pack of a chute always gave an added touch of comfort to my *derriere* not to mention my sense of security.

Upon my return from the aerial survey for the Engineers, I took on a new and different mission. I became a recruiter for the aerial photographic section of the Air Service Technical School, located at Chanute Field, Rantoul, Illinois. We selected Indianapolis, about ninety miles from Chanute, as the point from which to launch our drive. Our purpose was to get enlisted recruits to train to become aerial photographers and technicians.

When I arrived in Indianapolis with Andy Matos, we started taking aerial shots of towns and villages within a hundred mile radius of the city. Then we supplied all the newspapers in the area with prints. Our caption to go with the photographs was: "Join the Air Service and be an aerial photographer like Sergeant Matos, who took these pictures at 10,000 feet in an Army Air Service plane."

At the time, all we had to sell was the glamour of flying plus a new career. The down-to-earth reality of life in the Air Service for enlisted men and officers alike was not exactly pie in the sky. Poor pay (in November 1921, in an economy move, I was transferred

[3] Monthly *Air Service News Letters,* 1922.

to bachelor quarters at Bolling because the Air Service could not afford to pay per diem for officers to live in Washington). Slow advancement (I remained a first lieutenant for almost fourteen years from 1921–34). An uncertain future (due to the attrition of men and planes as a result of governmental economic policies).

In two weeks we had all the recruits we could handle for the next several classes. In fact, we did so well, the people at Chanute asked us if we'd do a repeat performance for their mechanics school. On this one we set up an exhibit at the Indianapolis Post Office of aircraft engines and accessories. Included in the exhibit was a tiny two cylinder Sperry "Messenger" airplane.

Lawrence Sperry was the designer and the plane could be landed practically anywhere, even on the Capitol steps in Washington, which Sperry did one day by mistake when he was demonstrating it to the lawmakers. But small as the plane was, we managed while driving it through the city to decapitate a whole row of street lights along a narrow thoroughfare. The city authorities were not pleased, but in short order we had all the mechanic recruits Chanute could handle.

In my various endeavors, I found there were a number of ways to sell an idea. One can use the direct approach, like recruiting; one can take aerial mosaics of a city or a harbor and sell the authorities on the value of aerial photography and the public on the peacetime uses of military aviation; and one can take advantage of opportunities that present themselves like will-o'-the-wisps.

Such an opportunity arose in April of that year when I was ordered to report to General Pershing.

I had met the Army Chief once very briefly when he had come through McCook on an inspection tour. I knew old "Black Jack" had a reputation of being stern and not easy to talk to, but on this spring morning I found him cordial and he quickly put me at ease.

"Lieutenant," he said, "General Patrick has reported to me the valuable work you people are doing. I know the importance of aerial photographic reconnaissance, of course, from France, and I'm wondering if you can help me out in a small matter."

He smiled as he said this last and then explained that he had a friend, a Dr. Lee, an archaeologist, who was writing a book on Indian mounds, and he was particularly anxious to get some aerial photographs of the Cahokia Indian mounds near St. Louis.

From a desk drawer, the General brought out a large map on which the mounds had been marked. "Do you suppose you could get some pictures of these within a week or so, Lieutenant?"

My answer was swiftly affirmative, and then I was off and running, figuring that time in this case might be money.

Before the day was over, Andy Matos and I, with some hard flying and good weather, reached the area to be photographed. On the following morning we took our pictures and were back at Bolling before sundown. We worked all that night to develop the film, and the next morning I delivered the goods to General Pershing with a letter from General Patrick. Pershing was impressed both by the quality of the prints and the speed with which he had received them.

Soon after I received a complimentary letter through General Patrick. You could say I was waiting in the wings for just such a cue, for I had learned long ago that the time to sell your wares was after you had performed a "meritorious deed."

When I went to call on General Patrick, I carried construction drawings and cost for a new photographic laboratory at Bolling Field. The good General smiled knowingly upon my salesmanship and wisely saw the necessity for the laboratory. He agreed to include the money for it ($12,500) in the Air Service's meager budget, and the amount was subsequently approved. It was my biggest financial coup of the period.

On another occasion when General Patrick called me in, the problem was somewhat removed from the normal.

"George, what's that friend of yours, Captain Stevens, think he's doing?"

"Why I don't know, sir. What is he doing?"

"Trying to break his fool neck I think. Here have a look at this." He handed me an official report, announcing that Captain Albert Stevens had established a new world's record with an unauthorized parachute jump from an altitude of 24,206 feet.

"Parachute jumping isn't his business, is it?" the General asked.

It wasn't an easy question to answer, for Steve appeared to make it his business to be involved in any phase of aerial research and development in which he could risk his neck.

I knew he'd made his first unauthorized jump when he and Leigh Wade were doing a mapping job in New England. Steve had suddenly decided he was going to find out what it was like to hit the silk. So far as I know, he was the first to perform the act without benefit of an emergency. He simply informed Leigh he was going to drop in on some friends and over the side he went. After that, he couldn't jump enough. In fact, famed test pilot John Macready found Steve to be the man who wasn't there. They had taken off together one fine day from McCook, but somewhere over Arizona Steve jumped ship without notifying Macready, who was unaware of his absence until he landed at Albuquerque, New Mexico, and found the rear cockpit empty.

In breaking the world's record, Steve had attempted to tie in the jump with aerial photography. As he explained it, the purpose of the flight was a high altitude photographic test. The negatives of the film he took were to prove what could be secured photographically through four and a half miles of air, dust, and haze. A secondary purpose was to check the altitude of the plane and, through measurements of ground distances recorded on the negatives, determine the correct focal length of the camera lens. The parachute jump had no photographic purpose whatever, and the reason for it might better be considered a demonstration of how an impatient man can reach the ground quickly.

Steve's equipment consisted of a 70-cubic-inch metal bottle of oxygen strapped to one of his legs, a chute behind and an eighteen foot chest patch in front. Altogether Steve and the three items weighed more than 250 pounds.

Over Dayton at 24,000 feet the west wind was so strong the special supercharged Martin bomber was backing up. After connecting his special oxygen supply, Steve dove head-first out of the rear cockpit. There followed a long plummeting free fall before he pulled the rip cord. The chute opened with a violent jerk, and the heavy steel oxygen bottle kept right on going down. Fortunately, he'd fallen so far he was able to get along without it.

But now as Steve descended, the chute rocked and tossed in the rough air, and after ten minutes of being whipped around he became extremely seasick. On top of that he was amazed at how rapidly the country was passing beneath him—almost as if he were in an airplane. Towns and villages swept by and he realized landing was going to be a bit sticky. Finally, he was so miserably sick, he pulled the lines on the side of the chute to spill the air from it in order to fall faster. Below lay a soft freshly plowed field, an ideal spot, but the wind took him over it, just clearing a barbed-wire fence. Ahead lay a grain field, coming up at him with awful speed. He assumed a crouching position in the harness and then *whamo!* he was threshing grain two feet high, and until he could manage to release his parachute harness, he became a human sled. In such straits he did a fine job of taking down a barbed-wire fence, cutting a swath through brush and brambles, and digging up a newly planted bean patch. Miraculously when Steve finally came to rest, aside from a few broken bones in his foot and thoroughly torn up hide, he was unhurt. But alas, that was the end of his sky diving, for even before his release from McCook Hospital, General Patrick sent orders forbidding him to make any more jumps and in the future to confine himself exclusively to testing aerial cameras.

There was something of Steve in all of us, or we wouldn't have been in the Air Service. While he had become intrigued with one-way vertical flight, I had been bitten by the horizontal speed bug. As the Syracuse (New York) *Post Standard* reported, I had "made a number of record flights, flying from Washington to Syracuse in 3 hours and 5 minutes; from Washington to New York in 1 hour and 50 minutes; from Washington to Dayton, Ohio in 3 hours and 20 minutes, and from St. Louis to Washington in 6 hours and 14 minutes with one stop."

I had made all these flights in a DH-4 not exactly noted for its speed, but by cornering General Mitchell one night at a party, I got his permission to requisition a single seater SE-5 for my own

private use. The SE-5 had its problems,[4] and I experienced most
of them, but in flying about the country in it, the desire for speed
and more speed overtook me.

Thus it was that I came to submit the following request:

July 27, 1922

MEMORANDUM for Chief, Training and War Plans Division.

1. It is requested that the undersigned be called to pilot an airplane in the Pulitzer Race, or in one of the other airplane contests,
to be at Selfridge Field in October 1922. I have had approximately
800 hours in the air. Most of this time has been on DH-4-B planes;
approximately 50 hours of this amount were on pursuit planes of the
following types: SE-5, Fokkers, including Fokker 300.

2. In case it is not possible to assign me to one of the high speed
airplanes, it is requested that I be considered as pilot for DH or
Le Père, or XB-1A, or Vought, which it is understood can be entered in the Observation Airplane Race by the Army Air Service.

George W. Goddard
1st Lieutenant, A.S.

Following my July memorandum, I stopped in at McCook and
while there I went to see my old friend George Hallett. I was anxious for him to show me the preliminary design of the 1000 horsepower engine which Billy Mitchell was vigorously promoting. It
had 18 cylinders and 72 spark plugs, four separate ignition sys-

---

[4] There were a number of SE-5 airplanes in use at Kelly Field at that
time, for single-seater training, and one of the flying instructors, Lieutenant
Birnn, expressed his views poetically in the Field newspaper.

Stone walls do not an aerodrome make, nor mud a landing field,
And quickly to a crosswind puff, the SE-5 will yield;
Beware the hill near Hangar Three, beware the thick mesquite,
If e'er you need seek landing field, this warning I'll repeat—
Stone walls do not the aerodrome make, nor mud a landing place.
So set her down on the landing gear and not upon your face.
This SE-5 it handles well when way up in the air
Except when you are pulling stunts there's small need to beware.
So take her off, my hero bold, you'll handle her with ease.
But when you come to set her down, *don't land her 'cross the breeze.*

tems, excellent power-to-weight ratio and the potential for great reliability.

While we were talking, George told me about a high-compression Liberty engine which he and his people were in the process of testing. He felt it would be a good workhorse for our photographic DH-4s. I immediately saw that it might serve another purpose and, in so doing, prove itself. I told him of my request to enter the National Air Races, and proposed that if he would see to it that I got to use the high compression Liberty, I was sure I could talk General Patrick into letting me participate on the basis of testing the engine.

A couple of days after I returned to Washington, the General added my name to the list of contestants, agreeing that it would be a good test of the Liberty, providing McCook Field offered no objection. A phone call to George Hallett and it was a deal.

For a week or so before the race, the mechanics at Bolling Field polished up one of our photographic DH-4s and added some streamlined fittings here and there around the wires and struts to cut down the drag and try to get a few extra miles per hour out of the bird. I took off from Bolling several days before the race in order to give McCook plenty of time to install the new engine. Just before leaving, an officer hitchhiked a ride part of the way, and going over the Allegheny Mountains I began bucking high winds which got stronger as I passed over into Ohio. I had to drop my passenger off in Columbus, so I planned to get gas there if necessary. But once on the ground with only 68 miles to go, I decided I had sufficient fuel to continue on to McCook. Airborne again, I could tell that the headwinds had increased. Apparently I had been too optimistic in my calculations, for a few miles past Springfield the engine quit, and I switched over to my emergency tank in the upper wing.

Again I had underestimated and almost to the edge of the field the ol' Liberty engine gulped its last drops of gas and I settled down in a pasture. Luckily, with the headwind and the airplane carrying a minimum load, I was able to make almost a helicopter landing. It didn't strike me as a very auspicious beginning for an

Air Race. However, the next day George Hallett and his men started to install the new Liberty.

Shortly before noon the day before the races I climbed into the cockpit and took off due west into the wind across the narrow part of the field. The Liberty was purring nicely and my morale was tops again when, without warning, the engine quit. I was about 300 feet over the levee headed across the river into a thickly populated section of the city. I immediately dropped the nose of the airplane and violated one of the aviators' commandments which says you never execute a turn with a dead engine. You always land straight ahead. At first I thought I would land south, downstream in the Miami River, but the big bridge nearby helped me make a quick decision to finish the 180-degree turn back toward the field. I couldn't lose much speed attempting a downwind landing with no brakes in a narrow field. Straight ahead lay the commanding officer's house. Just before I plowed into it, I hit full left rudder and ground looped the plane, completely tearing the upper and lower right wings off and ramming in some of the wooden pillars holding up the CO's porch.

A large crowd of military and civilian workers out for the lunch hour rapidly formed around the wreck and, before I could get out of the plane, up strutted the new commanding officer, Major John Curry, and General Patrick.

"Are you all right, son!" the General called.

"I'm just fine," I said disgustedly, "but I wouldn't give you much for this nag."

"Or my porch," Major Curry laughed. "Here, let me give you a hand, George."

Once I was out of the plane, General Patrick put his arm around my shoulder and said, "My boy, don't be discouraged, you'll be in that race tomorrow if it takes everyone on this field to build you a new airplane."

With that kind of support from the head man, I couldn't stay discouraged for long. He had just happened to be at McCook and was in a meeting in the CO's office when I had taken off. They had witnessed my departure and sudden return.

True to his word, he and Major Curry directed the chief of the shops to work around the clock in shifts in order to have the plane flyable by ten the next morning—including a new engine if necessary. A quick inspection of the Liberty revealed that a cotter key had not been used to lock the nut that secured the throttle rod to the carburetor and the rod had vibrated off during the take-off. This, of course, was easily fixed, but the big part of the job required splicing the wooden fuselage longerons near the radiator where the bolts holding the braided steel cables attached to the wing had torn loose.

But it was done and done in plenty of time, for the next morning at eight o'clock I was eagerly warming up the engine of my rebuilt plane. This time I obeyed the big sign along the front of the hangars—THIS FIELD IS SMALL—USE IT ALL. I took off to the south over its longest part.

Two and a half uneventful hours later I landed at Selfridge Field in Mount Clemens, Michigan. The programs for the races mentioned that this year's event would be as important as the national motor car races in the early days, because it would bring out the qualities and defects in the various flying machines. The main event was to be the Pulitzer Trophy Race, a contest for the fastest land machines. It was to be held over a triangular course totalling 160 miles (four laps of 40 miles each), the entire course over the water of Lake St. Clair, with the exception of the landing at Selfridge Field and between the Packard Field pylon and the lake.

I had never been in an official race before and the excitement was pretty keen as contestants worked on last-minute modifications of their ships, mostly streamlining any surface projections that would create drag. Some even waxed their planes hoping to cut down on wind resistance. There were lots of colored pennants attached to struts, and betting went on as though the affair was a big horse race. I figured there wasn't much point in being involved if I didn't think I'd win, so down went ten dollars on the nose.

There were plenty of familiar faces from McCook, and I got my fill of free advice on what to do, but most of it I didn't hear as I stalked up and down waiting for the race to be called.

I was a contestant in the fourth event (observation type aircraft). There were eleven of us, flying a variety of DHs, Voughts, and Le Pères. Flight altitude ranged from about zero to 100 feet, using full throttle in both the straight away and around the pylons. There was a mixture control beside the throttle, and in the straight away the idea was to jockey it expertly to get that extra burst of speed. Mastering this technique plus knowing how to get the best position in rounding the pylons is what weeded the men from the boys.

We got off to a roaring start about midafternoon. The Goddard blood was up, and I was out to grab the brass ring. As we entered the third lap over Selfridge, I was running third, moving up on Lieutenant Ted Koenig who was flying a Le Père. I was on his tail going around the pylon at Packard Field and had just rolled out of the vertical turn, my altitude 100 feet, when my engine popped, banged and quit dead. Luckily, straight ahead were several fields. It was dairy country and cows were all over the place. I had time to react and nothing more. I picked the best landing path I could and, except for one cow, I could have made it. However, I hit that poor cow right in the south end, tore off my left wing, did a dandy cartwheel of a ground loop, and generally rolled the plane into a compact ball.

Sitting unscathed amidst a pile of aeronautical debris, I was disgusted beyond words. As a racing pilot I'd made a good junk dealer, also I had some unkind thoughts about George Hallett's new Liberty engine.

In a few minutes there was a cloud of dust streaking down the road that turned out to be the ambulance. I told the attendants to see to the cow, that my injuries went deeper. Farmers were also on hand and presently I returned to Selfridge Field in the back of the ambulance and finished the day filling out government property damage forms.

The next morning I was flown to the Fairfield Air Service depot in Dayton where I selected another DH-4. On my return flight to Bolling, I decided that my forte was aerial photography after all.

Life picked up again on the day the K-3, "the between the lens" camera that General Mitchell had given me permission to order from Sherman Fairchild, arrived at McCook. It was most welcome, but like any new product it had its idiosyncrasies. The larger blades on the shutter occasionally jammed against each other because of a flutter caused by vibration, also we had trouble obtaining the right alloy of steel to withstand the severe shock when the blades hit the retard mechanism. But with considerable redesigning, testing and retesting, the troubles were eliminated and the Air Service had in the K-3 the most advanced aerial camera of the times.

Sherman Fairchild had returned from Europe shortly before we received the model of his K-3, and while he reported that the U.S. had the lead over other nations in the scientific development of aerial photography, he declared that in the practical application of the art, we lagged behind both France and Great Britain.[5]

[5] It is stimulating to learn that America leads the major European nations in the scientific development of aerial photography, but in the practical application of the art on a national scale we must look to France as the leader. The French, since the ending of the war with Germany, have systematically set about the development of aeronautics through utilization of every service offered.

Shortly after the Versailles Treaty was signed, a French law was passed requiring every city in the Republic, above a certain size, to be resurveyed within three years. It would have been physically impossible and financially impracticable to accomplish this by ground methods. The result was that mapping by air was adopted throughout and one company alone surveyed two hundred cities from airplanes.

Aerial mapping is being extensively used by the Ministry of Liberated Provinces. The areas of France devastated during the war are being resurveyed from the air, as in many cases not only were property lines obliterated, but the records of entire communities destroyed.

The city of Paris was mapped from the air to a scale of 200 feet to the inch, thus making it possible to identify even small buildings. Corrections such as new structures, streets, etc., were printed in red over the existing maps. For this air mapping work the French company received the equivalent of $400,000.

In Great Britain, commercial photography from the air has been highly successful. The government has underway an interesting experiment in mapping the Valley of the Nile. This is a part of the colonial development scheme. By means of aerial photographs the annual erosion caused by the river's overflow can be accurately recorded. Aerial photographs of the Mesopotamian desert, which anciently was irrigated by the Tigris and Euphrates rivers, is also being carried on by the British.

No doubt this was so, but the mapping demands being made on our photo sections were such that I went to see General Mitchell about it. I briefed him on Steve's research and development progress at McCook, the work of the Photo School at Langley, and then I gave him a long written report on the monumental work load of the photo sections, recommending that their number be doubled from 9 to 18.

I was naturally asking for a lot more than I expected to get, but Billy Mitchell was able to work the impossible on a fairly regular basis. There was simply no money available for the necessary expansion, yet he found ways to accomplish it. The increase not only took care of all our mapping requests, but also provided men and planes for mapping airways, patrolling borders and forests, and special forestry and agricultural studies.

With all that had transpired in the year to improve the state of aerial photography, it was no wonder that I chose to celebrate such progress by being evicted from Mrs. Bradley's exclusive Air Service supper club. Mrs. Bradley lived at 919 18th Street, N.W. in Washington, D.C., and out of the goodness of her heart, she had established a nightly open house for hungry pilots, offering us the kind of delicious cooking that one associates with home. We who belonged to the club paid for the food and had but one membership rule—only bachelors could belong.

As many before me, I made the announcement at a farewell club dinner. We all cried hard and long that night, singing a few songs into our glasses, and bravely toasting lovely Marge Mast, my bride to be.

We had met through her sister Isabel while I was still at McCook. Isabel was a violinist in a small orchestra at the famous old Gibbons Hotel in Dayton. I ate there often and one evening Isabel, who was engaged to a fellow officer, told me about her sister, Marge, a schoolteacher with a singing voice like a bird. I got interested enough so that I wangled an invitation to the Mast home in West Milton, a small town about twenty miles north of Dayton.

Marge was slim, dark haired, blue-eyed, and one meeting was enough for Lieutenant Goddard to know that he had been bowled over. In no time I became a familiar sight to the area and was frequently written up in the small town blabber sheet as that damn fool aviator who was disturbing the peace and tranquillity of West Milton. Romance can be dangerous, and the boys around the blacksmith's shop and the general store were making bets on just how long I'd last before I broke my fool neck. One day my antics resulted in the loss of a lightning rod from a farmer's barn, and a near miss of the village water tower. Of course, I told myself I was simply perfecting my acrobatic skill, like every other pilot at Mc-Cook with a girl friend within a radius of a hundred miles. Our aircraft carried very small identification numbers, so irate complaints made to headquarters seldom brought an end to low level loops and snap rolls.

Naturally all of Shorty Schroeder's good advice as well as just plain flying sense had no effect on one so smitten, but it was Marge who put me back on more or less the straight and level by threatening to terminate our courtship if I didn't cut it out. I continued to woo her by plane whenever I had the chance, but more gently.

A few days before Christmas 1922 we were married in Troy, Ohio. We came to Washington and moved into an apartment a few blocks from my office in the Munitions Building.

Like all newly married military aviators, it took me some time to convince my bride that aviation was my life's work.

"George dear, when are you going to give up flying?"

"Never, my love. Never."

After awhile Marge got the message and we settled down to married bliss.

## 8

In spite of dramatic aerial exploits such as the nonstop east-west transcontinental flight by Lieutenants John A. Macready and Oakley G. Kelly, the Air Service was in a bad state of decline. So bad that General Patrick was soon to state, "The Air Service today is practically demobilized and unable to play its part in any national emergency, or even to meet the peacetime demands for service with its present inadequate strength and organization."[1]

Billy Mitchell had, of course, been crying the same words in the wilderness of the War Department since 1919, but as time passed the situation only deteriorated.

What both men maintained was true enough with one exception —the aerial photographic branch. Then it was only half true. Once given the planes and the men, our photographic sections had become practically self-supporting. This was so because for every mapping job we did—be it county, state, federal, or military—we charged for our services—gas, oil, repairs, film, chemicals, per diem, the works. What we charged was acceptable because the nature of our work was deemed important and, under some circumstances, received Cabinet and White House approval. Thus while the deterioration of the Air Service was readily apparent, and more and more good men left it, we who were engaged in aerial photography were constantly airborne.

As a result of mapping tests that Howard Ramey and I had conducted over Washington, D.C., the Coastal and Geodetic Survey requested that we complete a mosaic map of the city of Los Ange-

[1] *Mitchell, Pioneer of Air Power,* Isaac Don Levine (Duell, Sloane & Pearce, 1943), p. 301.

les to a scale of 1/10,000, using the K-3 camera and coverage of Los Angeles County using the Bagley T-1, at a scale of 1/30,-000.

Howard and I figured we needed a new DH-4 for the job since it was a long hard flight to the West Coast. So with General Patrick's blessing, we traveled first class by train to San Diego to pick one up at the supply depot there. Howard, who bore the nickname the "old soldier" because of the squint in his eye, liked to play chess, but I was no match for him and he suffered stoically while I enjoyed the passing scenery and the growing warmth of the climate.

Before I had left Washington, Major Tommy Milling had given me a letter of introduction to Cecil B. De Mille asking him if it were convenient to provide me with a darkroom which would enable us to develop our films. We were delighted at the warm reception we received from De Mille, who turned over to us the facilities of the Lasky's Famous Players Corporation. We selected a spot in his laboratories which had dustproof clean dry air and special tanks and racks where we could hypersensitize our special aerial film. At the time film and lenses were quite slow and using a filter decreased the film speed even further. Prior to every flight, we used to hypersensitize the film in an ammonia bath and it was necessary to use it right away before it reverted to its former state.

De Mille told us he thought the Los Angeles Chamber of Commerce and the city council would be very much interested in our aerial photographic mapping project. He recommended that we pay them a visit and ask them to furnish an apartment as well as an automobile and the necessary gasoline and oil. Further, he thought we should be able to arrange a couple of guest cards to the golf courses in the Los Angeles area. De Mille had guessed right, and the city fathers couldn't do enough for us. We were sent to a garage to pick up a big six-cylinder Studebaker, plus gas and oil tickets. Guest cards to the golf course were mailed to us.

Although he never admitted it, we felt that the Hollywood impresario had had a hand in the warm all-out reception we received. Our only rejection came when we attempted to play golf at a very exclusive club and were denied the privilege because we were not Jewish. We considered it a first of some kind, and De Mille had a field day kidding the life out of the club's president, who was a friend of his.

Because we had to have an absolutely cloudless sky to do our work, it required about three weeks to photograph the 1600 square miles of Los Angeles County. This included processing our films and plotting each photograph in its relative position on the county map.

Our next job was to fly the mosaic of Los Angeles from an altitude of 12,000 feet. But again, we had to wait for ideal weather conditions. In waiting, we spent considerable time around Lasky's Famous Players' studio watching silent films being made. The studio was an exciting place. Gloria Swanson was the leading lady in the film *Bluebeard's Eighth Wife*, De Mille had his carpenters and other technicians making chariots for the *Ten Commandments*, and Theda Bara was also working on a film.

Theda Bara, a temperamental actress, insisted on having privacy during her love scenes. Her director was compelled to erect a heavy canvas screen around the set on which she was working. In time the screen was perforated with peepholes made with pencils, pocket knives, and a variety of other sharp implements.

The weather finally cooperated long enough to allow us to make all our pictures for the Los Angeles mosaic and after developing the film, we pinned the prints on large sheets of pasteboard to make certain we had the proper overlap in flight and from strip to strip.

De Mille came to see the mosaic and immediately decided this new method of map making would offer an excellent subject for newsreel coverage. He made a few phone calls and that afternoon the Pathé newsreel men arrived. They arranged to rent an airplane and mount a movie camera in it in a position where the camera would be shooting vertically through the floor. We were to repeat our initial mission at 12,000 feet flying one or two strips over the center of the city. The Pathé plane would fly a few feet above to catch the pilot and cameraman operating his aerial mapping

camera. At the same time it would show the city and the movement of the plane over the streets and buildings.

The completed film was titled *Army Aerial Photographers Map
Los Angeles from the Air*. Part of it had to be shortened for the
newsreel showings, but the entire footage was later used as a short
run film together with a feature picture. It turned out to be not
only educational, but also of great sales promotion value.

After the Los Angeles job was finished, we received orders from
General Patrick to go to San Diego and complete a mosaic map of
that city. The same treatment was accorded us regarding an apartment and a car, and living in Coronado was not hard to take.
Howard and I traded places on this mission as he wanted to get
some experience operating the K-3 camera.

Even before we finished the job, which took about ten days, we
received orders to report to Army headquarters at the Presidio in
San Francisco. Such orders were unusual, so we wondered what
was in store for us as we flew up from San Diego to land at Crissy
Field, where a portion of the Golden Gate Bridge now stands.

At the Presidio we were not kept waiting, but were ushered
immediately into the office of a colonel in G-2, Military Intelligence. Also present was a major from the Corps of Engineers.
After quick formalities, the colonel, a lean pipe-smoking type, got
down to business.

"Gentlemen, what we discuss here will not go beyond these
doors. Is that understood?"

It was, but it was *why* that counted.

"We have a photographic mission we'd like you to fly which is
somewhat other than routine. Major, will you explain the problem?"

The major unrolled a large-scale map which included the southern portions of Arizona and California, and the northern half of
Mexico, including the Mexican owned Baja California Peninsula
and Gulf. "According to treaty," the major explained, "Mexico is
entitled to the usage of a certain amount of the water from the
Colorado River. That usage entails the irrigation of these lands
here." He indicated a triangular piece of territory which was

marked in red pencil. Its northern angle ran along the border from Yuma, Arizona, to Calexico, California. Its southern angle, extended down to La Bomba, close to where the Colorado empties into the Gulf of California. The third angle ran from La Bomba back up to Yuma. In all, the area marked covered between three and four hundred square miles. La Bomba, the apex of the triangle, was fifty miles inside the border on the Yuma side and sixty-five from Calexico.

"We have reason to believe," the major continued, "that the Mexicans have extended their rights and are irrigating additional land in the area which means they are in violation of the treaty."

He glanced at the colonel who, having gotten his pipe fired up, took it from there.

"The Mexicans are not about to let us come in and see for ourselves, so we'd like you to fly over and photograph the territory." He tapped the map gently. "Think you can do it?"

"I think we can do it, sir," I said. "There's a field at Yuma we can fly out of."

"Good. Now this is both secret and of high priority. How long do you expect it will take?"

"We want a sixty percent overlap on the film strips," the major put in quickly. "We don't want to miss anything."

I glanced at Howard. All the old soldier did was squint at me with his game eye. When you saw Howard from the left because of his eye it appeared as though he were smiling. I always liked to be on that side of him because he looked so damned serious head on or from the right. "With any luck, we can get it done in two or three days."

It was Howard who got down to the matter of the kind of luck we might need. "Suppose we have to come down inside Mexico, sir?"

The colonel puffed thoughtfully. "I hope you don't. If you do it will create a very unpleasant international incident, and at best we'll get a lot of bad publicity." Obliquely he suggested what might happen to us. "You know about Lieutenants Wolfe and Usher?"

We did indeed. They had been flying the border on patrol and had got lost and landed inside Mexico. After having been beaten up and practically lynched, they'd been thrown into dungeons where they'd had a very rough time. It had taken the State Department nearly a month to secure their release and relations between Washington and Mexico City were at low ebb. If they caught us spying, we had an idea we'd end up on the short end of a rope or a firing squad.

As though to take our minds off such cruel eventualities, the colonel looked to the future. "When you have completed the mission you will personally take the films to McCook and develop them yourselves. No one is to know what you are developing. When that's done, you'll deliver the finished product to the Chief of the Corps of Engineer detachment at McCook. He'll take it from there."

I'm sure no two airmen ever took more care in seeing to their aircraft. Due to the wind there was a lot of blowing sand around Yuma, and we were worried about its effect on the engine and the gasoline. No one at the field knew what we were up to, although they may have noticed we were unusually quiet just before we left there.

Howard was at the controls and I was taking the pictures. Our plan was to fly east-west strips of the assigned territory, starting at the border and working southward. Our altitude was 16,500 feet, well out of the range of any rocks the Mexicans might throw at us, and high enough so that if the engine quit we might have a chance to glide back to safety. We had no oxygen and at flight altitude it was several degrees below freezing, a lot colder than we'd find it if we came down in the wrong place. The DH-4 was no U-2, but so far as I know, Howard and I were the first to overfly a foreign country with whom we were at peace to gather, by aerial camera, intelligence information.

The first day's three-hour flight went without a hitch, and we went back the next morning on our final mission in a far more relaxed mood.

After two hours or more of precision team work at a rarefied altitude in below freezing temperatures, the mind grows a bit numb and reflexes are slow, but when that Liberty began popping the old soldier and I became mighty alert. We were about ten or fifteen miles south of the border with a strong north wind to buck. Howard headed into it at once.

From the way the engine was missing, I knew it was ignition trouble or poor gasoline. I suggested that we switch to the emergency tank. The switch did no good and, almost at once, the Liberty gave a final pop and went stone cold dead in the market. There had been quiet times in the air before for me and there have been since, but that was a quiet time in which a landing feather would have sounded like a bomb.

Down we glided through air that was a hard clear blue. We could see for a hundred miles and we could be seen too. The rumpled arid land reached up quickly. No one had marked the border with a red pencil, but we knew where we were all right, and we knew it was going to be close. The slipstream whistled a soft dirge through the wing braces. Howard kept his eyes to the front and did not favor me with a look.

When we glided across the border we had something less than a thousand feet to spare. I began breathing again. Howard did a masterful job of setting the plane down in a potato field gracefully putting it up on its nose. From my perch in the rear cockpit, I looked down the fuselage and the old soldier turned to look up at me. It was his left side, the grinning side, and I grinned right back.

Returning to McCook with Howard to develop the Mexican films as ordered, I learned that Steve had been up to his old tricks. While Howard and I had been collecting clandestine aerial photographs, Steve and Jimmy Doolittle had set out to take aerial photographs at a record altitude. The plane they used was the supercharged Le Père with which John Macready had broken the world's altitude record by reaching a height of 43,508 feet.

Steve and Jimmy started out and flew west climbing until they were over Richmond, Indiana. During the flight they were trying out liquid oxygen in one of the very early experiments with it. They were both sucking on the liquid oxygen and apparently

Jimmy sucked a little harder than Steve did, because up around 38,000 feet—the highest they could climb—he noticed that Steve had slumped in his seat. Jimmy reached around to pat him on the back and see how he was. In reaching over, restricted by his heavy leather flying suit—with the temperature 60 below zero or lower—he also passed out. The airplane was stable and it flew for about thirty minutes. Jimmy was able to determine this because, during the half-hour period, Steve didn't take any pictures or make any notes as he had planned.

When they reached their maximum altitude they had encountered a phenomenon of which they had never before heard, but were later to identify as the jet stream. During their thirty minutes of unconsciousness, the airplane, flying full speed forward, had backed up all the way from Richmond, Indiana, to Columbus, Ohio, a distance of about a hundred miles. As the plane gradually lowered away they both came to and finished the mission.

In such fashion we went about our appointed duties. I never did learn if anything came of the Mexican photographs. However, as one might say, by hook or by crook we proved, sometimes privately and sometimes publicly, what a body can do when he gets off the ground.

One public proof came shortly after my return to Washington when the Shriners arrived for their week long national convention. With Air Service approval, Andy Matos and I took a photographic mosaic map of the city at 10,000 feet. The finished product consisted of one hundred 7×9-inch aerial photographs. We pieced them together to form a single picture of the entire city, 24 feet long by 20 feet high. We knew it would make a fine exhibit of our wares as well as an excellent guide map for the visiting Shriners. Permission was given to display our masterpiece at the very strategic corner of Pennsylvania Avenue and 15th Street in front of the Treasury Building.

There was only one hitch. We didn't have any lumber on which to mount the map. Bolling Field had none to spare and it was the same story with every other military installation at which we tried.

With the convention due to start, I decided direct action was in order.

At the controls this time of a six by six truck instead of the usual DH-4, I set forth on a reconnaissance mission in depth. With me were Andy Matos and several enlisted men from the photographic laboratory.

We soon spotted our target on Pennsylvania Avenue in front of the Willard Hotel. It was an excellent pile of lumber and we could see that it was being misused by a half dozen workmen who were building viewing stands for a Shriner's parade.

Halting the truck, I descended resplendent in my uniform.

"Whose in charge here?" I asked in my best military manner.

The workmen looked me over and then each other.

"I guess I am, Colonel," the biggest of the lot drawled.

Andy had stepped down to join me as aide-de-camp, short but powerful.

"I have orders to requisition this lumber for a special project up the street," I declared firmly.

"Well, I don't know nuthin' about it. We got orders to build some stands here." The straw boss rubbed his jaw stubbornly.

I reached in my pocket and drew out a bill from the Bolling Field Officers' Club. "This is the Willard Hotel," I said looking the hotel square in the eye. "Here are my orders." I waved the bill, "And as you undoubtedly know, a soldier has to obey orders."

"That's right, Buck," one of the workmen piped up. "He's got to obey orders. That's the way it was in France."

"This ain't France and I ain't no soldier and you shut up," Buck replied.

"Doesn't matter," another fine workman chimed in, seeing a possible way out of hard labor in the hot sun. "He's a soldier."

Andy seconded the motion with a vigorous nod and that eminently reasonable statement seemed to satisfy everyone, including Buck, who sighed and shrugged and said, "What the hell, if you want it, Colonel, take it."

The workmen helped us load our ill-gotten gains onto the truck and off we went to mount the map. On top of the map I had a sign painted which read: IN PEACE AND IN WAR—ARMY AIR SERVICE. To enable visitors to find their way to major points in the city, we had pinned colored tapes to the locations and run them in from a list to either side. So that the display could be seen at night, we made a deal with the First National Bank across the street to shine a searchlight on it from one of their balconies.

The Washington *Post* ran an editorial on our effort which read in part:

> Every Washingtonian should visit the interesting Army Air Service aerial photographic mosaic map located at the corner of 15th and Pennsylvania Avenue, because some day this is the way maps of cities, counties, states and, in fact, the whole country will be made. It is truly the future of things to come and do not miss the highly creditable job of our Army Air Service.

Some of those who did not miss our map were President Harding, former President Wilson, and Generals Pershing, Patrick and, of course, Billy Mitchell. We were highly commended for the job and the slogan. Remembering that I still owed that judge and the city fathers a map of the city, I got permission to turn it over to them at the end of the convention. I don't know if this helped take the mote out of the eye of the judge when Air Service officers were hailed up before him but it should have.

As for judges, while the Shriner's convention was still in progress, I was very nearly hailed before some judges and court-martialed. The incident occurred because I had been experimenting over a long period of time with developing and printing film and paper which would make it possible to take photographs in an airplane or balloon, and drop the finished prints to the ground in a matter of minutes. To demonstrate this new technique, I got permission to borrow a captive balloon. From it I planned to take pictures of the Shriner's parade and drop them to the press representatives to illustrate how high speed photography could work in a military operation.

We launched the balloon at the rear of what is today the Executive Office Building adjacent to the White House. An enlisted technician from our Bolling Laboratory and I were only a short distance above the ground when with a clatter of hoofs and a cry of "hold on there!" a general on horseback galloped up.

"You can't put that thing up now!" he shouted, standing in his stirrups and reaching toward the basket as though he was going to pluck it down. "We're holding a review at the Monument in five minutes. Bring him down, bring him down, I say!" he commanded the two enlisted men on the balloon windlass.

Rank has its privileges and down I came.

"You'll spoil our show," the general explained. "When the review is over I'll dispatch a messenger and you can go up in your balloon then."

That was that and soon the Mall and the Ellipse were jammed with spectators watching the cavalry go through its paces. After about an hour, however, newsmen who were anxious to use our pictures of the parade began flocking around me complaining that the Shriners were on the march and where were the promised photographs. After all the work I had put in on the experiment, I decided to take a chance. Bravely I stepped into the basket followed by my technicians and gave the orders to cast off.

At about three hundred feet I had a fine view of everything. I could see literally thousands of people running away from the cavalry show, across the Mall and Ellipse toward the balloon. Leading them I could see the general galloping hell for leather, and waving his sabre. Even at three hundred feet I could hear his voice clearly as he bellowed, "Pull him down! Pull him down, I say."

Apparently the enlisted men had had enough of the cavalry because some how the winch jammed. The general shook his sword at me as I peeked over the edge of the basket. The enlisted men slowly got out their repair tools, but the winch simply wouldn't repair. By now the balloon area was packed with people and only a few horse lovers remained to watch the cavalry.

The general, not wishing to make a public spectacle of his inability to command the situation, simmered away below.

"Why not take a picture of him, sir?" my companion in the basket suggested. "He might be pleased with how fast we can get it to him."

I decided things looked bad enough without trying to make them worse, but we did start taking pictures of the crowd beneath and the marching Shriners, swinging along Pennsylvania Avenue and down 17th Street. With the developing process I had evolved, we began dropping the finished results by small parachutes to the newsmen in an elapsed time of less than fifteen minutes. Some of the shots appeared in the evening and morning papers with due credit given to the Army Air Service for a job well done.

The cavalry was less appreciative. The general, seeing he wasn't going to get me out of the air any time soon, departed the field, leaving word with the troops that I would be court-martialed for insubordination. He also left instructions that upon reaching the ground I was to report immediately to the District of Columbia military commander's office.

When the boys finally hauled us down from our 300-foot perch and gave me the bad news, I headed for Air Service headquarters on Constitution Avenue and General Patrick's office. Fortunately, he and his executive officer, Major Tony Frank, were there, and I quickly explained my predicament. This was a matter between two different services, and since the balloon photography project was sponsored by the Air Service, I figured someone should get me off the hook.

The telephone wires hummed, some harsh words were exchanged over my fate, but sweetness and light and sound reason prevailed. The final result was that from then on until the end of the convention, the balloon continued making regular aerial photographic flights and the cavalry general, so far as I know, rode away into the Virginia hills and out of my life forever.

Good fortune seemed to be my constant companion that summer for by joint agreement, Generals Patrick and Mitchell dispatched me on a semiofficial mission to France and Great Britain to study progress of aerial photography in each country. I took only one aide with me, Marge, and in the course of our tour I returned to Tunbridge Wells, Kent, for a long overdue reunion with my family. It had been nearly twenty years since I had bid them goodbye, and though time had worked its outward changes, it was a wonderful experience coming back to see my parents and brothers and sisters once more. The only hard moment was saying goodbye again.

During the official part of the journey, officers of the French Air Force and British RAF showed me all they had in the way of research and development and aerial camera usage. As a result, I came back to Washington disagreeing entirely with Sherman Fairchild's earlier appraisal, convinced by what I had seen that we were far more advanced in all aspects of the art.

I repeated these observations to General Patrick, crowing our superiority to him and to anyone else within range of my voice. A day or two later, I received orders to report to Billy Mitchell.

He received me alone, and it took but one glance to see that he was fuming. "Goddard, don't you ever learn?" he snapped. "Has it been easy to get what you need to advance aerial reconnaissance?"

"No, sir."

"You're darn right it hasn't! I've had to fight for every nickel you've spent. All the times you've come crying to me . . . And now you come back from your investigation, popping off about how good we are. We've got the best cameras! We've got the best film! We take the best shots! We make the best mosaics! God in heaven man, how hard are you trying to shoot yourself down in flames!"

He paced up and down and I stood there feeling like the dunce of the class.

"I want you to get this through your head, and don't you ever forget it." He shook his finger at me. "Never . . . Never brag about how good we are. It's only by telling them how bad we are—by crying about how much better the other fellow is that we can expect to get any of the things we need!"

"We'll show them what we can do with the little we've got, but it's not enough, it's never going to be enough, and if people like you go around blowing off, we won't be getting anything at all. Now do you understand me clearly, Lieutenant!"

"Yes, sir."

"Good. See that you don't forget it. Good day!"

I left the General's office feeling like seven kinds of a damn fool, which I was. Needless to say, I never forgot the message and from then on I adopted the Mitchell approach in toto.

As for the General, he didn't go around crying wolf when none existed. Yet in having the uncanny capacity to be able to see things far beyond the immediate, he made many of his predictions sound like something out of Jules Verne. He had proved that battleships were no match for aircraft, but when he returned from Europe in 1922 and warned of the rise of German militarism and air power at a time when Germany's pilots were reduced to flying gliders, few paid any attention. Later, he was to issue the same warning about Soviet military designs. Most prophetically, in 1924 on the honeymoon of his second marriage, he conducted a remarkable intelligence investigation through the Far East. Following it, he predicted the advance of the Japanese Empire, the sneak attack on Pearl Harbor, and the invasion of the Philippines. In every single case he was proved correct, but at the time the developments leading to these events were in such an embryonic stage that his reports did little but gather dust.

On the home scene, however, he continued to see that the Air Service captured headlines by pushing flying exploits. Lieutenant Russell A. Maughan raced the sun on a widely heralded dawn-to-dusk flight from Long Island to San Francisco. Flying a new Curtiss pursuit plane, he made the flight in less than eighteen hours and, when he landed, he handed the Mayor of San Francisco *The New York Times* of the same day.

Even more exciting, in April of 1924, a long-planned project of Billy Mitchell's came to pass when four Douglas Air Service planes left Seattle, Washington, on the first leg of their round-the-world flight. (Two of the original planes made it all the way.)

Calvin Coolidge had become President and, unlike Harding, he had no interest in aviation. His send-off of the eight airmen (two

to a plane) was so rude and perfunctory, as was Secretary of War
Weeks', that the men departed on their epic adventure fed up and
disillusioned. These feelings were only aggravated by the fact that
in their globe circling they were warmly greeted by heads of state
wherever they stopped.

The President and his Secretary of War appeared to be about
the only people who weren't interested in the flight. It was uni-
versally agreed that this was an event that deserved to be recorded
on film. Since it was impractical to send a photographer around
the globe, General Patrick had decided to have films made by foreign photographers as the mission progressed. The countries that
participated were Japan, India, Turkey, France, and England. It
was to be our job to pick up the returning planes as they neared
the east coast and photograph them on to their starting point in
Seattle.

I was to be the pilot of the film plane, but the choice of the
lucky film photographer wasn't all that easy. There were at least a
dozen civilian candidates who were determined to get the assignment. A meeting was held in General Patrick's office where he explained that the Air Service could not spare more than one plane
for the job, so the only way to settle the choice was by drawing
straws out of a hat; the man drawing the longest straw would be
the winner.

The happy man was John Bockhurst of International News
Reel. Bulky as he was, Bocky on drawing the long straw practically flew around the General's office shouting, "I got it! I got it!"

Bocky was no stranger to me, for we had teamed up on a previous mission. This, too, was an occasion when he had been chosen by draw from a group of photographers. The event was to
film the dropping of the first 4000-pound bomb.

Our job then was to fly over the target and shoot the test all the
way from bomb drop to impact. We did that, and Bocky, standing
in the rear cockpit had just given me the okay sign when the
shock wave from the explosion hit us. The plane flipped violently
and out of the cockpit sailed Bocky. He wore no chute, and the
only thing that saved him was the rear gunner's safety belt which

he had snagged around his ample middle. I immediately put the plane in a vertical bank and he came back into the cockpit head first.

After he'd unscrambled himself, he stood up and shouted at me: "Keerist! What a way to take a picture!"

On this new assignment, in order to keep within Army Regulations, General Patrick decided to give Bocky a temporary commission as a second lieutenant in the Air Service Reserve. Bocky thought it was a great idea, but trying to outfit him was another matter. A connoisseur of the grape and rich eating, he protruded in all the places a uniform is supposed to fit snugly. I went through the entire Bolling Field Bachelor Officers' quarters trying to dress him. He ended up the worst-dressed second lieutenant I ever saw, but he was thrilled, and since most of our time would be spent in coveralls, I didn't worry.

"George, old buddy," he'd say, his rather bulbous nose sniffing the breeze for the scent of beer, "don't I make a helluva soldier!"

I could only agree.

Our mission was to take pictures from the air of the Douglas planes landing in formation at the fields along the way, and to leave ahead of them to record their take-offs. Captain Burdette Wright was to arrive in the cities along the route to handle the newsreel photographers on the ground at the various airfields. The films Bocky was taking were to be distributed to all newsreel companies with no special byline or preference given to International.

We first picked up the returning fliers along the coast as they entered the State of Maine. From there on, all along the route, every time we landed there were receptions and parties into the wee small hours of the morning, but the Texans at Dallas really topped them all. There were 40,000 people at Love Field to greet the fliers with bands, bouquets, and everything.

Leaving Dallas I had to land at Sweetwater to refuel for the nonstop flight to El Paso. I had planned to get to El Paso to refuel and be in the air so that Bocky could film the arrival. Again the Liberty engine was to do me wrong. We were a few miles north of

Barstow, two hundred miles or so from El Paso when it gave forth an all too familiar sputter and then quit.

We were at 6000 feet and the ground below appeared relatively flat. I felt that I could get down without serious damage to us or the airplane. At about 1000 feet small sand mounds began popping up and for every foot we descended they got bigger and bigger. Leveling off at one hundred feet I saw I was trapped—that I could not avoid plowing into at least one of these mounds, which were ten to fifteen feet high, with cactus trees growing out of them. Long ago in flight training I had been taught never to hit a hard object head on, so just before I plowed into the mound in front of me, I kicked the plane sideways and the left wing took the full force of the blow. The wing folded up like an accordion. The fuselage struck sideways, causing the engine to snap away from the wooden longerons and the tail to break off. This left the front and rear section of the fuselage intact with no bumps or bruises on either one of us.

Bocky had slept through the entire descent and crash landing. Now he sat up and shouted, "What the hell's going on!"

I explained.

"Know what," he replied after a moment, "That was the quietest ride I ever had."

We climbed out of the wreck and began collecting our belongings. It looked like we had a long rough walk ahead. To help us I took the compass off the instrument panel and got out a map. While I studied it, Bocky, who had recovered his camera and film equipment, broke open his special traveling case and selected a bottle of colorless liquid to give him added strength for the coming trek.

Suddenly over the dunes a couple of cowboys came in view leading an extra horse. They rode up and after surveying the wreckage, one of them asked: "How come you fellahs are alive?"

"Got a lucky horseshoe," Bocky grinned. "Care to step down and join us in a small libation?"

"That's right neighborly," the second cowboy said. " 'Pears like you got something to celebrate."

"Sure do," the first one said, shaking his head, "Worst wreck I ever seen. We brung the extra horse for . . ." he was too polite to finish.

"He can carry our equipment," I said. "How far are we from Barstow? We've got to catch the train to El Paso."

"For a fellah that should be takin' it real easy, you sure seem in a fired up hurry."

"Not that much a hurry," Bocky declared, passing the jug.

After a short pause, we cut up one of our parachutes and using straps and cords from it, tied our equipment and personal belongings on the extra horse. Riding tandem on the other two, we made our way toward Barstow a few miles to the south. It was not a method of travel I was ready to substitute for flying.

Much to our disgust, when we were a mile or so from Barstow we saw the only daily train for El Paso pulling out of the station.

That afternoon we finally hired an old man to drive us to El Paso in his model-T Ford. It was a rough ride, almost as rough as riding horseback, and just before midnight the old man dozed off and ran us into a ditch. We sat there disgustedly until a car came along and helped push us back on the road.

The rest of the trip was uneventful, and we arrived at the Fort Bliss flying field in time to see the round-the-world fliers take off for Tucson. The commanding officer understood our predicament and provided us with another DH, and we were on our way in a matter of minutes. In flight and during landing and take-off at Tucson, the plane demonstrated poor flying characteristics.

When I arrived in San Diego, I went to the engineering officer and asked to have my plane inspected. Examination revealed that one of the longerons back toward the tail was broken and another one was cracked. After an exchange of telegrams to El Paso, the engineering officer there admitted that one of his men had made a mistake and had given me a condemned aircraft.

I immediately forwarded a telegram to Major Tony Frank in Washington requesting that he direct the CO of the depot to give me one of the VIP airplanes being modified for station commanders. I gave him the number of a blue and gold DH with the latest improvements which was ready for delivery, and the local CO received orders immediately to assign it to me.

When we finally reached the flight's termination point in Seattle, we found that all the excitement was not quite over. The field was a long, narrow cut through a heavy stand of trees, with one end at the shoreline. The thousands of spectators stayed back along the sides of the field when the round-the-world planes were landing, but by the time we'd made the required pictures the crowd had swarmed over the field again and we couldn't land. For quite a while we just had to keep making passes over the field until, when we were almost out of gas, soldiers and police finally succeeded in clearing a strip for us and our job was finished. In all, Bocky had shot 15,000 feet of film of the historic aviation event. All of the film is preserved today in the National Archives.

## 9

In October 1924 I returned to McCook Field to resume again my old job as Director of Research and Development of the Photographic Laboratory. The return was due partly to my having completed my tour of duty in Washington and partly to the fact that Steve, in the summer of 1924, joined the Alexander Hamilton Rice scientific expedition, which Dr. Rice of Harvard University was to lead up the Amazon River some 2000 miles. Steve was to handle the photographic end of the exploration. This was recognized by the Air Service as an excellent opportunity to test its aerial cameras and laboratory procedures under severe tropical conditions. Steve remained with the expedition for over a year and the techniques he devised in working with aerial cameras and processing equipment in the middle of a steaming nowhere added much to our knowledge of the art.

For a long time I had been anxious to return to McCook, for I had been eagerly planning and replanning several new development projects. One was "Quick work photography" with which I had been experimenting at Bolling and had used in the balloon tests; long-range photography was another; the third was my old dream of night photography. But I should have remembered that the best laid Air Service plans were forever going astray because of lack of funds. The total yearly budget for aerial photography was $30,000 and that included everything from new equipment to travel pay. On top of that the Photo Laboratory staff had not been increased by much in my four-year absence; of the eight people assigned to me, five were mechanics whose primary function was to install cameras in aircraft.

I was bound and determined that aerial progress was not going to be stopped for lack of money. There had to be a way to get what I needed and, after a certain amount of cogitation, the answer sprang from my forehead like Athena from the brow of Zeus. I got in my plane and flew to Rochester to have a talk with Dr. Kenneth Mees of Eastman Kodak.

We had not seen each other in four years and he received me royally. Then we got down to cases. "Dr. Mees, you know as well as I that we're beginning to unearth great uses for aerial photography. But our thinking is pretty far ahead of our research and development. Our problem in the Air Service is money. Kodak's problem is to be sure that what it develops can be properly tested and then is marketable. I have an idea how we can join forces."

"Tell me about it, George," the doctor said dryly. "I had a feeling there was something on your mind."

I told him about my experiments with quick work photography. I wanted Kodak to endeavor to come up with a film that was both a negative and a positive, which would eliminate having to make prints from negatives. Such a "negapositive" would save much time and would permit a photo reconnaissance plane to take its pictures, develop them far more swiftly than I had done in the balloon, and get them in the proper hands much sooner. I also wanted Kodak to pursue its research into higher speed films and higher speed shutters on aerial cameras. This was because the higher the speed of both, the sharper the definition of the object photographed. Finer grain film would add to this sharpness as well. In the area of long range photography, I wanted Kodak to start working on a 36-inch lens. The largest at that time was 20 inches. The increase would naturally mean we could take pictures at a far greater distance.

And with all that I wanted Kodak to get cracking on, what could we offer in exchange? Dr. Mees was curious to know.

"Doctor, we'll handle all the flight testing. We'll prove the product. When I can show my superiors and the public what we've got, that's going to mean orders for Kodak. It's also bound to bring orders from civilian firms. You do the research, we'll do the testing. It will cost you money in the beginning but you'll make it up, and we'll all end up on top."

Dr. Mees looked out the window a moment and then turned and smiled at me. "George," he said, "you make it sound interesting."

Dr. Mees took my proposal to other colleagues at Eastman Kodak and they, too, saw benefit in it. They were particularly intrigued by my wish for a 36-inch lens because its development would make it the first long range high efficiency system ever produced in the U.S., especially designed for aerial photography. Their enthusiasm fortunately was not tempered by a lean purse. The company had a budget of $5,000,000 for research.

Having inaugurated a reciprocal gentleman's agreement with Kodak which took on the epithet of "chizzlin' research," I knew for the testing that lay ahead I needed a partner who was a thoroughgoing expert in the field of chemistry, optics, and physics. I was a man who had ideas on how to get the best out of what was available and on how to develop what was on hand into something better. Along with the ideas I had a practical knowledge of the materials needed to execute them. My constantly stained and burned fingers attested to my being a self-made chemist. My understanding of the mechanics of aerial photography and its component parts had enabled me to carry out on my own certain improvements in the art, and my knowledge of optics was such that I was forever seeking new ways to improve lenses. But now, in having the responsibility of testing all that Kodak was going to turn out for us, I wanted to be back-stopped by someone who was a bonafide expert. I wanted a partner with whom I could work on the ground and in the air, one with whom I could undertake my number one project—which I had not discussed with Dr. Mees or anyone—night photography.

In being lucky in selling Kodak, I was equally lucky in finding the man I sought—Dr. Sam M. Burka. I had first heard about him through the Bureau of Standards where he had formerly worked and had been held in very high regard.

Despite his youth, he had been recognized since his graduation from Johns Hopkins as a keen physicist and inventor. His scientific knowledge was utilized by a number of laboratories at McCook, and he was in constant demand at the Office of Engineering School helping students with higher mathematics. Further, whether it was optics, chemistry, or navigational equipment, his contributions were important to the Air Service.

I first cornered Doc in a laboratory where he was working on an altimeter. It wasn't hard to do because he was a little bit of a fellow.

"Dr. Burka?"

He looked up from his work with a boyish smile. "Some people call me Doc, some call me old Doc," he spoke very softly.

"You look too young for an old doc. I'm George Goddard."

"Oh yes . . . I've heard about you," he said.

"I've heard about you, too. In fact, I've been checking up on you."

"Is that so!" He made it sound incredible. "And tell me, what did you find out?"

"That a laboratory like this is much too confining for a man of your talents." I shuddered as I looked around the small room. "You need broader horizons than just tinkerin' with altimeters."

"I do? What do you suggest?"

"Waal, I think what you need is a job in which you get to fly every day, a job in which you'll be technical adviser in the testing of all the latest Eastman Kodak aerial photographic developments from film to lenses, and one in which you'll be regularly rubbing noses with Eastman Kodak's top research people, such as Dr. Kenneth Mees, Dr. Arthur Chapman and John I. Crabtree."

My explanation had opened Doc's big brown eyes, not to mention his mouth. He put down his screw driver, rubbed his hand on his coveralls and thrust it out. "George, I like the way you paint a broad horizon. Where have you been hiding?"

In order to pry Doc loose from his laboratory job, I had to get

the Chief of the equipment section, Major Ed Hoffman, of parachute fame, to release him. This took a bit of doing until I
gave Ed a confidential explanation of my plans to undertake night
photography tests and my need for a man of Burka's caliber.
At the time I was stretching the string a bit because I had neither
funds nor official authorization to proceed with such tests, but I
did have enthusiasm and since Ed could see the vital importance
of the project, I got the Doc. It was one of the best pieces of
good fortune in my entire career.

Doc was a man of many talents both on and off the job.
Every pilot from coast to coast knew his name and fame . . .
as a bartender. In the dark days of prohibition, he was a ver-
itable Merlin amongst the host. He could turn stone-like liquids
into golden libations, and every pilot coming into McCook after
a long hard flight from somewhere was anxious to pay his respects
at Doc's apartment by the Miami River where he lived in splendid bachelorhood with Lieutenant Bert Lewis, a pilot envied by
his brethren.

Soon after Doc was transferred to aid me, I confided to him
my ideas for night photography and we began making plans as
though we already had money and approval. To take aerial
photographs at night there was one major difficulty and several
fundamental problems to overcome. The difficulty was that the film
at our disposal was approximately one tenth of the speed of
present-day films. This meant that we had to create enough light
of the desired quality so that the object photographed would register on the film. The only way to produce such a light was with
flash powder. The fundamental problems were: How much powder should be used; what method would be used to ignite it;
what altitude would provide the maximum brilliance; and how
could the ignition of the powder be synchronized with the shutter opening of the camera?

I had a good many ideas, some of them feasible, some of them
not. As for those that were not, Doc had no hesitation in saying,
"George, you're wrong, you're absolutely wrong. You'll blow us

out of the sky." And when I'd ask why, Doc would explain why, and I would see that he was right. While he was not the sort who came up with the original thought, he knew how to advance or to reject it, and so we made an excellent combination.

The opportunity to stop talking and get down to serious business occurred when General Patrick came to McCook on a periodic inspection. At every laboratory he received a complete progress report, and when he came to mine, I was well prepared. I gave him a blackboard briefing and told him of my arrangement with Kodak, saving night photography for last. At once he grasped the tremendous military potential involved; his approval was immediate and enthusiastic. As for the necessary funds, "I'll see about that, son."

The necessary money had to come out of the general fund that McCook Field was allotted every year by the War Department. From this fund each laboratory was doled out its portion. The only way you could expect to get more than your share was when Washington stepped in, and this was one reason why a quick quiet trip to Air Service headquarters sometimes helped. Now General Patrick brought his influence to bear and suddenly I had a budget on which to proceed with preliminary tests.

My first idea was to build a small wooden glider with a five-foot wingspan and to fill the fabric-covered fuselage with 30 or 40 pounds of flashlight powder for the initial test. As these tests progressed, I could then vary the amounts of powder necessary to make the correct camera exposures, according to the different altitudes we were flying. The glider's design was readily handled by our engineering division and, in a few days, it was constructed in the main shop.

The glider was suspended under the fuselage of the DH. A two-way wire cable was attached to its nose and secured to a windlass in the rear cockpit. When the glider was released it would trail out behind the aircraft. When it was a safe distance to the rear, an electrical charge was sent down the wire to ignite the flash powder that lit up the sky and went off with a helluva bang. At the moment the powder ignited, the same electrical impulse came back up the wire and tripped the K-3's shutter.

On our first daylight test over Patterson Field, we used a reduced charge of powder because we were anxious to test the flash and shutter synchronization. It worked perfectly and Doc and I were elated. But we realized the glider concept was not practical from an economic point of view because it made but a single flight and then was blown to smithereens, so we decided to start using small bombs attached to rope cables. The bomb was released from its shackles beneath the fuselage. In the drop the cable unwound to its full length of several hundred feet. The first jerk of the extended rope tripped the camera shutter in the aircraft while the second ignited the fuse on the bomb. The idea was all right, but the timing was not dependable because there was no way to control either the bomb or the cable once it had reached its full length. In seeking better control, I turned next to attaching the bomb to a small parachute made fast to the end of the cable. This gave us a slower drop and a better method of timing the camera shutter and detonation.

It was all trial and error and we knew we had a long way to go before we were going to get what we wanted. Of course, all members of my staff, as well as a good many others at McCook, either contributed to, or were interested in, our tests.

In the beginning I would leave Dayton early in the morning with Doc and my civilian assistant Bill Oswalt and drive to a fireworks company in Redding, Ohio, not far from Cincinnati. There we would decide on the proper mixture of powder for the test, encase it in the bomb and drive back to Dayton. That night, Doc and I would fly into the dark, light up the sky with "Canned daylight," come down and develop the film and decide on the changes to be made at the fireworks company the next morning.

It was quite routine and it precluded blowing ourselves up at the fireworks factory, or in driving back to Dayton, or while airborne at night. Miraculously we succeeded in avoiding such an obliterating departure, but the citizenry of Dayton got fed up with our nightly bombing. Not appreciating our scientific pioneering, they, in turn, began bombarding the newspapers with letters of complaint such as the following:

> It is about time some drastic action were taken against this dam-nable night bombing by McCook fliers. No consideration is given to whether the physical condition of some of our citizens permits such nerve-racking playfulness, and that is about all it amounts to.
>
> My permanent home is in Cleveland, Ohio. We do not have a great deal to crow about in that city. However, such practice would be stopped in a minute. Neither do we have a spineless worm as a city manager who would tolerate the many things that you people in Dayton have to put up with.[1]

A few stalwart patriots wrote: "Bravo! Keep up the good work, boys. We would rather listen to your bombs than those of the enemy!"

We weren't sure who the enemy was, but we approved the sentiment and went on about our business. In our tests there was always the problem of a dud, a bomb that failed to explode. This could present an extremely hazardous situation because some unknowing person might pick it up by mistake and the results could be instantaneous, loud, and not redeemable. Though the chances of such a mishap were unlikely, it was a possibility we always feared and sure enough one night while carrying out a test, the bomb did not explode. We knew the approximate area where it had landed in a new housing subdivision called Dayton View.

The following morning bright and early Doc and I went on a ground reconnaissance mission in depth. We spent practically the entire day in and out of backyards and vacant lots. Nothing turned up. I was becoming increasingly concerned. In such a state of mind we were driving down a street in the gathering dusk when I saw an elderly gentleman picking up pieces of wood around his newly constructed home. A very strong hunch came over me

[1] The Dayton *Herald,* December 15, 1924.

Sergeant Andy Matos and I fuel up our DH-4 at Moundsville, West Virginia. *U.S. Army Air Service*

Sergeant Andy Matos, seated left, and I standing (center), after landing the DH upside down in a cornfield. *U.S. Army Air Service*

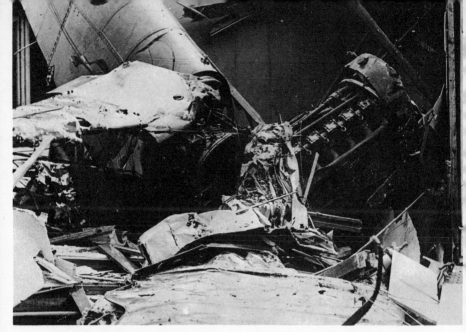

Stevens and MacSpadden make contact with the CO's bed at Mitchel Field. *U.S. Army Air Service*

The Army Air Service dirigible *Roma* about to depart on its last flight, February 21, 1922. *U.S. Army Air Service*

The invincible "Bocky" and I prepare to set forth to film the returning "round the world" fliers. *U.S. Army Air Service*

President Calvin Coolidge and Secretary of War John W. Weeks greet "round the world" fliers, September 1924. *U.S. Army Air Service*

Five who survived being blown up by a Goddard flash bomb. Left to right, Bill Oswalt, Colonel John C. "Magilicutty" McDonnell, Captain Albert Stevens, Lieutenant Gene Batton, Lieutenant George W. Goddard, March, 1927. *U.S. Army Air Service*

The Douglas C-1, hiding its broken bones beneath a wrinkled skin. It too survived the Goddard flash bomb. *U.S. Army Air Service*

The interior of the Douglas C-1, showing the effects of the bomb damage —snapped faring, bent longerons and torn fabric. *U.S. Army Air Service*

and I pulled over to the curb, stopping the car and noting that the new home owner wore thick glasses.

"Excuse me, sir—ahhh—we're looking for a wooden object."

"Plenty of wood around here," he said with a sigh.

"This is a special kind of laminated wood. It's about two and a half feet long, about this wide and so round." I had gotten out of the car and was using my hands to indicate.

"Nope. I ain't seen anything like that." He looked around the yard. "Got other kinds though."

Doc had started to turn away, but my hunch had a severe not to be denied feeling. "You don't mind if I look around, sir, do you?"

"Look all you like. Find anything that strikes your fancy, take it away."

He moved toward the cellar entrance and I followed him like a moth to the flame. It was dark in the cellar but not that dark, for my eyes immediately spotted the missing bomb stacked up with other yard wood right beside the furnace!

After that close call, we made certain that our bombs would be released over the Miami River alongside the field, and so night after night we continued our bombing with all kinds of variations on the same loud theme.

Dayton View, however, was still not free of McCook's dedicated testing, for we learned that shortly after we had been over it, a couple of stalwart pioneers looped a Martin bomber and it was reported that tools fell out of the sky into Dayton View like raindrops.

In late January of 1925, our tests were momentarily interrupted by the historic total eclipse of the sun. Dr. David Todd, one of the country's most noted astronomers, working through Congressional contacts, arranged with General Patrick for me to fly to New York State in the vicinity of West Point to take photos at maximum altitude of the celestial spectacle.

Along with the eclipse I was also to photograph the advancing and retreating shadow of the moon as it raced across the earth's surface. This would be no mean feat and would take terrific timing to catch both shadow and solar corona at the right moment.

On Friday, the day before the big event, Doc and I arrived at Mitchel Field. It had been a cold and snowy flight from Dayton, and the weather prediction for Saturday was ten below on the ground. I'd had plenty of experience in trying to start a Liberty engine on a cold morning with the oil practically frozen solid, so that evening I had the plane brought into the hangar and the oil drained. In the morning it would be heated and then poured back into the engine.

My pilot for the flight was Lieutenant George C. MacDonald from the Photo-Section at Langley. Doc was to fly in another plane whose photographer had become sick.

We all rose up in the frigid dawn. The snow bordered the field in frozen drifts. For once the weather man had been correct and it *was* ten below. A fairly heavy overcast at about 6000 feet worried us. What worried us more was the thought of the temperature at 16,000 feet. In the hangar, George and I had the mechanics heat the engine oil over a stove while we got dressed for the ordeal. We put on all the clothing we could carry, sweaters, jackets, several pairs of wool socks, heavy duty flying suit, fur-lined leather gloves, boots, face mask, helmet.

Our Liberty fired up at the first push of the button, and we learned later ours was the only plane that got off from Mitchel on schedule, the others suffering bad cases of congealed oil. Poor old Doc and a bunch of other frustrated photographers were left on the ground as we climbed up the icy blue.

The overcast was broken and we were on top in a cloudless sky at 10,000 feet. Before we'd reached our optimum altitude of 16,000, my face and oxygen mask were frozen stiff, and to George I looked like a frosted snowman standing in the rear cockpit. The K-3 camera was mounted on the gun scarf and fortunately the shutter switches on each side of the camera handles were activated by pressing down with the thumbs. Anything more intricate would have been too difficult to accomplish, for with all that I had on, my movements were clumsy and, as we finally leveled off, I realized I'd never been so cold in my life. The icy blast came right through all my clothing and grabbed me in an aching vise, numbing the life right out of me. It was a fight to concentrate on the momentous moment that lay ahead and what I must do to capture it on film.

At the instant of total eclipse, I was too occupied to realize that the temperature had plummeted another twenty degrees, which must have made it about 40 below. Perhaps we survived the cold because of the transcendent awe we experienced in viewing earth and sky, sun and moon at that moment of rare blending. Those watching below could not see the spectacle as we witnessed it. They could not see with our clarity the magnificent grayish blue streamers of the corona arching gracefully in the instant of climax across millions of miles of space. They could not see at all the hurtling lunar shadow, as wave-like it sped darkly over the snow-white landscape, its rim shimmering with the colors of the spectrum. We saw it, and I photographed it, and then we came back down to the earth again, numbed to the bone but warm in spirit.

The next day, Sunday, January 25, a banner headline in the New York *Herald Tribune* read: ECLIPSE REVEALS NEW SECRETS TO SCIENCE: CORONA AND SHADOW RECORDED BY ARMY FLYERS AT 16,000 FEET. The subhead beneath ran: Dr. David Todd Succeeds in New Aero-Astronomy Tests Carried Out by Two Pilots at Risk of Lives.

In the page one story that Dr. Todd wrote for the *Tribune* on the eclipse, it was noted that as professor emeritus of Astromony at Amherst, the doctor had observed seven partial and twelve total eclipses in his fifty years of astronomical observations.

He wrote in part:

". . . All my previous experiences covering the face of the earth were but rehearsals for this one, and the aid of aviation brought me nearer than I had dreamed to the realization of a lifetime . . . Lieutenant Goddard, United States Army, who took these photographs

was at a vantage point above more than a third of the earth's en-
folding atmosphere. He was above the smoke drifts and mists, which
we do not see on even the clearest days below, but which mountain
climbers have always seen in valleys and with which every aviator
is familiar . . . Lieutenant Goddard's photographs of the solar
corona obtained yesterday from this exceptional vantage point show
clearly much more extended streamers of the blue corona than could
possibly have been caught by the astronomers below. What these pictures mean to the new science of Aero-Astronomy is obvious to
everyone."

The pictures I took that day appeared in hundreds of newspapers and periodicals throughout the U.S. and foreign countries.
The solar shadow photographs were of particular interest, and
George and I were given due credit for nearly freezing to death
to record the phenomenon. From then on, whenever I saw one of
the photographs, I never failed to consider that I had deeper
respect than most for life in the Arctic.

A hoax came out of the eclipse of which only a very few
people were ever aware. A commercial photographic outfit had
contracted with a number of newspapers to supply aerial pictures
of the event. They did so, but not by leaving the ground, or for
that matter by even going out of the laboratory. They slipped
into the dark room where they suspended an orange in front of a
mazda lamp. Click-click went the shutter, and they had a home-
made eclipse. While their photographs lacked the solar corona,
they bore a close resemblance to the real thing and the newspapers paid for and carried the results, never the wiser.

Returning to our night tests, Doc and I decided we had to do
something about our fireworks bombs. Though they offered the
necessary amount of light, they were too primitive for us to attain
the precise kind of timing needed. We flew down to talk to the
Ordnance people at Picatinny Arsenal and Aberdeen Proving
Grounds, and their research branch set to work on developing
what we came to call flashlight bombs. What I was after was a
triggering mechanism that would explode the device when it had

dropped two-thirds of the way from the aircraft to the ground. This was no easy request because of the unreliability of fuses.

About the same time Doc and I and the Ordnance people were scratching our heads over that one, Kodak, true to its word, began supplying us with film for tests in quick work photography. This was almost as exciting to Doc and me as night photography, and, of course, went hand in glove with it. One meant a hostile force could no longer conceal its movements under cover of darkness, and the other meant you could get photographic evidence to where it was needed that much faster.

But like night photography, quick work offered its problems, too. In this case what we were doing was transferring the laboratory darkroom to the small, unstable confines of the cockpit. This meant we had to have a small enough container in which to put chemicals and film equipment. When Kodak began supplying the film, Doc and I set to work on designing the equipment. Temperature was one critical factor that constantly plagued us and, during the hot summer months, we often carried a block of ice to keep things cool. One of the chemicals with which we had to work was sulfuric acid. We could not prevent spillage in rough air and we had a pan in the floor of the cockpit to catch it.

We didn't give much thought to the corrosiveness of the acid or the fact that the pan was not really adequate. It was another example of how carelessness around an aircraft can bring bruising results. The mechanics in inspecting our plane after a long flight found that the acid had spilled from the pan and run back onto one of the elevator control cables near the rear of the fuselage. The acid had eaten into the cable and it was about ready to snap. Had it snapped in the air, we might have been able to bail out, but had it happened on landing or take off, or when we were too low to bail out, that would have been that.

As Doc, rather white-faced and shaken, put it, "Gee, George, we'd better be more careful, or this work could get dangerous."

In struggling to find ways over, through and around the obstacles that confronted us in all areas of testing, I did some of my best thinking in the cockpit, and one day at about six thousand feet a bolt came down from somewhere above and germinated into a full-winged idea. In the development of aerial night photography, the speed of the flash was important because it was at its peak that the picture was taken. We needed to know how to measure the length of the flash and to determine when the peak occurred. The answer to that need was what hit me. It was a simple and inexpensive device that would indicate the duration of the flash, just how long in fractions of a second it took to reach the peak, and provide a spectral analysis of the light as well.

The unit I constructed was basically an old secondhand phonograph. Instead of putting a record on the turntable, I had Kodak sensitize some circular glass plates and used them in place of the standard records. The speed of the turntable was one revolution per second. The phonograph was placed inside a dark chamber facing the sky. On the upper surface of the chamber we cut a series of small holes which were covered by different spectral filters. To show the duration of the flash there was a row of holes covered by certain density filters. If the entire flash was a sixth of a second, it recorded the time accurately in a circle around the sensitized surface. The peak of the illumination was recorded through the heavy density filters in the upper surface of the dark chamber. Even Doc agreed it worked just fine.

After I had made a night flight over Dayton using the flash recorder, I mailed one of the resulting photographs to General Mitchell, together with a copy of my patent application covering the device. A few days later he breezed into my laboratory.

"George, my boy, how are you?" he said, slapping me on the back in greeting. "Up to some new tricks, I see."

"General, wait till I show you. We've been laying eggs and scratchin' worms out here."

It had been quite some time since we'd last talked, and although his manner was just as sharp and invigorating as it had ever been, his face looked drawn and there was something in his eyes that indicated frustration and weariness.

We spent a pleasant half hour together and, while I needed nothing to stimulate my own morale, I had a feeling I helped his a bit because he showed genuine excitement over our progress.

In the course of our conversation, he'd told me that he had come to Dayton by train and was going back the same way. After he'd said, "so long," I suddenly got a bright idea, and next morning shortly after the train had pulled out of Dayton and was toddling along to Washington, Doc and I were airborne. We caught up to our target and I began buzzing it, diving down and flying alongside and then pulling up and away. Sure enough after a couple of dives we saw Billy Mitchell step out onto the observation platform. On the next pass, Doc had the camera in action. While I raced ahead of the train looking for a place to land, Doc developed the pictures. When the train pulled into the next station, we were there waiting for the General to hand him some prints of himself standing on the observation platform. He was so pleased I think he showed everyone in sight those pictures, including the engineer.

It was only a very short while after this episode that the bad news hit McCook like one of Billy's 4000-pound bombs. He'd been replaced in his post as Assistant Chief of the Air Service (by Lieutenant Colonel James E. Fechet), demoted in rank to Colonel, and assigned to a meaningless job at Fort Sam Houston near San Antonio, Texas. The reason behind the move was that Secretary of War Weeks, with the strong support of President Coolidge and the War Department, had had enough of Billy Mitchell's speaking out on the wretched state of our air defenses.

Most officers would have considered such a demotion an engraved invitation to a quick resignation. Not Billy Mitchell! He accepted his new orders calmly and although he'd been deprived of his authority, he still managed to come winging into McCook to inspire us and give us the benefit of his thinking. In a sense the demotion had a somewhat opposite effect than was intended. Everyone on the Field, whether he agreed with his unorthodox manner or not, felt that he had been unjustly treated. As a result, both military and civilian aeronautical engineers were even more anxious to show him what they were doing and get the benefit of his knowledge. Thus in the months following, his visits became highly heralded occasions on which the red carpet was rolled out.

For me in the months following, improved weather meant improved night bombing tests, and a proportionate increase of complaints. As author Kent Sagendorf put it:

> Not even love's young dream veered Goddard from his quest. Asked to avoid cities in the future, he began blasting holes in the moonlight over a river. He didn't know that the river was full of canoes at that season of the year. He found out about it later, when the indignant owner of the canoe concession appeared at the Field and demanded redress. It seemed that just about the time the boys and girls in his canoes were getting chummy and comfortable, along came the unromantic Goddard bent on bombing. At the paralyzing flash and its roll of thunder, paddles would go one way, pillows another, the canoes would all but capsize and that ended the evening as far as the boys were concerned. Doggone it, said the man, it had to stop.[2]

Finally under the deluge of protests, Major John Curry, the CO, recommended that we do our bombing over Patterson Field. We were not too happy about this, for we did want to test our equipment over areas where we could see considerable detail of buildings, railroad yards, autos, trucks and people, if possible. We finally settled for the area of Patterson showing hangars, depot buildings, railroad equipment, etc. Then the management of a large Portland Cement plant at Osborn gave us permission to take night pictures of their plant and yard area. This was ideal, because the large plant did not have any windows in it and, at night, most of the workmen were inside the plant, which was not close to a residential area.

About this time I got a chance to explain publicly my side of blasting holes in the moonlight and interrupting love's progress. The fad of having a radio set, either a ready-made crystal set or a home-made rig, was sweeping the country. The McCook radio

---

[2] Kent Sagendorf, *Thunder Aloft* (Reilly & Lee, Chicago, 1942), p. 52.

research laboratories equipped two planes with radio transmitting equipment and each laboratory was directed to fly on certain nights and give lectures to the tuned in public below. In short order listeners from as far away as Tennessee began monitoring our airborne broadcast every Tuesday night at seven o'clock. Our popularity grew and the mail poured in. One dear old lady wrote to express the hope that the flyer was "right with God."

We hoped so, too, but we also hoped to get our message across. Major John Curry talked about the purposes of McCook Field; Jimmy Doolittle about speeds, stunts and stresses; Ted Barksdale, noted test pilot, took on the subject of performance testing; Tommy Milling, described an aerial defense; John Macready explained flying on top of the clouds; Victor Bertrandis handled commercial aviation, and I held forth on aerial photography. I explained why Doc and I had been lighting up the night sky and producing thunder claps. I also described Eastman Kodak's contributions to quick work and long-range photography.

In the latter there was big news, for Dr. Mees and his assistants had completed what the newspapers referred to as "the five mile high" camera.

"This photographic apparatus will be used by Lieutenant George W. Goddard in a flight soon to be made from Dayton, Ohio," said *The New York Times*. "The eagle eye of this aerial camera is the largest photographic lens ever ground. With its aluminum mounting the lens is nine inches across . . . Lt. Goddard hopes to obtain an aerial picture having a panoramic range of 318 miles."

My plan for the test was to take a picture of Detroit which lay two hundred miles north of Dayton. Theoretically it would be possible from 25,000 to 30,000 feet, if there was not too much smoke over the city or south of it. Unfortunately, Detroit experienced its clear weather when the wind was from the west, northwest or north. From this direction the wind blew the smoke of the city directly across or down the path that I would follow in taking my picture.

I planned to put the 100-pound camera in the rear cockpit

of a new high altitude aircraft, the SCOS-A, and mount it so the lens would stick out through one side, and the film magazine through the other. From my front cockpit I could actuate a lever that would remotely control the camera and take sequence pictures. I also planned to install a glass viewfinder alongside my right eye, so that what I could see through the viewer the camera would photograph when I pressed the exposure button.

The SCOS-A, with its supercharged Liberty engine, had unusual flying characteristics and, with the engine on full power, it would continue to climb rapidly with the nose pointed far below the horizon.

On the first test—using oxygen—I flew to about 20,000 feet and was quite comfortable in my uniform shirt with the heat from the engine flooding up through the cockpit. Before I realized it, however, I was at 27,500 feet and, in maintaining this altitude, I had to keep the nose down and throttle back the engine considerably. As I had feared, the smoke was too thick to see Detroit, so from a point several miles north of Dayton, I took a picture over a hundred miles away of a section of Canada in the vicinity of Point Pelee across Lake Erie from Sandusky. It was a good picture, the only one of its kind at the time, and it pointed the way for further research and development of long-range photography.

When I had first gone to Dr. Mees to make my "chizzlin' research" proposal, I had not mentioned aerial night photography. I felt it was a project that at least in its formative stages should be buttoned up at McCook. However, as we progressed, it was natural that I should discuss certain aspects of our endeavors with Dr. Mees. He was particularly interested in the simple device I had dreamed up to measure the speed and intensity of the flash. This was an area in which he had been working, and he asked me if we could come to Rochester and conduct some night flights so that he and his people could try out their more precise and sophisticated equipment which would also determine the actinic or spectral quality of the light.

For these tests Doc and I decided to have another glider constructed. It would allow for better targeting because we could trigger the flash directly over the Kodak equipment.

Since there were no landing lights on the DH or around the airfield, we prevailed on the station chief of the New York Central Railroad to give us a supply of 15-minute burning flares. I positioned three of the flares at the end of the runway and used them as a guide to take off. For landing, I had a Kodak man at each of the four corners of the field and when the tests were completed, they were to light up, and I'd come in and set down in the middle of the area.

I did have red and green wing lights so the ground researchers could track us, and I carried a Very pistol to signal the start of the test. At 6000 feet just as we had made our final turn and were headed toward the field, a couple of miles away, Doc released the glider and the windlass started to unwind slowly. Suddenly, when the glider was about fifteen feet back of the tail, the windlass jammed.

Caught in the slipstream of our airplane, the glider began crazily hopping and spinning around. I could see it easily because of its wing-tip lights, and right then I knew I had serious trouble. There was no communication system in the plane except pencil and paper, so Doc and I kept exchanging suggestions back and forth reading them by flashlight.

Apparently a bolt on the windlass reel had come loose, and Doc had no tools with him with which to fix it. In its gyrations, the glider began braiding its own cable and the more we flew the closer the monster with its fatal powder charge inched up on the tail of our plane. I knew if we couldn't get rid of it fast, we were going to have to bail out.

I informed Doc that I was going to gain some altitude and then put the plane through some violent maneuvers and try to break the glider loose. I went through sharp turns, dives and nearly everything that I'd learned during my acrobatic training. Talk about traveling with the fear of a fire in your tail! Every time I looked back, the thing seemed closer.

Apparently we had the Lord with us that night, because after about thirty minutes of wild maneuvers, which had made Doc thoroughly sick, the desperate try worked and the cable pulled the nose fitting off the glider. About that time there were a couple of guys at 8000 feet in the pitch darkness singing "Yankee Doodle."

Doc Mees and his Kodak troupe of researchers on the landing field were really puzzled and beginning to wonder if it were all a joke. They thought differently, however, when they saw two sets of wing lights following each other down. The glider was aerodynamically well designed, for it gracefully spiralled to a crash landing hardly a mile or so beyond the field. By this time we were making a fast descent for a quick approach. I fired the Very pistol and, shortly after its vivid explosion appeared, the red railroad flares were lighted and Doc and I glided in for a landing. And what a welcome landing that was.

The flight was not all on the minus side, for we had learned something—namely to abandon the glider idea once and for all! Doc Mees and his crew helped us search for the beast, which was not too difficult to locate because one wing light was still burning. We trailed some of the powder away from it, lit a newspaper and, in a few seconds, it exploded the charge with a brilliant flash.

"I sure as hell won't miss seeing that thing again," Doc sighed.

It was little more than a week after we had been chased all over the Rochester sky by our lethal creation that Doc and I got orders from Washington to take on a special mission. We were to intercept and fly alongside the U. S. Navy airship *Shenandoah* as it passed over Dayton on its goodwill flight from Lakehurst, New Jersey, through the Midwest.

When we arrived at flight operations at 6:30 on the morning of September 3, 1925, we were notified that the *Shenandoah* had crashed a short time before somewhere in the vicinity of Cambridge, Ohio. It would be our job to make a complete series of photographs of the wreckage.

Soon after we passed Columbus, Ohio, I spotted a mirror-like object glistening in the sun on a hillside. As we approached, I could see that it was the forward section of the airship. The control cabin had fallen several hundred feet away, and we learned later that everyone in it, including the *Shenandoah*'s popular young skipper, Lieutenant Commander Zachary Lansdowne, had been killed. We made a wide search before we found the tail section. Miraculously when the airship had come apart in the clutches of a violent line squall, most of those in the tail and another smaller section, managed to survive. The helium gas which remained in some of the rubber gas cells kept them airborne.

We made aerial photographs of all the wreckage from various angles then flew sadly back to McCook. Our pictures were developed and printed before noon and all morning long we received phone calls from the news services trying to get prints. Private planes began converging on McCook to try to get pictures for the press, in fact, one service offered several hundred dollars if I would give them exclusive photographs.

By noon Doc and I were ordered to fly a complete set of the pictures to the scene of the wreck for the use of an investigating board from Naval headquarters.

It was a grim and somber experience, infuriating too, when we learned that before the authorities had arrived, souvenir hunters and just plain scavengers had come swarming across the countryside like locusts and literally picked the remains of the *Shenandoah* and its dead crewmen clean. Someone had actually stolen Lansdowne's Annapolis ring from his finger.

On the scene I met Lieutenant Walt Richardson, my photographic counterpart in the Navy. He had been in the tail section of the dirigible when it had torn loose. Shaken and stricken as he was by the loss of men who were his good friends, he described the hell of being flung about in the violent turbulence, "like dice in a cup," as he put it. Their ordeal had seemed endless and they had finally descended by ripping open some of the gas cells, being slowed down by dragging through the tree tops of a woodland, and finally hitting the ground in a nearby valley. Of the eighteen men in the tail, fifteen survived. Like Walt, the shock of their experience was not only coupled with the death of

their friends, but also with their outrage at the wanton dese-
cration of their comrades' bodies.

There was another kind of outrage over the fact that the accident had occurred at all. The public uproar was galvanized by
Billy Mitchell, who forty-eight hours after the *Shenandoah*
crashed, charged the Navy and the War Department with "in-
competency, criminal negligence and almost treasonable administration of the national defense."

"All aviation policies, schemes and systems are dictated by non-
flying officers of the Army and Navy who know practically nothing about it. The lives of the airmen are being used merely as
pawns in their hands." His statement was 6000 words long and
it was all in the same vein of blunt and insubordinate accusation.

We knew there could only be one answer to it—court-martial
—and it was soon apparent that this was exactly what Billy
Mitchell wanted.

He was laying his entire career and future on the line, and
popular as he was with the public and many of the legislators,
we didn't see how he could expect to win out.

Very quickly President Calvin Coolidge moved to take some of
the steam out of Mitchell's damning accusations. He appointed
a board of seven outstanding citizens, headed by the noted attorney Dwight W. Morrow. Its purpose was to make "a study of
the best means of developing and applying aircraft in national
defense." No one could argue with such a move, and the Navy
immediately set up its own court of inquiry into the crash of the
*Shenandoah*. As for Billy Mitchell, it was announced in due
course that he was to be tried by court-martial, charged with
violating the 96th—or old lady's—Article of War for conduct unbecoming an officer and gentleman. Thus the War Department
determined not to try him on the merits of his accusations but
under an article of war that you could be tried on for as little as
kicking a horse. The trial was not to take place for several
months, the delay intended to let public opinion calm down, and
so we who were Billy Mitchell's strongest supporters could only
get on with our work and speculate on the coming clash.

Some months earlier when I had been testing quick work photography over Rochester for Eastman Kodak, I had read an announcement by the American Telephone & Telegraph Company describing a new piece of equipment they had developed for transmitting pictures over telephone lines. This gave me an idea —why not get together with them to demonstrate how we could take air photos in flight, drop the pictures to a transmitting station and send them out over the telephone lines instantly?

Through our local radio researchers I was able to locate the president of AT&T and arranged to see him a few days later. I had to operate in established channels, of course, so I obtained permission from General Patrick, who seemed very enthusiastic about the military possibilities of the idea.

My meeting with the phone company executives in New York was most encouraging. They agreed to send the picture transmitting equipment to the Army Command Staff School at Fort Leavenworth, Kansas, and the picture receivers to San Francisco, Chicago, and New York. The plan I had worked out was that the students at Leavenworth would witness the test in which the airplane would take the picture and drop it in eight minutes to the transmitter installed in a baggage car on a railroad siding nearby. Then the picture was to be transmitted over the wires and received simultaneously by the Corps area commanders in the three cities.

In late September we flew out to Fort Leavenworth and put on the demonstration as planned. A few days later the Chicago *Tribune* ran an editorial that told the story and indicated the effect:

> It is impossible to estimate the value of the latest development in aerial photography in time of war . . .
> The purpose of the test made by the American Telephone & Telegraph Co., and the army air service was to show the practicability of the device developed by Lieut. George W. Goddard. The picture of the Fort Leavenworth barracks, the theoretical base of the enemy, was snapped at 10:48 a.m.; developed in the air in seven

minutes, and two minutes later was dropped by parachute to the Fort Leavenworth station, and in eight and one-half minutes it was going over the wires. At 11:17½ the completed picture was ready for inspection and study.

The development of this photographic device is only another instance of the valuable work army officers are doing. Lieut. Goddard was told that to enable the commanding officer to make proper and effective disposition of his forces he required a photograph of the enemy's position within half an hour. The lieutenant went aloft, located the position of the enemy, made the exposure, and had the developed negative in the hands of operators ready for transmission by telephone in nine minutes.

Without having landed he had completed his assignment 21 minutes sooner than his commanding officer required, and was on his way back to continue his observations of the enemy's movements.

I have often found that one good idea can help to stimulate another. For months Doc and I had been working to solve the critical problem of synchronizing powder flash and shutter opening. We had made considerable progress, but until we could evolve a dependable solution, night aerial photography was going to remain in the realm of hit or miss. And then as I was flying back from Fort Leavenworth to Dayton, the answer came to me.

At Fort Leavenworth I had watched telephone engineers operating their picture transmitting equipment. Inside the revolving drum which held the picture during transmission was a photoelectric cell—the first one I had ever seen. When light struck the cell, it produced electrical energy. Couldn't this energy, I asked myself, be amplified to actuate the shutter of a camera? If so, when the light from the powder flash struck the photoelectric cell, which we would locate in the tail of the plane, it would trigger the camera shutter. It was simple, it was wonderful, and I knew it would work. I began to sing and Doc took fright thinking I had been possessed by cloud nymphs.

The next day I made some drawings of what I envisioned and filed a patent disclosure with the McCook Field Patent Officer. Then I flew to Pittsburgh and landed on a golf course not far from the Westinghouse research and development laboratories. There I met Vladimir Kosam Zworykin, whom I had learned was one of the world's authorities on the development and use of photoelectric cells. I told him my plan and explained the assistance Eastman Kodak was providing. He became enthusiastic and, not to be outdone, said that Westinghouse would develop and produce a prototype of the photo-cell amplifying system. When I asked him how soon it would be ready, he estimated sometime early in 1926.

With that agreement, I felt it wasn't going to be long before we made the breakthrough. However, I was impatient, for Doc and I had come a long noisy way in our testing and we had reached a stage of advance where we were rarin' to demonstrate to the Army, the public, and Kodak just how far we had progressed in being able to take a night aerial photograph. So after due cogitation over one of Doc's tankards of ambrosia, we decided to really light up the sky.

We selected Rochester as the testing place because Dr. Mees and his assistants wished to place their light recording equipment on the roof of their eighteen-story office building. Also Rochester with its rail terminus, industries, and river would make a good military target.

We set the date for Friday, November 20, 1925, and I told Dr. Mees I would pass over the Kodak building at about nine o'clock that evening.

At McCook Field we had rigged up twin Liberty engines on a Martin bomber for the test and Lieutenant Don Bruner, chief of the equipment section's night flying branch, agreed to pilot the airplane. Don was about as big as a minute and he had a deep voice that made him sound eight feet tall. Garbed in a parachute he took on the stature of a midget and I always swore that if he ever had to bail out, he'd fall right through the chute harness. But Don's heart was as big as he was small, and he was one helluva good pilot, too. Lieutenants Dick Copeland and "Froggy" Reed of the Army Ordnance Corps, Doc Burka, and I made up the rest of the crew.

Several days prior to the test I labored in our field wood-working shop in order to make up a super-size bomb, fourteen feet long and eight inches in diameter. I constructed the bomb casing of several layers of laminated wood and glued them to form a thickness of an inch or so. At each end I fashioned two solid oak plugs six inches in diameter and six inches long. I installed several veins or squibbs up and down throughout the eighty pounds of powder in the bomb, the idea being to explode the powder evenly. This would build up terrific pressure so that the wooden casing would explode in a one-hundredth of a second flash, sufficient to stop motion and record a picture through the open camera lens. The bomb was equipped with four separate time fuses which were to be pulled as the bomb left the airplane.

We left Dayton early November 19 in two planes and landed at a new airport in Cleveland for refueling. It was a sod field and very soft after several rainy days. In taxiing across the field to the hangar both planes bogged down in the mud and things began to look gloomy for our test in Rochester. Finally, we hired a farmer to pull the Martin out and, in doing so, damaged our landing gear. This we finally managed to fix and, well after dark, we all took off for Rochester in the one plane. Just before take-off, I had the field superintendent telephone Dr. Mees to tell him to get set for the bomb drop at 3000 feet over his building between ten-thirty and eleven o'clock.

We arrived over the city shortly after eleven and dropped our bomb, which was suspended on a parachute. In about twenty seconds it exploded with a tremendous blast and a brilliant flash which was so fast it took the place of a shutter in the camera. Using the remaining New York Central flares left over from my previous visit, we landed at the Rochester airfield extremely anxious to learn the results. At first they weren't what we were looking for because when the bomb went off that late at night, it raised havoc with the unsuspecting populace.

Near the airfield we tried to use a telephone to call the Seneca Hotel, but we were told by the operator that there had been a big explosion in the city and phone lines were jammed—

we'd have to wait until things died down. As we drove along the streets to our hotel there were groups of people standing around trying to figure out what had happened, and newspapers the following morning described wild scenes in town the night before. Rochester had a central heating plant and when the big blast occurred the city fire department nearby figured that the boiler house had exploded and dashed for the plant. Telephones were out for several hours and there was a near panic in the city.

I didn't know whether to hide out or head for Dayton.

None of it phased Doc, who was beside himself with joy, "What's the matter with you, George, it's the picture that counts, man, the picture!"

I could see a picture of me in the guardhouse and headlines screaming: *ARMY AIR SERVICE CREATES CHAOS IN ROCHESTER!*

Maybe I was a bit weary at the moment because later the afternoon papers proudly displayed the world's first photograph ever taken at night from an airplane. Little was said about the uproar and all we received when we got back to Dayton was a letter from the CO saying from now on dammit let the people know before you scare the hell out of them . . . and congratulations for a terrific job.

Naturally, this photographic first attracted nation-wide attention, but several weeks later Representative Martin B. Madden, Republican from Illinois, and a powerful member of the House Committee on Appropriations, let go with a blast maintaining that the Air Service in general and McCook Field in particular was wasting the taxpayer's money. The accusation really lit a fuse in me, and since I was in Washington at the time, I let go with a counter blast that found its way into *The New York Times*.

"We have not scratched the surface yet in aerial photography," I said. "Recently Congressman Madden made a wild statement, claiming the Engineering Division at McCook Field had not developed a thing and had wasted lots of money. Believe me, he is sadly misinformed, for every day very valuable developments are made at this Division which benefit aviation in general both from a military and commercial point of view."

The Congressman did not respond to my rebuttal and fortunately the Army didn't either, possibly because at that moment all eyes were focused on the outcome of a far more serious and spectacular drama, Billy Mitchell's court-martial.

At the very time we succeeded in Rochester, the court-martial was reaching its climax in Washington. At it, the findings of the Morrow Board were released which maintained: that the country was in no danger of attack; it compared favorably in air power with other nations; that a unified department of national defense was uneconomical and inefficient; that the American tradition required the separate development of civil and military aviation; that there was no evidence of officers being compelled to fly unsafe planes; that air power at the expense of battleships would merely substitute more deadly armament and was not conducive to disarmament.

The Board proposed the appointment of assistant secretaries for air in the War and Navy Departments, and adopted a few of the recommendations proposed by the buried two-year-old Lassiter Report.

On the one hand Billy Mitchell had been tried for conduct unbecoming an officer and, on the other, this was the government's answer to his charges. Without his years of prodding climaxed by his charges, there would have been no answer.

None of us was surprised when Mitchell was found guilty and swiftly resigned from the Army. But we were plenty angry about the whole thing. As one of the boys put it, it was like having our best friend shot down by our own side. It made many around me feel like quitting the Air Service, and morale hit an all-time low.

Of course, we were not objective, how could we be? Of the two schools of thought at McCook, there was one that believed he should have been more flexible and not thrown his career on the block, but whatever school of thought, we had considered ourselves Billy Mitchell's boys. For us, it was a very sad end to a bright year.

As to the good that came out of Mitchell's unceasing efforts, Frank Tichenor, editor of the popular *Aero Digest,* voiced our sentiments: "He has done more for the cause of aviation than any other man in the nation's history except the Wright brothers. If it had not been for him, there would have been no President's Aircraft Board, no Air Commerce Act, no under secretaries for air in the Department of War, Navy and Commerce."

I have a picture of Billy Mitchell that can never fade, not one on film, but one etched across my memory. He sticks his head into the little office I had at McCook and with that wonderful grin of his says, "Well, George, what have you got to show me today?"

# PART II

---◆---

*The Lean Years 1926–1936*

## 10

In July 1926 the Air Service, by an Act of Congress, had its
name changed to the Air Corps. At the time the only observable
difference this Act wrought at McCook was the need to reprint an
awful lot of letterheads on official stationery. Other than that, for
me the year was marked by three notable milestones—I won a
budgetary battle; night photography took a giant step forward, and
because of some dirty work at the camera shop, I nearly resigned my commission.

The budgetary battle took place early in the year when Major
Bagley of the Corps of Engineers protested to the War Department that too much money was being spent on quick work and
night photography and not enough on new mapping cameras. Because the Major had high-placed friends in the War Department,
I saw our efforts to continue our progress and establish true acceptance of aerial reconnaissance, day or night, in danger of being brought to a standstill. No one could deny that in spite of
always having to make do with too little money, we had, with
the aid of Dr. Mees and his staff, been successful in improving
the state of the art, and now I was damned if I was going to sit
still and have our program set back, particularly when I knew
that even while the Bagley T-2 and Fairchild K-3 cameras were
doing an excellent job for aerial mapping, there were already
newer models in the development stage.

Fortunately, our work had aroused considerable interest in the
upper echelons of the Army, and I decided to stimulate that interest further. Through Major Curry, a group of staff officers

from Washington were invited to McCook. We had them placed in front of one of the hangars, and then Doc and I took off into the night. At 3000 feet we snapped their picture with the aid of a 40-pound flash bomb. Ten minutes later we taxied up to the group and handed over the finished product. It showed the assembled in exceptionally sharp detail, and they returned to Washington duly impressed. The upshot of this demonstration was not less money but more, plus several additional technicians for my laboratory. Elephant-like, however, the Corps of Engineers was not to forget, and my heading them off at the pass would come back to plague me later on.

The giant step in night photography followed the completion of Dr. Zworykin's specially built T-shaped photoelectric cell unit which had been specially constructed at the Westinghouse Laboratory. Personnel from our radio laboratory helped us rig the equipment under the tail of a DH and in mid-July the great night arrived. Over downtown Dayton, I made the first test of the system and the results, equaling aerial photographs taken at midday, were published and displayed far and wide. No more would I have to drop bombs attached to parachutes or tow a glider full of powder. All the pilot had to do now was to release a flash bomb and when it exploded, the light at the peak of the flash, working through the photoelectric cell, would trip the camera shutter and in so doing unwind the next exposure automatically. For the next thirty years my patented system was used as standard night reconnaissance equipment by both services and during World War II by our allies as well.

The Dayton success brought the following official note from General Patrick: "There have just been received in this office samples of the night photographs taken on the 14th of July, and I want to let you know how greatly pleased I have been with the excellent results obtained. This development is of real importance, you have worked at it consistently, effectively and intelligently. For your efforts and the success you've attained, you deserve this commendation."

Between July and December, Doc and I continued our work in the same general vein, and in so doing we advertised our accomplishments as frequently and as widely as possible. The most famous recipient of quick work photography was President Coolidge. We took a picture in the air of New York City and delivered it to the White House lawn by parachute two hours later. During the six month period we also took photographs of many Midwestern and Eastern cities. In our activities we were building not only a case for the value of quick work and night reconnaissance but also the training techniques to carry it out. In my own mind a solid amount of research and development lay ahead. Thus when I received a call to report to the Adjutant's office one December day, I was not prepared to be blasted out of the sky like a glider full of powder. Orders had been received from the Chief's office in Washington stating I was to be transferred for duty in the Philippine Islands to take command of the 6th Photo-Section at Camp Nichols in Manila.

Some months prior there had been an official War Department release, declaring that all officers must have overseas duty and that those first lieutenants who had not served in such capacity could expect to soon. However, my tour at McCook was not due to expire until October 1928. On top of that General Patrick had made it clear he expected me to continue in my present capacity. Both Majors John Curry and Ed Hoffman, the CO and my section supervisor, were as flabbergasted by the news as I was, for as Curry put it, rubbing his hand through his thick mop of hair: "George, I've had every assurance you were staying right here . . . I think you'd better get this straight with the Chief the next time you go to Washington."

I was airborne within the hour, plowing through foul weather in a foul mood. No one had ever accused me of being unable to find my way around the red tape maze in which the Army is knit. I knew that all kinds of strange orders had been issued because stupidity is not special to any rank. Since I also knew that my orders for transfer would have to be approved by General

Patrick, I suspected some lower echelon wizard had made the error and somehow it had gotten past the General.

I was only half wrong.

"You've been transferred where?" General Patrick looked at me in amazement.

"To Camp Nichols, Manila, sir." I handed him the orders.

"But this can't be," he said, studying the document. "Your name wasn't on the list of officer transfers. I signed it on Tuesday."

"Well, it looks like it is now, sir."

"We'll see about that!"

Almost at once he had the chief personnel officer, a retired Air Service lieutenant colonel, before him. The personnel officer had the offending document in hand, and my name had been added to it.

The General bristled with anger. "Perhaps you can tell me how Lieutenant Goddard's name came to be put on here after I personally approved it with his name *not* on it."

The retired colonel was bland and noncommittal. "I really can't say, sir."

"Well, I want to know how it got there, and I want to know how it got there right away."

"I'll do my best, sir."

I was somewhat surprised that the General had not simply ordered personnel to correct the mistake. Instead, he waited until we were alone again before making any further comment.

"George," he said with a sigh, "that transfer list has already been approved by the Chief of Staff . . . It has become official."

The way he said "official" meant final. The surprise showed on my face. He turned and looked out the window, his words not coming easily. "The timing couldn't be more unfortunate . . . I can't rescind what the Chief of Staff has already approved . . . Recently there have been a rash of complaints because of changes in orders made in this headquarters after having been officially accepted . . . I've been accused of not knowing my own mind."

He shrugged and swung around to face me. "George, if I changed your orders now, the War Department would not accept it . . . I'm sorry. I'll be sorry to see you go."[1]

I've never been one to dwell on what might have been if things were different. But I knew as I listened to him, and by his words saw a glimpse of the daily battles he must have to fight with higher command, that were Billy Mitchell still on the scene the orders would have been changed. As it was, General Patrick went on in his fatherly way, trying to placate me, telling me that the two-year tour would be most valuable to me. He had been informed that several extensive aerial photographic map revision projects were being planned by the Philippine U. S. War

[1] WAR DEPARTMENT
OFFICE OF THE CHIEF OF AIR CORPS
WASHINGTON

December 29, 1926.

My dear Lieut. Goddard:
Orders have been issued for you to go to foreign service, sailing about two months from now. I want to tell you how much I appreciate the excellent work you have done in connection with the development of aerial photography, the processes you have devised for finishing prints in the air and for taking such photographs by flashlight at night, all of these things are due to your having initiated them and they are of great importance.

It is gratifying to know that you have had the ability to conceive, to undertake and to carry forward these many things and for your work you deserve high praise and much credit.

I shall see that the facts are duly set forth and made part of your military record, but especially, before you leave the United States, I want you to know the high opinion I have of the service you have rendered and of the excellent work that you have done.

I hope that you will find your tour in the Philippines interesting and I am satisfied that there will be there opportunities for you to illustrate the methods you have devised and thus greatly improve that part of the work which the Air Corps must do in that Department.

With kind personal regards and best wishes to you and Mrs. Goddard, I am

| | Very sincerely yours, |
| --- | --- |
| 1st Lieut. Geo. W. Goddard, A.C., | Mason M. Patrick, |
| McCook Field, | Major General, Air Corps, |
| Dayton, Ohio. | Chief of Air Corps. |

Department and I would no doubt play a leading role in the operations.

"You know, son," he said putting his arm around my shoulder, "those two years will go by in a wink, and I promise you I'll see that you go back to McCook as soon as they're completed."

When I had left the General's office, I walked a long way to Constitution Avenue, the cold December air matching my mood. I was not placated; I was sorely disturbed. Even with his promise, it seemed to me at the moment that I was being deprived of two years of time to pursue aerial photographic developments we had brought to a new threshold in a single year. Behind it all there lurked a faint but persistent suspicion that my totally unexpected transfer had not been brought about by administrative error but by direction.

On the face of it, it hardly seemed to be a reasonable suspicion. Not everybody loved Lieutenant George W. Goddard, and no doubt there were some who would be pleased to see him disappear over the horizon, but so far as I knew my work had been well received and no one in General Patrick's office wanted me out of the way. Yet, that was where the change had been made and someone in the personnel office had made it. I decided to see if I could at least lay the suspicion to rest before returning to McCook.

All that I learned before my return was that, due to a lack of shipping space, Marge and I wouldn't be departing for two or three months. This was good for several reasons. It not only gave me time to get used to the idea, it also helped to ease Marge over the hurdle. Like any Air Corps pilot's wife, she did a lot of socializing with other Air Corps wives and it seemed they spent a good part of their time together, playing "can you top this" on the horrors of their husband's next duty station. On top of the hazardous flight conditions, supposedly current in the Philippines, Marge had her ears filled with the rough climate and poor living conditions with which she would have to contend.

Sherman Fairchild, hearing of my transfer, added to the problem by offering me a job as a foreign sales representative for his company. The salary, of course, was far above anything the Air Corps could offer. His company now had the contract for producing my night photoelectric system. Although there was no financial benefit for me in being the inventor, because what was mine was also the government's, he agreed to pay me a $250 royalty on each foreign sales of the system.

And so here I was once again faced with a situation in which the grass looked greener, much greener, on the other side of the fence. But once I had calmed down and talked the problem over with people like Doc and John Curry and Ed Hoffman, I began to get some perspective on it. As General Patrick had said, two years would go by in a wink, and experience in the Philippines would be valuable. After nearly a decade of aerial photographic pioneering and flying service, I was not about to give it up for the sake of more money.

"No," I said to Doc. "We're going to go, and then we're going to come back here."

"Older but wiser," Doc said. "Here, try this. It's my newest. It won't make you any wiser but you'll feel maturity setting in fast."

Shortly, with the aid of Doc's newest, I began to see duty in the Philippines in a calmer, more amber-colored light.

"There's still something I'd like to know, though . . ."

"Yeah, who the buzzard was who put your name on that list?" Doc said.

"Yes . . . if there was such a buzzard."

There was, I believe, although I didn't learn about the circumstances all at once, and what I learned I could never prove, nor did I ever attempt to.

For a number of months prior to my unexpected orders the sales representative of a manufacturer, trying to sell us some photographic equipment, had been conducting an intensive campaign for his product at McCook and in Washington. Since I took a personal interest in testing most new equipment, I knew that until serious malfunctions in the product were corrected, no sales campaign was going to work. I explained this to the salesman on several occasions, for he kept coming back and trying to get acceptance through others on a higher echelon, all of whom referred him to me.

One day early in December he came storming into my office and announced, "This has got to stop! I see you've turned us down again."

"That's correct," I said. "Do you think I'm going to recommend an inferior piece of goods? I've told you before, and I'm telling you again, until the mechanism functions properly, I'm not interested."

"We'll see about that, Lieutenant!" he snapped, the emphasis on lieutenant, and out he sailed under a full head of steam.

In the interim between receiving orders and my departure, I saw no more of the salesman and in fact, completely forgot him until a few days before leaving the States. I was in Washington, clearing up some last-minute business, and the retired Lieutenant Colonel in Personnel, whom I had formerly known, invited me home to have dinner with him and his wife. He had never supplied General Patrick with a satisfactory answer as to how and by whom my name had been added to the transfer list, and I accepted his invitation, anxious to see if I could find out.

He greeted me at his apartment door, effusive and cordial, and as I entered the foyer I noticed in the open closet a large trunk, lid up, filled with bottles of Scotch whiskey. During prohibition this was in the nature of rare treasure, and I was surprised to note on the trunk the name of the manufacturer whose salesman had been trying so hard to sell his unperfected wares.

I didn't get the answer directly from my host that night. Whether I got the answer indirectly I was never sure, but a year later I did learn that the equipment I had rejected was approved and procured by the Air Corps. Within the next year all units of the product were returned to the manufacturer for further improvement at a considerable cost to the government. It was safe to say that among other things, the episode added to my experience, and from then on I was always on the alert in the presence of salesmen.

Another episode took place before our farewell that nearly

made the journey academic. Steve, back from the rigors of the Amazon, was to take over as director of the photographic laboratory in my absence. He reported to McCook in fine fettle, but since he'd been out of the picture, so to speak, I gave him a complete briefing on developments.

The "K" series of cameras were in general use in all the photographic sections. The K-3 had been modified for night use, its number changed to 12. A whole series of faster lenses were on order. Kodak's contributions to long range photography and improved film was an on-going project. There were many other advances, new to Steve, but the one he was keen to see in operation was our night photo system, and since he'd never been on a night photo mission, we decided it was high time.

The aircraft I arranged to borrow for Steve's debut was a single-engine Douglas C-1 cargo plane, the first of many transports Donald Douglas was to design and produce. It was a bi-plane with a two place open cockpit forward and a five man interior cabin aft.

To make the exhibition a truly gala performance, I invited the Air Corps' Chief Photographic officer, Colonel John C. "Magilicutty" McDonnell out from Washington as an observer.

With Bill Oswalt, my staunch civilian project engineer, I constructed four 60-pound flash bombs, each equipped with twin fuses, an extra safety measure we had used to good advantage in prior operations.

Steve observed the preparations having little to say and when I asked him if something was wrong he grunted, "I hope you know what you're doing."

"I'd better," I said, "because you'll be doing it after I'm gone."

Lieutenant Gene Batton, a McCook test pilot and good friend, took on the job of flying the C-1 and "Magilicutty" McDonnell volunteered to act as co-pilot. Steve, Bill, and I piled into the portholed cabin. On to an opening in the floor we had fitted a laminated wooden collar and over the collar went the camera and view finder. Our plan was to climb to 3000 feet and photograph a building area at the north end of the field which had a couple of red identification lights on the roof.

We had only our flashlights for illumination, and as we rumbled across the field toward our take-off point, using mine I went over the order of events with Steve.

"Now when Bill sees the target coming up through the view finder, he'll simultaneously flash a signal to Gene and one back here to me. When he does, I'll release the bomb through this chute in the floor. There'll be a twenty second delay and then the bomb will go and the picture will be taken automatically. Simple enough for you, boy?"

"There's something about that bomb I don't like."

"For a man who had a dark room in a Brazilian ant hive, what are you worrying about? I told you the fuse won't ignite until twenty-five feet have unraveled."

I could see his ears flapping in the glow of the flashlight, shaking his head in doubt. He said something but I couldn't hear what it was over the roar of the engine as Gene poured the coal to it and we began our take-off run.

"Keep calm, child!" I shouted, "and maybe I'll let you drop the second one!"

At drop altitude Gene made his turn and we headed toward the target. I knelt on the floor waiting for Bill's signal. When it came I released the bomb down the chute and started to stand up. And then, amidst the most godawful blast of sound and blinding flash of light, I continued my progress upward, right through the roof of the cabin. Stunned, deaf, and blind, like a fly in a spider web, I struggled in a tangle of wires spanning the fuselage top between the two main longerons. My vision returned swiftly and, dazed as I was, I could see that Steve and Bill were similarly enmeshed, and if it hadn't been for the wires the three of us would have been blasted clear through the top of the fuselage. Now with badly bruised wits, we clung on to the wires to keep from falling through the floor of the aircraft because the floor wasn't there any more. With it had gone extra bombs, tool chest, assorted equipment and most of the fabric in view.

Almost at once the aircraft had begun going through a series of wild gyrations, up, down, round and round, the engine wide open and the breeze funneling through the shambles. Somehow, Bill Oswalt had retained his flashlight and in its wandering beam I could see he was wearing something unnatural around his neck. I came to realize it was the wooden horse collar on which camera and view finder had rested. Fortunately, in the blast, they had gone sailing through the roof without making contact.

As the plane continued its frantic maneuvers, it became a question of whether we should bail out by dropping through the gaping hole in the floor. We had no way of communicating with Gene or "Magilicutty" or for that matter very coherently with each other. Steve was close by with his head jammed through the upper wooden faring.

"You and your goddam bomb!" he shouted at me.

"If they keep up these acrobatics, I'm gonna get sick!" Bill gasped.

The plane had no lights. The field had no lights, but all at once in the wild and woolly blackness, we hit the ground and up we went again and it seemed like another forever before we came back down again . . . and again! . . . and again! and again and came to a staggering halt.

They say any landing you can walk away from is a good landing. On that basis, without a doubt, it was the best landing I ever survived. We staggered out of the wreckage in front of operations and saw that practically every piece of wood in the airplane had been splintered and that all the fabric on the bottom of the fuselage and much of the wings and tail was either gone or hanging in shreds. By every law of flight the plane could not fly.

Gene Batton said that after the explosion the only way he and "Magilicutty" could get the plane into a relatively level position was by holding their knees against the controls with the engine wide open. We learned that the reason we were alive was that the Douglas Company had replaced the structural wooden tail ribs with metal ones a few days before the flight. The ribs had bent but not shattered. Still when the Douglas engineers saw the plane

one of them said, "I'll never believe it was landed in that condition."

Donald Douglas and his chief engineer together with McCook
engineers later thanked me for giving them test data on the effects
of antiaircraft shells exploding under an airplane in flight. It would
be so useful on future designs of combat aircraft. What caused the
bomb to go off prematurely I did not learn. Nothing like that had
ever happened before, and I had personally supervised the installation of the fuses. Even after we had gone up again with Bill and
Doc, and run through a number of tests, the look on Steve's face
indicated a deep suspicion that I had somehow blown us all up on
purpose.

Aside from downright survival, the best I could say for it was
that I departed McCook with a bang and not a whimper.

## 11

The journey from Brooklyn to the Philippines aboard the troop transport *Somme* was a delightful six week cruise. Considerations of war in 1927 were absolutely nil, and our sailing schedule was geared to thoughts of peace and prosperity. Still, I managed to arrange a demonstration of aerial photography for those on board, consisting of military passengers plus many Congressmen and their families. I knew that the CO of our Panama Photo Section was Lieutenant George C. MacDonald, who had been my pilot for the eclipse flight. With the aid of the *Somme*'s captain, I sent a wireless message to George requesting that he take aerial shots of the ship as it entered the Atlantic side of the Canal and deliver the finished product p.d.q. He complied in short order, and just as the ship was passing into Lake Gatun, down he zoomed, dropping on the deck a package of a couple of hundred aerial photographs of the *Somme*.

The stunt made a most favorable impression and through it I got to know some of the Congressional voyagers and their families. On the military side, a number of artillery officers, assigned to Corregidor, asked me if it would be possible to take night photographs of the gun emplacements on the island. I said it would be my pleasure, if they would arrange for the proper orders to be issued. And so, as we slowly sailed into the west—via San Francisco, Hawaii, and Guam—I managed to mix a little business with a great deal of pleasure.

Since we supplied our own entertainment, on a couple of talent nights I even got a chance to go back to my old trade of drawing cartoons—in this case mostly caricatures of the solons. Marge sang for the multitude and all assembled were highly appreciative.

In every way the entire voyage was a leisurely and enjoyable interlude. It was climaxed as we approached Manila Bay by the sight of a large Army and Navy formation of fighters, observation planes and bombers. They escorted us in with a spectacular air show, including a fighter that buzzed the decks and sent passengers scurrying for cover. For a while it was like being back at McCook during the noon-hour break.

But just as the performance ended the journey, so did it end the dream. The awakening was rude and jarring. Waiting for us at the ship's gangplank was Lieutenant John Hammond whom I was to relieve as CO of the 6th Photo Section. Hammond looked like he needed relieving. He was pale, skinny, worn out and the pallor of his skin was not far removed from the whiteness of his uniform.

Almost at once I could understand his condition, for the heat and humidity hit us like a suffocating blanket and the only things that seemed to be able to move swiftly in it were the clouds of flies and mosquitoes.

By the time Hammond had us on board his model-T, we were wringing wet and as we proceeded along the coast road toward Camp Nichols, we were assailed by a stench that defied description. It was a conglomerate odor issuing from a low hanging cloud of smoke created by the natives living in shacks near the river. They did their cooking, washing, and other rituals beside the river and in it. Garlic, rice, and fish were their main staples. The smell left me feeling nauseated and Marge with her handkerchief to her nose. Hammond laconically observed that we'd get used to it. We'd get used to it and the chuck holes in the road filled with filthy water all set to douse you if you forgot to close the windows. It was a long painful ride, and arriving at Camp Nichols did not remove the far away I-want-to-go-home look in Marge's eyes or mine. It just became more fixed.

I had two immediate reactions when we entered onto the base at which I was to serve for the next two years—what a helluva comedown from McCook, and why hadn't I accepted Sherman

Fairchild's offer. The buildings were of the so-called temporary sort, grayish, wooden and temporary until they caved in from rot. There was a main headquarters structure dominating the scene, a row of houses for senior officers plus a number of lesser buildings including a goodly number of two-story barracks for the enlisted men. Palms and assorted flora dotted the base edging off into a swampland. The airfield was small, sod covered with no runways, a railway track flanking one side of it. There were two rusted metal hangars and a scattering of planes before them.

Camp Nichols was the home of the 26th Observation Squadron and I was to learn later that it boasted a total of twenty-five planes, most of them DHs, a couple of fighters, a Martin Bomber and several Loening amphibians. For the photo section there were a pair of DHs. I was struck by the smallness not only of the base but also by the very few aircraft in evidence, either on the ground or in the air. I did not realize that this last was a reflection of the base CO, Major "Jan" Howard. The major was the kind of officer who did not expect his men to do anything he wouldn't do himself and since he flatly refused to fly more than the minimum four hours a month, enough to receive flight pay, the aircraft and flight crews at Camp Nichols spent most of their time on the ground.

My first official duty in reaching the base was to report to Major Howard. I had known him at McCook, but never on a working basis. A West Point graduate[1] who had matriculated early from the Artillery to the Air Service, he had served under Benny Foulois in the 1916 Mexican affair and, following stateside duty in World War I, had taken an advance course in aeronautical engineering at MIT. After that the rumor around McCook was that Howard knew more than anyone else in the world and had become dedicated to letting everyone, particularly his subordinates, know about it. I knew he had the reputation of irritating his men by constantly taking issue with their actions, and as I entered his office to present myself it was apparent that tropical duty had done nothing to improve his disposition.

[1] He was in the same class as Generals Eisenhower and Bradley.

Beneath a short cropped pelt of dark hair, his round Irish-looking face was tight-skinned and perspiring. His quick brown eyes showed restlessness and irritability. I went through the formalities of reporting in swiftly, a growing sense of emptiness rising in me to blend with the humidity.

After departing the headquarters building, Lieutenant Hammond escorted us to the Officers' Club, always a sanctuary on any base, and here Don Bruner and his wife Dottie were waiting. Seeing them again was the first touch of light in all the darkness. Don hadn't grown any taller, but his voice was just as deep and warm in greeting.

Because there was no housing for junior officers on the base, it was necessary to find quarters in the city. And this was no mean problem, for adequate housing was in short supply and what was available was pretty primitive and expensive. Wives of officers banded together to help new arrivals get adjusted to the change and the realities of a different kind of living. The Bruners, old McCook friends, had volunteered to assist us and having an apartment of their own, offered to take us in until we could find our own accommodations.

Gratefully I left Marge to the tender care of Dottie Bruner, and then I accompanied Lieutenant Hammond to the Photo Section to meet my men and take over command.

The men, all twenty of them, were fine, so were the two DHs assigned to us. They were the newest model with metal frames in place of wood, the latter subject to rot in the tropics. I was somewhat surprised to find both planes in the hangar, but surprise turned to dismay when Hammond escorted me to the photographic lab. Located in a concrete building, I found it to be a steaming mess. Cheese cloth-covered racks were used on which to hang and supposedly dry photographs. The method of using cheese cloth was Neanderthal in its obsolescence, and the idea of drying anything under the climatological conditions existing in the lab were practically non-existent. This was a basic problem. It had to be solved or there was no point in being in the aerial photographic business.

"Sure a lot of work to be done around here." It slipped out, and I glanced quickly toward Hammond to see if he'd taken offense. In his pale eyes there was a far away home sweet home look. "Yesss," he murmured.

I've heard it said that you can get used to living most anywhere, and after the events that took place during the first week of our new life, I knew it was so. In fact, we not only got used to it, we actually came to enjoy it. But that first week!

Dawn came early to Manila that first morning. It erupted furiously about 4:30 to the caterwauling of what sounded like a zillion roosters each trying to outdo the other. The din was continuous; its utter cacophony beyond description, swelled by the cackling counterpoint of an equal number of hens. The cause was cock-fighting, the national sport of the Philippines. Practically every red-blooded Filipino had a stable of these noble birds that each day donned their razor-edged spurs.

As for spurs, very shortly I found I was to acquire a pair, too. Don brought up the matter as we were driving to the base in his model-T, and I was marveling at his dexterity in dodging goats, water jugs, trolley cars, bicycles, automobiles, carabaos, and natives, all of which cluttered the road in a welter of disorder.

"George, how are you with a saber?" Don rumbled, his eyes busy with the traffic.

"You want me to go ahead of you and mount a charge?"

"Hmm? No, no, how about spurs, do you own any spurs?"

"No, and I'm not a polo player either, Don."

He grunted, just missing a goat and its shouting owner. "Well, even so you're going to have to get a saber and maybe spurs and polish up your Sam Browne belt. Every morning at eleven sharp the good Major Howard conducts sabre drill on the parade ground. He expects all officers to attend."

The evening before Don had enlightened me on the CO's minimal attitude about flying. Now he was giving me more bad news.

"The heat really has got him," I said, trying to digest this latest.

"No, he likes the heat. You'll see what I mean when he gets out there."

"Hell, I don't know anything about saber drill."

"You can get one at the Cavalry PX."

By 11 A.M. the tropical heat was intense. On the merciless parade ground Major Howard, weapon in hand, faced his neatly
aligned and properly spaced officers, some thirty-five in all. They,
too, grasped their weapons. Heavily uniformed and belted, they
awaited their leader's opening command. And then for the next
forty-five minutes all saluted, slashed and waved their swords,
drowning in their own perspiration.

I had never learned saber drill, and before my debut I had
made a few tentative cuts before a mirror. During my initial encounter, I nearly managed to slice my ear off and I was grateful
that no other officer was in reach of my swing.

It was an exhausting and purposeless hour and near its end, I
heard a voice behind me gasp, "Let's scalp him!"

It seemed like an excellent suggestion, and before my first day
of duty at Camp Nichols was half over, I realized that the morale
among the officers was as low as a fog bank and I understood
why.

Another factor adding to this condition was that practically all
the officers at Camp Nichols were first lieutenants, having been in
that grade for about ten years, and any chance of promotion
looked grim, regardless of an officer's accomplishments. Evidently
this situation came to the attention of Congress, because the
Manila *Times* ran the following article a short while after my
transfer to the Philippines.

Lieutenant George W. Goddard, Army Air Corps, stationed at
Camp Nichols, recently received favorable mention in the House of
Representatives, according to information received here. During a
discussion of the War Department appropriations bill Representative
Barbour of California remarked that "there should be some way of
rewarding that enlisted man or that commissioned officer, some way
of recognizing the exceptional service that has been rendered."

Representative Wainwright added, "I think we should adopt some
system by which there could be some reward granted to men of this

kind. As I understand it, there is no provision for reward in such cases."

Representative Barbour replied, "I understand that is true. There have been officers in the Air Corps who have made the most wonderful inventions. I call to mind now the invention of First Lieutenant George Goddard of the Air Corps, in the field of night photography, a most remarkable invention. Yet Lieutenant Goddard is still a first lieutenant in the Air Corps, enthusiastic about his work, and in my opinion there should be some way of recognizing distinguished service of that kind."

My "distinguished service" at Camp Nichols was recognized by making me Officer of the Day on my second day of duty. It just happened to be the wildest night of the month because it was pay day for the enlisted men. This was indeed the night of nights, for hardby the entrance of the camp, and in the little villages surrounding it, were many night clubs, bars and brothels. The 750 or so men of the command descended on them like locusts, welcome locusts, and all through the magic hours, the MPs, utilizing their motorcycle sidecars, hauled in the joyous merrymakers who quickly overcrowded the guest houses in the stockade.

My job was not only to fill out the multitudinous forms each case required, but also to conduct running investigations into breakage, brawledge, and general umbrage. The evening was climaxed by a soldier who suddenly decided that the heat was too intense and so he divested himself of all clothing. This would have been all right but he was in a large, well-populated bar filled with both sexes and some present took exception; others took his clothing. The result was that a huge donnybrook ensued in which our naked warrior, using a chair like the jawbone of an ass, did battle and wrecked havoc.

I arrived on the scene to catch him as he came hurtling through the open door, propelled by a combined force stronger than his own. The MP and I planked his battered form into the side car and away they went, leaving me to face the well-stirred mob. They say clothes make the man, and, in this case, I fully believed it was only my uniform that stood between me and a very one-sided battle. The heat was intense until the MPs returned in force. Then the temperature dropped a few degrees and sweet reason prevailed. We never did recover any of the naked soldier's uniform and all he had to cover him for a while were his lumps of which he had a great many. Following this long night of glory, I devoutly hoped I would never again get the job of Officer of the Day on pay day night.

This ennobling experience was quickly topped on the third day, however, by an earthquake. It was our first earthquake and quite a severe one. It occurred shortly after midnight and we were suddenly awakened by an ominous rumbling and the sickening realization our room and the entire building was gyrating in a circular motion.

"Don!" I shouted to our host, "What the devil's going on!"

"House is in a spin!" he boomed back. "We'd better bail out!"

By the time Marge and I had our bathrobes on and were staggering toward the door, I felt as seasick as any new mariner. We were on the second floor, but we went down those heaving stairs in what seemed like one long leap, bits of plaster and wood raining down around us.

The rumbling and the rotating of the earth continued even after we reached the comparative safety of the street, and we were all violently sick to our stomachs. I had read of earthquakes and the ground trembling, but never had I known it could actually gyrate in a spinning motion.

In all, it lasted about two minutes, but to us it seemed much longer. There did not appear to be much damage, but we were hesitant about going back in the building. We didn't know if another shock was in the making, and we couldn't tell in the darkness just what kind of shape the building was really in. The street, of course, was filled with excited people. It was also quickly filled with swarms of mosquitoes, and it was their insistence that drove us back inside. There were no more shakes that night, but there was no more sleep either while we sat there doing the quaking.

The blessed weekend came, and we attended a party at the

Army and Navy Club. While there we were introduced to the Commanding General of the Philippine Department, Major General Fred W. Sladen and his wife and daughter.

When I told Mrs. Sladen I specialized in photography, she asked me if I would be kind enough to take an interior picture with her and her daughter in the living room of their quarters along Dewey Boulevard.

I said it would be a pleasure and we made a date for Monday. The Commanding General and his staff lived in a small court facing Manila Bay, and the large wooden homes for military personnel had been there many years and were in constant need of repairs. At the appointed time, Mrs. Sladen showed me into the living room, which was beautifully furnished and decorated. Taking a flash photograph of the room with a single flashgun presented a difficult problem, for it was fifty to seventy feet long. Anyway, I was there to take a photograph, so I posed Mrs. Sladen and her daughter alongside the piano, toward the rear of the room, and poured a heaping amount of flash powder in the metal trough of the flashgun. At a given signal came the big flash, then, much to my amazement and horror down came the entire plaster ceiling. Through the dust and debris, I rushed to Mrs. Sladen and her daughter, first to see if they were all right and then to pour forth my apologies for the awful mess I had caused.

Mrs. Sladen, in her gracious manner, said, "Young man, please don't feel badly about this. After that last earthquake the ceiling was badly cracked and had been condemned—we were going to have it replastered in a few days anyway."

That picture actually turned out to be one of the best interior photographs I had ever made. It had been exposed a fraction of a second before the shock wave started peeling the plaster off the ceiling. When I delivered the prints the following day, the plasterers were busy on the job trying to finish the work before a scheduled cocktail party.

In all, it had been quite a week of indoctrination, but now it was time to get down to the business at hand.

## 12

Although Major Howard's unwritten motto appeared to be "Keep Them on the Ground," he could not keep our photo section out of the air because the Philippine Islands were practically virgin territory when it came to aerial mapping. He could and he did find excuses for responding negatively to requests from the Corps of Engineers and the Philippine Department to do large mapping jobs, using adverse weather and hazardous flying conditions as reasons. But we managed to skid around him on small assignments in the general area of Manila. We undertook a number of missions for the Philippine Forestry Department, photographing mahogany stands and other timber tracts. From these pictures we would make a mosaic and then the Forestry Department would take their own planes and fly over the area in question and, using the mosaic with the various shades of green, locate the different stands of timber.

By keeping myself in the air I avoided the deadly routine that was the fate of most of my fellow flying officers. Aside from the daily saber dance, they were required to attend classes that had nothing whatever to do with their profession as pilots. Courses in court-martial procedures, military ground tactics, administrative responsibilities, etc., were their diet. To men in love with the smell of gasoline and the wild blue yonder this was no life and the grumbling grew accordingly.

I kept as distant from Major Howard as duty would permit, but I sensed a certain inevitability in our crossing swords and not on the parade ground. I knew that since I was managing to fly in spite of his authority (through the orders of higher command), he was adversely aware of me. He made this manifestly apparent soon after my arrival.

Trying to solve the problem of temperature and humidity in the photo-laboratory was of prime importance. For better print drying I even had my men bring in stoves, but that only made the place so hellishly hot and unbearable that we dropped the idea fast. Then almost by accident I found a heaven-sent solution. At one end of the building in which we had the laboratory, there was a room that I had been told was for storage. One day I went exploring and found it was for storing leather fur-lined flying suits. It was full of them, brand new and never used and, except for high altitude work which only we would be doing, they were of no use to the rest of the squadron. To my amazement they were kept in A-1 condition because the room had an air conditioner! The air conditioner was the perfect answer to humidity in my laboratory, for keeping the dark rooms cool and the water and chemicals at proper temperature. To have requested such a piece of equipment through Air Corps headquarters would have required reams of forms and years of waiting. All it would take was an okay from the Major.

I prepared my request carefully, explaining that, without the proper laboratory, the 6th Photo Section could never fulfill its potential, and that to utilize the air conditioner would not cost anyone a red cent. The answer was a flat unequivocal "Absolutely not!"

It wasn't air conditioners, however, but the infantry that brought the confrontation between Major Howard and myself. The officers I had met on board the *Somme* stationed at Fort McKinley had not forgotten my acceptance to take night aerial photographs of the Fort. They prevailed upon General Sladen's office to inquire into the matter. The inquiry came to the major, who, in rejecting it, was careful to do so on the basis that had Camp Nichols night flying facilities he would have granted his approval.

In hearing about the rejection, I suggested to one of my infantry friends that perhaps they could provide Camp Nichols with night flying facilities by bringing in one of their big search lights. I had heard of a case when a search light was used for this purpose before. I knew if it were placed at the edge of the field and pointed horizontally in the same direction I was heading, I could use the beam to take off and land by. Without making too much noise about it the searchlight was trucked into the camp one clear night, set in the proper position and with its broad beam cutting a path of light across the darkened field, I took off beside it, finding that it worked just fine.

Over Fort McKinley the pictures were taken and when I returned to the field there was the light to guide me to a landing. In the cockpit with the cool night air rushing by, I descended smoothly through the darkness toward the golden finger. It drew me down out of the sky with such geometric nicety that I thought: You know, George, you've got a helluva an idea here! This is one facility you can really put to use.

Coming in to land, I'd forgotten about Major Howard. He summoned me to him the next morning, on the double.

First lieutenants don't stand much chance against majors when the party gets rough and from the look on the major's face and the glint in his brown eyes, it was going to be just that.

He did not put me at ease but kept me standing at attention even after I had saluted him, attending to more pressing matters at his desk. When he looked up, his expression was flat and unfriendly.

"Lieutenant Goddard, who gave you permission to fly last night?"

"No one, sir. I didn't know that I—"

"Be still, sir! . . . I'm the one who's asking questions here. You deliberately disobeyed my orders. I believe you went behind my back and conspired with the Infantry, didn't you?"

"No, sir. I didn't conspire with anyone. I simply suggested a way we could have night flying facilities and I could demonstrate my new night photo system."

"When I say there are no facilities for night flying, there

The first 9X18 Fairchild K7 camera, mounted in DH-4 with Goddard and Bill Oswalt ready to brave the upper air. 1926. *U.S. Army Air Service*

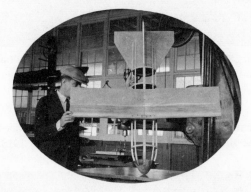

My devilish flash bomb glider in the laboratory at McCook Field. *U.S. Army Air Service*

In the cockpit of the SCOS-A with the first long range high altitude camera. Perfected by Eastman Kodak, its 36-inch lens enabled me to photograph objects 100 miles away and was the great grand daddy of today's long range aerial cameras. 1926. *U.S. Army Air Service*

Dr. Kenneth Mees, on the far left, and his assistants, waiting for the big moment on the top of the Eastman-Kodak office building in Rochester, New York, November 20, 1925. *Eastman-Kodak*

The big moment. The first night aerial photograph ever taken. The scene is the center of Rochester, New York November 20, 1925. *U.S. Army Air Service*

Over the mountains of Luzon in my trusty DH-4, Philippine Islands, 1927. *U.S. Army Air Corps*

I explain the mysteries of aerial photography to some interested if skeptical observers. *Merle LaVoy*

The Bataan bat that nearly got "Deacon" Welles. Sergeant Art Stockwell on the left, Captain Hill, the Deacon, center, GWG to the right and Sergeant Bill Patterson. *U.S. Army Air Corps*

Goddard and friends. 1929. *Merle LaVoy*

are no facilities, and I don't need the Infantry and you sneaking around behind my back to try and prove otherwise!"

The more he orated, the angrier he got until he was beating his fist on the desk, and I could see that any attempt to reason was out of the question. There was much more of it before I managed to get out of his office. I had gone behind his back. I was going to be shoved further into his dog house. No one was going to flaunt his authority, etc., etc.

I was badly shaken by the encounter, although I had certainly anticipated it. More than his threats, it was the thought of having to face several months of duty under his command that undid me, particularly now that I was number one in his black book.

I had never checked when his tour of duty would be up, but lo and behold, Christmas came early that year for the officers and men of Camp Nichols. Major "Jan" Howard received his orders to return to the States, replaced in his command by Major Walter "Mike" Kilner.

We made it a joint celebration, honoring the personnel officer in Washington who had issued the Major's change of station orders, and the blessed arrival of Kilner.

I had known and served with Mike Kilner during my four-year tour in Washington. One of Billy Mitchell's early adherents, Mike was a pilot's pilot. He had been made Chief of the U. S. Flight Training Center at Issoudun, France, during the war and his specialty following it was directed toward flying Operations and Plans. At work he was all business and no monkey shines. Socially, he became the life of the party, and almost secretly, he was a music lover and a fine violinist.

Ruddy complexioned, with a close-cut pelt of dark hair, topping a hard square face and perceptive blue eyes, Mike Kilner didn't take long to change the climate at Camp Nichols. The morning he took command he appeared before the officers at saber drill.

"Men," he said, "put those sabers away. You won't need them any more. We're going to start doing what the folks back home expect us to do and that's to fly hell out of those airplanes stored in the hangars."

A collective sigh went up, morale rising with it.

As for the planes, they really had been stored, for when they pushed the Martin bomber out on the flight line they found that mice had built a nest in one of the fabric-covered wings.

Whereas, under the stewardship of Major Howard life at Camp Nichols had been rather dull, under Mike Kilner there was both purpose and method, although the latter was frequently blocked by those who had not been sold on aviation, higher up in the Department.

His purpose was the protection of the Philippine Islands through air power. Part of his strategy called for the utilization of flying fields to be located on the string of small islands stretching north from Luzon almost to Japanese Formosa. These islands were flat and flying fields could be built on them with ease. In his plans, submitted to the staff in Washington, he asked for approval to begin work on several which our section had photographed, his idea being to station fighter and bomber units on them. The cost would have been small because they had natural drainage and harbors were available. The biggest problem would have been protection from typhoons but labor was cheap and it would only have required construction of revetments and concrete housing for personnel.

Mike, like Billy Michell, fought hard for his beliefs. However, he could not win this battle, not in 1927—not even if it had been 1937—and instead of receiving approval and the additional aircraft requested, the staff in Washington sent polo ponies for the relief and entertainment of the troops. There were, of course, other far-sighted officers like Mike Kilner, but I believe that had these islands been developed and equipped as Kilner had recommended, history might have told a different story in 1941. As late as November 1940, the aerial defenses of the Philippines consisted of one squadron of obsolete bombers and twenty-eight equally obsolete Boeing P-26s. It is true that as of December 7, 1941, this strength had been beefed up to consist of thirty-five

B-17s and about a hundred P-40s. But it was much too late and much too little.

As for the Japanese, I had personal knowledge of their early planning soon after I arrived at Camp Nichols. I was at 10,000 feet one day and I happened to look up and see far above me an object glinting in the sun. I only caught a fleeting glimpse of it, but I knew it was another aircraft. When I reported the sighting, everybody thought Goddard should change his brand. At the time I didn't realize it was a Japanese plane, but I later came to believe it couldn't have been anything else.

On the other hand, if a Mike Kilner could not get the whole loaf, he'd do the best he could with the half, and the 6th Photo Section was at least a slice of it. Once he was situated and firmly in command, he called me in and said, "George, let's get these islands properly mapped. I've been talking to Colonel Tyler, Chief of the Engineers, and he has had some definite plans for a long time. I want you to go talk to him."

"With pleasure, Major, but I've got a real problem."

"I know you and your problems, George. What do you want?"

I told him about the air conditioner and explained that our laboratory was not suitable to accomplish large mapping jobs and considerable expansion would be necessary. In short order I got the air conditioner and the necessary funds to do the remodeling. With my twenty technicians plus some native help, we put in more darkrooms, better lighting and plumbing, and in a few weeks we had a nice concrete photographic laboratory, cooled by the air conditioner with darkrooms, water and chemicals kept at the proper temperature. It didn't take long for a mess of winter flying suits to be on board a transport headed for more suitable climes.

I reported back to Mike and said we were ready for real business. Colonel Max Tyler decided that our first project would be photo coverage of the Bataan peninsula from Corregidor north, one hundred and fifty miles and from the coast inland, for seventy-five miles. I had two aircraft to do the job and some real pros to assist me.

At McCook my principal photographers had been Benny Thomas, Louie Hagemeyer, and Doc Burka, at Bolling, Howard Ramey and Andy Matos and now at Camp Nichols, Sergeant Art Stockwell. There was much about Art, in looks and manner, that reminded me of Hagey. Tall, rangy, and immensely strong, he was known far and wide as "round-the-clock Stockwell" because he never seemed to stop working. He loved everything that had to do with airplanes and there wasn't much he couldn't do around one. He was as good a mechanic as he was a photographer. Like Hagey he stood tall in the cockpit, and when I'd turn around to look at him, I had to look up and invariably there would be a grin on his good natured, rather homely face, his teeth sticking out in the breeze.

Another man who really stuck up out of a DH was Lieutenant Harold "Deacon" Wells, the pilot of the section's second aircraft. Deacon, or "the old preacher" as he was also called, was as tall and skinny as he was serious. Fair-haired, with pale grayish eyes, he wasn't much on words or at least speaking them, he figured that they were all in the Bible that he carried. With it he also carried a slide rule, a symbol of his years at MIT. Deacon was somewhat of a paradox, intensely religious on the one hand, mathematical on the other, and in the air, cool and daring, but whether in the air or on the ground, curious about everything around him.

His second man was Sergeant William Patterson, and like Art, Sergeant Patterson was a Chanute Field graduate, trained as a mapping camera operator.

My first flight presented a very difficult problem, particularly to the Engineer Corps. The country from our usual mapping altitude of 16,500 feet was like one giant green carpet with very few landmarks such as roads, fields or rivers. It would be extremely difficult for the engineers to plot each picture in its correct position on the existing maps and for the ground surveying parties to use these pictures. We decided to use two airplanes, one flying at 16,500 feet taking the pictures and one to fly close to the ground exactly along the same flight lines drawn on our flight maps. The plane flown by the Deacon at low altitude would precede my plane by a few miles and drop small white parachutes on the treetops so that they would be seen in the high-altitude pictures as small white dots.

The Corps of Engineers had established a station on top of the five-thousand-foot Mariveles Mountain on the Bataan Peninsula and, using their triangulation sighting equipment, they could record exactly the correct position of these individual parachute markers along each line of flight. It sounded like a good idea, but carrying it out was something else. There were many natives living in the forests and it was uncanny how fast they could shinny up a tree and get a nice white G-string or sarong.

An almost fatal situation developed on the first day's mission. I was watching the Deacon dropping chutes four or five miles ahead and Stockwell was recording them in his pictures, when all of a sudden no more white dots appeared. Circling around for several minutes I became apprehensive and went down to treetop level but could find no trace of the Deacon, so I headed back to Camp Nichols. Coming in for the landing I could see a large group of mechanics forming a ring about a hundred or so feet back from the Deacon's plane, the fire department hosing it down. As I jumped out of my plane I saw the firemen flushing large bats from the crosswires between the upper and lower wings of the DH.

The Deacon explained in his thoughtful fashion what had happened: "I was following the flight line . . . following it rather well, you know. It passed through a narrow canyon . . . I would imagine I had at least twenty feet of clear air to either side . . . And then quite suddenly the air was no longer clear. It was full of bats . . . swarms of bats and all of them looked immense. They began slamming into the crosswires and struts . . . I thought they'd knock us right out of the sky. Then one ponked the radiator and I knew we had trouble . . . The canyon ended and I managed to do a one eighty and get back here . . .

I had help," he raised his eyes skyward, "or I would never have made it."

I wasn't about to argue. The creature that had done the "ponking" had a four-foot wingspan and a body the size of a cat. If he had hit the radiator any lower, the Deacon would have lost his cooling water in a hurry, burned up his engine, and gone down in the impenetrable forest. Any plane missing in Philippine territory of the sort we were flying over was immediately posted as "lost" and that usually meant permanently.

The reason the crowd was standing some distance away while the firemen washed off the plane was because of the sickening stench emanating from the bats.

After this experience the parachute triangulation surveying idea was abandoned. The bats were not the sole reason, however. We found that many of the parachutes often landed in positions where they could not be sighted from the Corps of Engineers' station on Mariveles. It finally ended in ground parties setting up a series of white cross markers throughout the area and also pacifying the natives and obtaining their cooperation.

The worst enemy we had to contend with was the weather, and a perfectly clear, cloudless day in this area of the Philippines was hard to come by. Often I would wake up in the morning and figure we'd finally gotten the day, hustle out to the field to take off with Art Stockwell and his Bagley four-lens camera loaded for a three or four hour mission. Many times, after we finished a flight strip or two, the little white cloud puffs would begin appearing and before long the day's mission would have to be scrubbed. This was a common occurrence and, while we got in lots of flying experience, it caused trouble for the Corps of Engineers because of the lack of necessary reference points to rescale the photographs. We could not accurately match the same scale of the pictures taken on the different interrupted flights. Also, it was difficult from 16,500 feet to locate the exact area where the flight was terminated the day before.

After we did finish the aerial photographic mapping of the Bataan Peninsula, General Sladen's staff was swamped with requests for the services of the 6th Photo Section and there just wasn't sufficient cloudless weather to meet all of these requests.

General Sladen, his chief of staff, Colonel C. D. Herron, Major Kilner, and I attended a meeting in the General's office to decide on a schedule of mapping projects and it was determined that we should first cover the northeastern section of Luzon requested by the U. S. Coast and Geodetic Survey, the Philippine Forestry Department, and the Philippine Bureau of Public Lands.

The most important goal of this project was furnishing to the Geodetic Survey a set of photographs to be used as plane-table sheets for adding ground topographical information. We were also to gather information that would enable the Bureau of Forestry to conduct a timber survey, and the Bureau of Lands was interested in finding out whether a portion of the territory might be suitable for settlement. The area to be covered encompassed about five thousand square miles, all of it densely forested. Our first base of operations was to be Aparri, the northernmost port in the Philippines. Our plan was to take the two DHs plus the Martin bomber for ferrying the necessary supplies to set up camp and to act as shuttle link.

When our three-plane flight was ready to start out, we were literally loaded to the wings, with crates of equipment tied on them next to the fuselage. The twin engine Martin carried a ton of supplies for although we knew we had a field of sorts to operate out of at Aparri, we had little else and we were going to have to be self sufficient. Even our gasoline had to be flown in in five gallon cans.

We figured if nobody else got off the ground the Deacon would, because the Lord was on his side, so we let him take off first. The Lord was definitely on his side, and He couldn't have been too busy that day because I got an assist as well, and so did Don Bruner in the Martin. All three of us headed north with underbrush sprouting from our landing gear. Later we decided from an aerodynamic point of view the field was too short, and the gross weight of each plane too great for thrust to have overcome drag and produced enough lift for any of us to have become airborne.

The trip to Aparri usually took four days by boat. We made 350 miles in little more than three hours, and then down we came beside the scrofulous little village known as the jumping-off-place for China and Japan. We could understand anyone's eagerness to make the jump. The village was best epitomized by its single boardinghouse; its kitchen and its open toilets were joined together and the fly population had the benefit of both.

We slept in tents and ate canned food in preference, and, of course, as soon as we had landed crowds of natives turned out to see us. Young and old came from miles around, whole families from the Spanish-owned tobacco plantations, tribes of them. We quickly hired constabulary guards to watch the planes and the stores night and day. Since we knew that Aparri lay in the path of most typhoons originating near Guam, we made arrangements also to store planes and supplies in an old Spanish church built of stone which lay close to the field. The elderly padre was most accommodating, offering to delay Mass if necessary to get the aircraft inside.

In the beginning it wasn't so much the curiosity of the native population and the threat of typhoons that concerned me as it was something else. Over it, I held a briefing powpow with the Deacon and Sergeants Stockwell and Patterson.

"We should consider the possibility of what to do in case one of us has a forced landing. If we keep in visual contact during the mapping, and one of us goes down the other will not only know it right away, he'll know where."

"How could you land a plane in the kind of stuff we'll be flying over?" the Deacon asked.

"If you couldn't glide to the coast and land on the beach, you'd have to bail out," Sergeant Stockwell said.

"You'd land in the trees and your chutes would show from above. Even if they didn't the other plane could drop smoke flares and come back here and get Lieutenant Bruner and the Martin. When those who were downed heard the Martin coming, they'd light the flares and supplies would be dropped until such time as a rescue party could make it in."

"Gee, sir," Stockwell said, "you've got it all figured out. But I know the best way to handle it . . . Bill and I'll keep these old Liberty's running . . . I'm not much good with a parachute."

On that reassuring note we began our mapping operations. We were using the Bagley four-lens camera in both planes and we found that it took us about an hour of climbing to reach our operating altitude of 16,500 feet. Our routine was to take off from Aparri about seven in the morning and, weather permitting, put in three or four hours of mapping a day.

Almost at once I saw that my survival plan wasn't going to work. We were able to stay together until we'd leveled off and started taking pictures, but after that we soon lost sight of each other. On a big mapping mission we had many details to attend to and a two-man team has to concentrate on its own assignment and nothing else.

Soon my apprehension faded and I was trusting Art to keep the old Liberty purring. After twelve years of refinements, we figured it should be dependable, and then on one morning I thought it had failed me for sure.

I had lost sight of the other plane, as usual, and we were about half through the morning's work when the engine began to sputter and showed every sign of giving up the ghost. I figured we had enough altitude to get to the Pacific on the east side of the island, so we turned around and started a long glide. I switched over to my emergency gasoline tank in the upper wing of the airplane and pumped the wabble pump frantically. We were at about a thousand feet when we reached the coast line, but one look at the enormous swells dashing against the rocks and I knew we would have done better to have bailed out when the Liberty started missing.

It looked like suicide to try them in a land plane, but the rocks on the beach were worse. I had two bad choices and we were too low to use our chutes. Just as I was getting ready to ride the waves, the engine started to pick up again and allowed me to tenderly nurse it back to life. We headed for Aparri and landed, shaken but safe.

Hard on the heels of this hair-graying flight, I made another that had in it the taste of salt water.

One morning when it was perfectly clear and looked like our kind of weather, I was in a rush to get ready and failed to check both magnetos separately.

The throttle was pushed forward as far as it would go and, with our full load of fuel and the heavy camera, we lumbered down the strip with chickens, dogs, pigs, and people scampering to get out of the way. Much to my sudden dismay the engine was not revving up to full power, but by this time I was out of flying field and my wheels were off the ground a few feet. Fortunately there were no high trees or buildings in the way from the end of the runway to the China Sea, so I kept going. When I would try to pull the plane up it would "mush" and settle and lose precious altitude and the same thing would happen if I tried to turn. It was straight ahead or into the drink, so I kept going not more than twenty or thirty feet above the water, headed for China.

We had a speaking tube in the plane, so after ten or fifteen minutes of flight—and, fright—I said to Art, "I'm not getting any altitude, and I don't think we can make China this week . . . We may have to drop your camera to lighten the load."

I gave a quick glance over my shoulder and for the first time I did not see a smile on Sergeant Stockwell's face. It wasn't fear that erased the grin but the thought of having to part with his pet camera. It was like asking him to throw his teeth overboard. His feeling was that, as long as our tail wasn't dragging in the water, we were airborne and there was no need for anything else going into the briny.

Gingerly, I had been gradually flying the aircraft around in a wide circular course, at the same time trying to nurse a little altitude out of the half-powered DH. Once I had fifty feet I began to breathe easier. When the village of Aparri came into view it looked great. The approach to the field was over low Nepa shacks but no high trees. I hoped the natives and their livestock would scatter, but there was nothing I could do to help the situation.

Very little wind was blowing, so with the heavily loaded plane, in we went with a stuttering clatter and a *swoosh!* Just as soon as the wheels touched the ground Art Stockwell was out of his cockpit, straddling the fuselage, sliding down it to force our tail skid down and provide some breaking action. His quick thinking saved us from overshooting the field and going into a ditch.

When we'd come to a stop at the edge of the field, he swung off with a grin and said, "Never knew I was broncho buster for the Flying Dutchman, did you?"

I didn't have anything coherent to say in reply, so when he'd climbed back into the plane I taxied over to the supply tent. There the mechanic checked for the trouble and found that a small cap had been left off the end of one of the magnetos when it was cleaned a few minutes prior to the flight. This taught me a great lesson and I never again failed to check *both* magnetos prior to take-off. Also, we had been on this "Cook's Tour" without life preservers, so we hurriedly had several flown up to us from the Air Corps amphibian base at Kindley Field on Corregidor. We had to wear heavy leather flying suits so from then on we always took two life preservers each on our overwater trips.

By using a portable photographic darkroom tent laboratory which we constructed at Nichols Field, our work at Aparri was efficiently accomplished within a month's time. The small lightweight tent was easily carried in the bomber. We set this up under a larger tent and after landing we would make tests of our film on the spot, so we could tell just what we were getting. Processing the test strips of film was done at three o'clock in the morning when the temperature was down around seventy-five degrees. The lab included a collapsible darkroom and all necessary paraphernalia. It served the same purpose as the quick work laboratory I had developed in the States.

As with Bataan, through it all, the greatest difficulty was the weather. At first regularly each morning, between seven-thirty and eight o'clock, clouds would form along the mountaintops. After a frustrating series of cloudy days, clear skies did finally appear and we got on with the job.

If I was the one who had problems in keeping out of the treetops and the water, it was the Deacon who had trouble with other flying objects. On one occasion he had lost himself and didn't show up until about half an hour after I had landed. While I was waiting for him, I noticed what looked like a great dark cloud moving in from the jungle area. It was an enormous swarm of locusts, attracted by our field—the only grassy place for miles around. In some years, before and during the rainy season in the Philippines, locusts are a great pest, doing incalculable harm to agricultural lands. This cloud of insects kept coming toward the field and hovered over it, darkening the sky. Just then I heard the hum of the Deacon's motor.

He said afterward that squinting down out of the cockpit, he could not tell what in the world was the matter with the field. It had turned from kelly green to brown. It looked like heat waves from up above. When he descended and saw what it was, his curiosity got in the way of his better judgment and he decided to fly into the swarm. The locusts simply plastered the ship—flattened out all over it. The Deacon's goggles were so splashed he couldn't see. The insects got into his mouth, nose, and ears. Instinctively he zoomed up out of the danger zone and retreated to the upper air to do some heavy figuring. Our landing field was the only place in northern Luzon where he could come down safely. He was low on gas and he spent an anxious half hour circling until luckily the swarm settled down over the field in a shimmering blanket. Then, recognizing a quote from his Bible—"and the locusts shall cover the face of the earth"—he landed amidst them.

It's an ill wind that blows somebody good because our hazards provided a banquet for residents of the place. They came out with big baskets and gathered the insects to their hearts' content. Fried locusts are considered a great delicacy by some Filipino tribes.

After we had completed mapping the northern end of the unexplored territory, we returned from Aparri to Manila to pick up a new aircraft. It was a Loening amphibian with an inverted Liberty engine, more suitable for the work and safer. It had just arrived from the United States and was the same type being flown by the Air Corps fliers at Kindley Field on Corregidor.

Starting out again one morning, heavily loaded, with two sea-planes from Corregidor as escorts, we flew the two hundred miles northeast from Manila to Casiguran Sound, on the southern rim of the unexplored territory. Now we were living on the very edge of the area over which we had flown before, and had a good chance to observe the wild Negrito tribes. Before starting work again we made one trip inland on foot to seek prospects for a landing field up near the lava beds that surround the course of a river emptying into the sea. We found nothing suitable but we gained a better idea of what a forced landing would mean in this region—nothing good.

In Casiguran Sound we tied up to the *Fathomer,* U. S. Coast and Geodetic Survey boat, which had been dispatched to this point with our gasoline and supplies. All the seamen on the boat were native Filipinos, according to the agreement with the Philippine government, and the only Americans were the three commissioned officers. Captain G. C. Jones was the skipper, Lieutenant Hoskinson was his executive officer, and Dr. Scroggs, a lieutenant, was the medical officer. A boat on a mission of this sort can do more to make friends for the United States than all the missionary or financial foreign assistance programs yet devised. The one thing the natives out there needed above all else was medical attention and Dr. Scroggs was busy fixing broken bones, doing minor operations and fighting diseases common in that part of the island.

The Deacon, Sergeants Stockwell and Patterson, and I thoroughly appreciated living on the *Fathomer*. Every night the boat was anchored out in the middle of Casiguran Sound far removed from mosquitoes, gnats, and flies that made life on land unbearable. The boat was equipped with a refrigerated storage room, which was stocked with delicious foods and the very latest medical supplies that made it seem just like being back in the States. We slept out on the deck without any of the mosquito nets we had to use every other night during my entire tour in the Islands.

The Negritos we found were rather short and slight and dark-skinned. They wore a minimum of clothing and had many unusual customs and characteristics, one of them being their great love of dogs, which were valuable to them for hunting purposes. They regarded these animals as their most treasured possessions and treated them as their children. If a mother dog were killed they would feed the puppies until they were old enough to be on their own, even if one of the women had to breast feed them.

The Negritos swarmed about the planes whenever we taxied ashore. They were frightened at first, remaining in the background behind trees and bamboo groves, but they soon discovered that the "big white bird" was not harmful, and they made the most of our visit. It was just like a world's fair to them, the biggest event of a generation. They came from miles around, bringing offerings of bananas, coconuts, lemons, and papayas. In exchange, we gave them empty five-gallon gasoline cans, and no offering could have pleased them more. They hugged those cans, carried them around for days, slept with them. We could have had in exchange anything we could carry back.

The *presidente,* a wizened old fellow with sharp eyes, and his wife and daughter were our most distinguished hosts. The *presidente* received four pesos, or two dollars in gold, per month from the Philippine government for keeping his tribe in order, and was rich beyond the comprehension of his subjects. But our empty gasoline cans started a new vogue in tropical currency. Madame Presidente put most of her husband's salary on her back, judging from appearances. She was the best-dressed woman of all the tribe. But she could no more resist the tremendous appeal of an empty gasoline tin than could the lowliest tribesman. She carried hers around with her for days, and slept with it, like the rest.

They were crazy to fly. As white men, we ourselves were objects of curiosity, but the planes came in for special tribal adulation and wonder. Whenever they could get our attention they tapped themselves on the chest and pointed to the sky with a beseeching look. I am sure they attached some supernatural significance to the "big white bird." They never discarded the notion that the plane was a species of fowl. Some of the crew on the Survey boat, who had been charting the coast for years, understood enough of their language to learn that the natives had decided that the wheels, which drew up under the pontoons, were the bird's claws. One old fellow spent hours squatting in front of the plane, trying to make his arms go around like the propeller. If he could once get the hang of it, perhaps he might fly by himself!

The plane was undoubtedly "good medicine." All who could crowd close enough to it touched and fondled the wing surfaces and fuselage. Becoming bolder, they climbed all over it and into it. At night they went to sleep on the sands close by, with oil cans for pillows. The *presidente* wanted to know how big the stars and the moon looked when we went up in the plane at night. I had had Americans living in our own country ask me the same thing.

A very amusing incident occurred one evening when, unannounced, we ignited a piece of obsolete airplane flare which produced about 500,000 candlepower. The light, which was located at the edge of their settlement, gave the natives quite a scare and practically all of them took off for the mountains. We learned later that they thought their god, which is the moon, had fallen to the earth and was about to punish them. The next morning runners carried the news that the Americano had caused the light and that everything was all right. They immediately returned and requested that we repeat the spectacle, which we did a few nights later for their amusement and for motion pictures of their dances. To them, it would seem, the Americano could do anything. They had seen his cigarette lighters, cameras, field glasses, airplanes, had undergone minor operations and been cured by medicine, and so our light business was not so puzzling after all.

Our work on the southern edge of our territory was about the same as from the Aparri base. We spent the morning in flying and mapping, and were tired out at the end of four or five hours. The sudden climb from tropical heat to the frigid upper air was debilitating. We wore suits of sponge rubber which were unbearably hot on the ground, but we needed all the protection we could get from the cold at the twelve to fifteen thousand foot levels. Everything, including ourselves, sweated copiously on the descent. The camera equipment in the planes got as wet as if we had been parked out in a rainstorm. It was a problem to keep the film dry under these conditions and when we unloaded the film from the cameras it was sopping wet for several feet into the roll.

The results of the trip were very encouraging from several points of view. Our aerial photographs saved the various government agencies for whom they were made an enormous amount of time on their preliminary survey work, and showed sufficient detail on which to base valuable government reports. Even the underwater detail to a depth of twenty feet was shown in certain localities along the coast line.

While we were on this mapping project, General Sladen finished his tour of duty in the Philippines and left for the States. His replacement, Major General Douglas MacArthur, had arrived and had moved into Sladen's quarters. Apparently General Sladen had been pleased with the work of the 6th Photo Section, for I found a letter of commendation from him waiting for me when I returned.

HEADQUARTERS PHILIPPINE DEPARTMENT,
OFFICE OF THE DEPARTMENT COMMANDER.

In reply refer to:
HQD AG (Off Div)                                  Manila, P.I.
201 Goddard, George W.                            April 16, 1928.

Subject:  Commendation.
Thru:     Commanding Officer, Camp Nichols, Rizal,
To:       First Lieutenant George W. Goddard, Air Corps,
          6th Photo Section, Air Corps.

The zeal, efficiency and cooperative spirit which you have shown in carrying out various photographic missions in this department have been repeatedly brought to my attention. Conditions here in the tropics are such as to demand careful work by highly trained and skillful technicians to produce satisfactory photographs. The problems are numerous and varied and flying conditions are difficult and hazardous. Under these handicaps you have obtained exceptionally good results.

In view of this I wish to express to you and your command, the 6th Photo Section, 4th Composite Group, Air Corps, my sincere commendation.

FRED W. SLADEN,
Major General, U. S. Army,
Commanding.

# 13

General Patrick had predicted that my two years in the Philippines would go by in a wink. Actually it was not so much a wink as it was a *whoosh!*—a variety of adventures strung out above and below the palm leaves in kaleidoscopic fashion.

I brought night aerial photography to the Islands for use during Army maneuvers. But just as the event had not come to fruition in the States without a certain amount of trial and error, that, too, was the way of it in the Philippines. At my request Wright Field supplied our photo section with the components for six test flash bombs which consisted of powder, fuses, and bomb casings. It wasn't exactly like having the makings of a cigarette and rolling your own, but the casual manner in which we assembled the parts might have given the same impression. The men loaded fifty pounds of powder per bomb and handled it as though it were no more lethal than loose tobacco. The casings were square and wooden and fabric-covered and one spark and we'd all have been on our last flight. Perhaps it was the Deacon standing close by, Bible in hand, that reassured us.

Once the fuses were installed we had our shop make four square metal cans to hold the bombs. Then we fitted two apiece under the wings of our DH. The cans had hinges at the bottom and the idea was that the photographer would trip a release, the bottom of the can would open and the bomb would drop out.

I was to be the bombardier-photographer and while the Deacon wanted to be the pilot, we decided it would be better if Don Bruner was at the controls because he was both an expert in night flying and had had prior experience in dropping photo flash bombs.

On the night of nights the troops were holding their field maneuvers near Fort McKinley and our plan was to catch them in action. However, just before we took off we mutually agreed it would be a good idea to run a test drop first in the vicinity of our base.

At 3000 feet Don leveled off and throttled back. The lights of Manila, like the lights of any city seen from the air at night, were a conglomerate scattering of precious stones, some laid down in mathematical order, some clumped helter-skelter but collectively compelling in their setting against the black of earth and sea. Their glow afforded us a greater degree of illumination as we coursed the night sky.

When Don was ready, he gave me a hand signal to fire one. I activated the release and then . . . no flash . . . no nothing.

Don's voice rumbled through the speaking tube. "What happened?"

"Must have been a dud."

"I didn't feel it leave."

"We'd better try another. If it was a dud at least it went into the water."

Again Don gave me the signal and again I activated the release . . . nothing.

"What the devil is going on?"

"The release is working okay. Could be bum fuses. Could be the powder."

"Well, we'd better try again."

We tried twice more with the same results.

"You sure you know how to make flash bombs, George," Don muttered.

"Listen, I think you were right the first time. I don't think any of them dropped. You throttle back and I'll have a look."

Don slowed the DH down close to stalling speed, and I unhooked my safety belt and lowered myself head first out of the cockpit, holding on with knees and feet. One look was enough. Dangling in the rushing night breeze, I saw all four bombs were hanging halfway out of their containers. The shop had done a fine job of making them too small for the load.

The question was now how did we get rid of two hundred pounds of angry flash powder without getting rid of ourselves? We couldn't land with it. We could bail out, but that would mean the loss of the plane and an uncertain descent by parachute into who could say what.

We talked it over. "Got any ideas, George?"

"Not many. Is there some way we could shake them loose?"

"I was thinking I could pull her up into a whip stall. When she stalls that should jar hell out of her and, if the wings stay on, the bombs might fall out."

"Give it a try, boy."

Don gained some altitude and then making sure I was ready hauled the nose of the plane up almost vertically, with engine wide open. The DH hung on her prop, trembling violently, clawing at the sky. Then she slid backward on her tail, stalled dead, and before Don could check her, whipped over into a tight spin. I had seen the bombs fall free as we hung nose up. Now I gritted my teeth as we spun down after them. All four of them went off at the same time in a blinding flash and roar of sound. They really lit up the sky, and why their collective explosive impact didn't peel us like a grape I left to the Deacon and his fellow theologians for discourse. One moment we were spinning and the next I was hanging blinded upside down while Don fought for control.

The quadruple flash had taken place over a barrio or native village near the edge of the base and later, when we drove through it, still benumbed, the streets were jammed with people trying to figure out if a piece of sky had fallen. They were sure an airplane had blown up but where were the pieces? We didn't stop to enlighten them or the excited crowds milling about all the way into Manila.

We found the entire telephone system in the city area was jammed with calls, and it wasn't until the morning newspaper arrived on the stands that people calmed down. Our attempt to take a night aerial photo had been a failure, but I couldn't help seeing the similarity between the attempt and the first successful exhibition over Rochester, New York. Don Bruner had been the pilot on that one, too.

"Do you think maybe we're a bad mixture?" he asked me the next day.

"Well, we certainly know how to attract attention, boy. I admit some of the maneuvers you do scare me a little."

"The way you drop flash bombs doesn't exactly soothe my jangled nerves," his bass voice boomed out of his half-pint frame.

"Well, we're going to get another chance to improve our technique. The *Free Press* called. They're wild to have a midnight shot of the city."

"And you, of course, told them, yes."

"Sure. I think it's the least we can do to repay everyone for losing so much sleep."

"You know, son, that was one helluva blast. Wonder it didn't take the wings off."

"We'll see that it doesn't happen again."

It didn't. Having corrected our flash bomb release mechanism, we made a fine shot of the city from three thousand feet up. We took it over the Manila railroad terminal, and it was sharp and clear showing people on the station platform. Don and I then went on to greater glory participating in night military maneuvers at Fort Stotsenburg.

The *Free Press,* pleased with our illuminating efforts, ran a story of the 6th Photo Section with many of our aerial pictures used as illustrations. The four-page article was headed "Risking Their Lives to Make Our Maps" and read in part:

The photographic work that has been done and is presently being done in North Eastern Luzon is among the most dangerous jobs the Army has ever tackled in peacetime. If anything goes wrong there is simply no place to land, except in the ocean, which beats over reefs in huge waves the year round. From Aparri down below the Tayabas boundary line the country is mountainous. Something goes wrong with the engine and it's just too bad . . .

I had thought the conditions described in the article were pretty well accepted by us who were doing the job. But doing it is one thing and then reading in cold print about the hazards you take for granted is another. The Deacon came to me, *Free Press* in hand, a worried look upon his lean visage.

"George, I want to ask you a personal question."

"What's the matter, don't you think it's a good story? Aren't you proud of that subhead: 'Brave Officers and Men of Air Corps Driving Ahead!' Don't you like driving ahead?"

"Yes . . . I think it's fine to be a hero." He was very serious, looking out across the jungle. "But—"

"You don't mean you want to quit, Deacon! Hell, you can't believe everything you read in the newspapers."

"It's not that. It's you." He turned his mournful gaze upon me. "Do you mind telling me, when is your birthday?"

"Birthday! What's that got to do with the price of film?"

"I'd like to know."

"You haven't taken up astrology, have you?"

"No, I want to give you a present."

"Deacon, are you all right? What do you want to give me a present for? I'm not expecting a birthday for at least two years."

"Well, I have one, and I think you should have one, too. I've read this article and I want to give you a Bible."

Graphic newspaper descriptions of our work aside, the basic mapping we did of Bataan Peninsula, Luzon, Lingayen Gulf, and other parts of the Philippines was to prove of inestimable value to our forces in the retaking of the Islands from the Japanese some fifteen years later.

Our working hours in the photographic laboratory were from seven o'clock to three o'clock in the afternoon, including Saturday mornings. One morning, soon after seven, a staff car drove up and in strode General MacArthur's Chief of Staff, Colonel Charles D. Herron. Herron wore glasses and was a thin scholarly soft-spoken officer. He said he wanted to look through the laboratory to see what was going on. He walked into one of the rooms where our technicians were making prints from some aerial negatives and asked where they were taken and on what project. I explained that they were pictures of a flying field on the island of Mindoro, an official assignment ordered by the local CO. In another printing room he made the same inquiry and was told that they were prints being made for Fort Stotsenburg. The same questions and answers took place in a third printing room where we were developing prints in connection with our work for the U. S. Coast and Geodetic Survey.

In our largest workroom he found laboratory technicians piecing together a mosaic that was eighteen feet square. This was a section of the mosaic map of the Bataan Peninsula and Corregidor, and we had it fairly well assembled into one large picture.

The colonel, whose principal hobby was photography, was intensely interested in the Bataan mosiac and spent considerable time looking it over and asking questions concerning flying, camera details, and laboratory operations. He remarked that he thought the 6th Photo Section was a real business organization and said he would bring General MacArthur out some morning to see it.

It was then that we learned the reason for his impromptu personal inspection. The preceding day he had unexpectedly visited another military laboratory in Manila, and when he went into the darkrooms and pulled prints out of the sinks all he saw were pictures of nude women. The colonel failed to see the artistry of the effort and he instituted immediate action to close the laboratory and to take the necessary disciplinary measures against the CO. At the laboratory the colonel was informed about the 6th Photo Section at Camp Nichols and he thought he would personally make a surprise inspection.

We continued to work on our Bataan mosaic, and about three days after the colonel's visit a staff car flying a two-star banner pulled up at the front door of the laboratory and out stepped General MacArthur and the colonel. The General was wearing his cream-colored britches, Sam Browne belt, high boots and spurs, and carrying a riding crop. Everything was spic and span.

He walked in and, after the introductions, he said, "Young man, what is this?"

I replied, "Sir, this is a map of the Bataan Peninsula."

He said, "Young man, that is not a *map,* only the Corps of Engineers makes maps."

Thinking of all our hours of flying and laboratory work, I answered, "According to Mr. Webster, sir, a map is a representation of the earth's surface and here is one without any human errors."

He sort of chuckled at the remark and said it still was not a map, and then went on to praise us for the wonderful work we were doing for his chief engineer, Colonel Max Tyler, and the Philippine government. He went all through the entire operation and told me if we ever needed anything to contact his office. As he was passing by the mosaic map on his way out he said, "You understand, young man, that's not a map . . . yet."

After he left I realized I was wrong and should not have called it a map. Instead, it should have been referred to as a mosaic from which a map would be made, with the help of ground surveyors. Also, although I was not aware of it then, the General had gone from West Point to the Corps of Engineers, and in his early days in the Army he had done a lot of mapping work.

I really made a friend of MacArthur and the colonel, who did several favors for our photo section. On one occasion I wanted to get Marge on a Navy transport, the *Shaumut,* which was going to Hong Kong and Shanghai, and the ship was fully booked. I called Colonel Herron and he said, "Come on down and we'll see the General, maybe we can get her on board."

When I arrived Colonel Herron said, "The General wants you to use his speed boat and go out to Admiral Bristol's flagship, the U.S.S. *Pittsburgh,* anchored in the Bay. Tell him to help you out in this matter if possible."

If I had ever been in a first class speed boat I couldn't remember it, and whatever kind of boat I'd been in, it had never sported a two-star flag in the bow. At first I was only impressed by my style of travel, but as we approached the imposing cruiser, I could hear bugles blowing all over the ship, and since it wasn't mealtime, daybreak, sunset or any other occasion when bugles are blown, I was puzzled. Moreover, the urgency of their collective call sounded like something out of *Ben-Hur* or the summoning of the praetorian guard.

The crewmen of the speed boat brought her smartly to the gangplank, and I stepped off and ascended. It suddenly seemed terribly quiet and then as I rose toward the level of the deck a shrill whistle pierced the silence and unnautical as I was, I knew what it and the bugles had been calling for . . . me!

I stepped off the gangplank onto a deck resplendent with lines of sailors standing stiffly at attention. Before them was brass, miles of it, not the kind you polish but the kind you salute. And for an instant, they were all saluting, not a two-star general named Mac-Arthur, but a one-bar lieutenant named Goddard, sporting a hateful pair of wings. It was a tableau to make strong men weep . . . or possibly to throw an unexpected visitor over the rail. But discipline has its purposes and while the salutes were quickly retrieved and startled looks locked in cold storage, a quick thinking officer—who may have been promoted to admiral the next day —gave a swift command, the bugles sounded, and the ranks melted away to continue their appointed duties.

One would have thought that Admiral Mark L. Bristol might have been tempted to make me walk the plank or suffer keel hauling. Instead, he was a mariner with a sense of humor and an understanding compassion for wives who wanted to go to Hong Kong. Some orders were given, a few aides dashed about, and Marge was booked on the *Shaumut* for points west. A few days later I was able to hitch a ride on a destroyer and I joined her in Hong Kong and we went on to Canton and Shanghai. After that kind of service, I never again harbored any unkind thoughts about the Navy.

One high point of our journey was meeting the Chinese Lindbergh, Major Tieu Lai-huang. He had made many long-range flights around China and Asia and his exploits fascinated millions of Chinese.

A man who fascinated the Filipinos and in turn fascinated me was Merle LaVoy, a civilian free-lance photographer. Merle had taken possession of the islands a short time after my own arrival. Oddly enough it was Lindbergh's flight to Paris that had brought him to us for he had heard that everyone in the Philippines was "nuts" about aviation. This may have been so but most all the flying being done over the islands was military, and Merle quickly saw that he had an opportunity to get some rare footage of our ,activities for motion picture consumption at home.

The result was that I first heard about him when I got a call from the Philippine Military Department, instructing me to show him all the courtesies and to take him anywhere he wanted to go, to film anything he wanted to film, providing it was feasible. Since there was little I considered unfeasible, Merle and I became fast friends.

He steamed into my office one day, short and bulky with a magnificent belly and a gargantuan laugh which I was to find went well with his exuberant manner and prodigious appetite. Despite his bulk and his constantly perspiring face, Merle had a zest for living that even the oppressive temperature could not hold down.

"Well, sir! By God, sir!" he greeted me, doffing his gray fedora and thrusting out a meaty paw, "I'm Merle LaVoy, and it's a pleasure to meet you, sir!" His booming laughter was contagious and it was a pleasure both to meet him and to fly him about the islands on my many assignments. Planted in the rear cockpit, roaring a bawdy song into the breeze, he used his Bell & Howell camera to good advantage, and it seemed that all of the footage he took brought him fat rewards from the States.

It wasn't just aerial photography that captured his imagination. He was crazy about the people, and they took to him, particularly the primitive tribes, and thanks to his canny use of tobacco, beads, and fire water, there wasn't much they wouldn't do for him.

On one occasion we flew to Mindoro and landed at the field which had been built by Sugar Central, the combine that ran all the sugar plantations on the island. Merle thought he might find some good local color in the plantation operations, but when he looked around he got other ideas.

"By God, sir!" he proclaimed, smacking his forehead with his palm. "What an idea!" He was focusing on a carabao, a Filipino water buffalo, ambling along a dirt road.

"What have you got in mind, life amongst the carabaos?"

"Better than that, sir! Better by far! We're going to have a contest, Sir George, the greatest yet!"

He loved contests, and he loved action, and I wasn't far behind what he had in mind when he announced, "I'm going to film a carabao race. No one's ever done that before, sir!"

I didn't point out that so far as I knew no one had ever done it before because no one had ever thought to hold such a race for what I considered a very basic reason.

"Merle, I hope you plan to film it in slow motion. Those nags would drop dead if they ever got up to a good trot."

"You think only an airplane can fly, sir! By God, sir, you don't know carabao! Under the proper stimulation, sir, they can run like hell!"

"I'll believe it when I see it, pal."

"And see it you shall, sir!" He gestured grandly.

He had the real impresario touch. In less than two days he had an advertisement drawn up announcing the contest, which was distributed by the head men of major island villages with an agreement to run preliminary races, the winners to compete in the final event. The whole island went wild with excitement, the betting fierce.

Merle was everywhere, stamping about with his "By God, sirs!" or squatting on the ground beside his ever-present black film bag, loading and unloading his cameras, preparing his equipment, even burying some of his film in a container in the ground to keep it from spoiling in the heat. One could argue that not all Merle's films were Air Corps motivated, but certainly I learned a lot just by watching him perform.

The great day arrived. The whole island was rocking with the build up. The twelve finalists might have been Derby triple crown winners the way their partisans treated them.

Certainly, by bulk, inclination, and configuration, a carabao was never designed for racing. By temperament they are mean and until ringed by the nose and broken to the plow, they can be dangerous. Under any condition they have a low boiling point. It was on such characteristics that Merle was banking. He encouraged all the riders to tape sharp pieces of metal or nails to their heels to act as spurs. Numbers were painted on the rumps of each animal. The main road was the race course and it looked like it was crammed with every native on the island above the age of three.

The din was at concert pitch, the race about to begin, when Merle approached me, a camera in each hand. "Well, sir!" he blared out, "I need your services above the ground."

"You don't think I'm going to film this from the air, do you?"

"I do, sir. I do! Right up on the branch of that tree." He pointed behind me at a limb extending over the road near the halfway mark of the course. "From that vantage point, you will get some spectacular footage, sir!" He clapped me on the shoulder proudly and thrust the Bell & Howell into my hands.

"But what about you? Where you going to be?"

"Why at the finish, sir! At the finish!"

There was no arguing with Merle and besides the limb of the tree did seem like a good spot to get some interesting footage. It looked that way at least until I had crawled out on it and the race had begun.

Those carabao, infuriated by the goading of their riders and the roar of the crowd, came thundering down that road balls out and hell bent for tomorrow. The closer they came the more the limb bent and cracked. Through the camera view-finder I could see that the enraged beasts had but one goal in mind and that was to make instant hamburger out of George W. Goddard. It surely would be spectacular footage! And I could hear Merle exclaiming, "By God, sir! Wasn't that a show!"

Then somehow the mass of packed horn, bone and meat hurtled by beneath me and I was left dangling limply, choking in a cloud of dust.

We heard later that the film made a great hit with audiences back home. But Merle was never one to rest on his last picture, he always had a new project to undertake and a new angle by which to approach it. For a long time he wanted to film the primitive tribes in the Bontoc country in northern Luzon, but there was no place to land and he didn't like to drive. So I was surprised one day to hear him calling outside the laboratory, "Sir George! Sir George! Come out and see my new car!"

I went out and there he was ensconced beside a driver in a brand new model-A Ford.

"By God, sir! Isn't it a dandy!" he gestured broadly. "This is Mister Meeker, he runs the Ford agency in Manila, and he's consented to drive us to the Bontoc country. Mister Meeker, meet Lieutenant Goddard, sir, the most notable flier west of Charles A. Lindbergh!"

The introductions over, I learned that Mr. Meeker's model-A was the first in the islands and Merle had talked him into giving it a widely publicized demonstration test by driving us to the Bontoc country. Merle had invited me to come along and since my orders were to accompany him when feasible, we were off and running in no time, that model-A getting a rugged workout on the so-called roads we traveled.

It took us several days to reach our destination, and while Mr. Meeker and the model-A were on display at a nearby terminus, Merle and I made our way by foot to the native village. They were a primitive tribe living in mud and straw huts, and the first night Merle arranged to film a dance around the campfire.

The natives thought it was a great idea and they took to Merle, howling with glee everytime he rolled his eyes or smacked his forehead or let go with his belly laugh. Everything was fine until I lit a couple of flares to provide illumination. Then it was scatter and head for the hills! Never having seen such light before, the natives were terrified by it. Merle spent all the next day getting runners to go out and find the departed and assure them "By God, sir!" that everything was all right.

That night the dance was filmed but Merle didn't want to stop with that. He had learned that it was the custom in the tribe for girls when they reached the age of fourteen, to leave home and live in a brush igloo until they were married. The young Bontoc boys would visit these sorority houses and marry the girls as they became pregnant. This system insured that there would be no childless families. Girls who did not become pregnant became igloo dwellers the rest of their lives.

The igloos held forty to fifty people, and were very dark inside because there were no windows. Nevertheless, Merle was eager to film the homey scene.

"To think of coming all this way and not getting such footage would be a crime, sir! A crime!"

"I'm not thinking about the criminal aspects of it. What about the lighting? Certainly not enough light from the doorway."

"I have the answer to that, sir. We can use another flare."

"We've got just one flare left. You want to shoot the whole thing on that scene?"

"No, sir, I do not. You will saw one-third of it off. That will give me one minute of light, and that, sir, will be ample. You will plant the section in the doorway and at my command ignite it." He had an answer for everything and it usually made sense.

The residents of the igloo were not aware of our intentions, but other members of the tribe got the point as Merle stepped into the darkened interior, camera in hand. They gathered around giggling and laughing as I prepared the flare.

On Merle's "Fire, sir!" I lit the fuse, and suddenly there was light! With it there came a collective shriek and then out of the doorway poured a welter of terrified young people, arms and legs flailing and again, it was head for the hills! I only regretted I didn't have a camera myself because I would have gotten some footage comparable to the carabao race.

As for Merle, he was last man out, appearing in the doorway on hands and knees, having been bowled over in the rush. "By

God, sir!" he panted as I helped him to his feet, amidst the howls of laughter from the rest of the tribe, "wasn't that a pretty sight!"

Just as we were about to leave the area and return to Manila, Merle heard about another pretty sight. He confronted me with news of it the following morning. "Sir George, sir! We must go north! North!" He was really excited as he mopped his dripping face with a red-checkered bandanna.

"What's up north, Merle?"

"A member of the Ifago tribe, sir, I have simply got to photograph. The Chief told me about him."

"Well, what about him?"

"He is a medical wonder, sir!" Merle rolled his eyes. "Fantastic from the Chief's description!"

"How? What's he got, two heads?"

"Equipment, sir! Equipment!" He indicated. "Utterly beyond belief, sir. My medical clients will want footage of him for their studies. We must go north, Sir George, north!"

And so with Mr. Meeker and his wonderful model-A, we bounced and sputtered our way north in search of Merle's medical wonder. We stopped at every village in the general area to make our inquiries and while Mr. Meeker displayed his Ford, we went on foot over trails to tribal settlements. Suddenly we found that there were natives who felt that they were as well-equipped as the Ifago we sought and for a price we could film them, too. It appeared to be more than a matter of professional jealousy. Tribal pride was involved and with a man of lesser talents than Merle we might have gone broke and used up all our footage before reaching the object of our hunt. But reach him we finally did, and by that time he was well aware that we were on his trail, and he suddenly had become remote and modest . . . and like a movie star not willing to be filmed unless he was paid the proper price.

The three of us sat squatting on the ground, Merle constantly reaching into his black bag and taking out odds and ends of film and equipment.

"Look at this beauty, sir," he exuded, holding up an empty can of chemical. "What a treasure, sir! What a find!" He tried to give it to the Ifago. The Ifago impassively shook his head, and the one-sided dickering went on until Merle called his bluff by arising suddenly, and gesturing me to follow, stalked off, black bag slung over his shoulder.

The native quickly caught up to us and a deal was made.

Merle did his filming gasping with awe, his by God sirs! ringing through the jungle. I knew one thing. That Chief hadn't exaggerated a bit.

Before we had gotten back to Manila, Merle had thought up a name for our medical find—"Pump Handle Pete." And somehow it did not seem right to us that such an unusual discovery should not be shared with others. Consequently a good many post-card sized prints were made of old Pete, and some of them found their way into the post-card rack in the Manila Hotel.

The hotel was located in the dock area and the placement of the cards happened to be on the day that a round-the-world ship was visiting the city. Sitting in the main lobby, we watched the tourists come storming into the hotel, and of course, they all headed for the post-card and newspaper counter. Soon we observed a lady who had found one of Merle's cards. She gasped and paled, hand going to her mouth. Then she summoned her husband, whose eyes went wide in disbelief. He roared with laughter and called a friend. That really started a scramble and soon the post-card rack was spinning around, the assembled fighting over it like it was bargain day. Before long the hotel manager appeared on the scene and, with the aid of several bellboys, the offending rack was dragged from the clutches of an incensed mob of tourists.

"By God, sir!" said Merle, clapping his forehead, "that was the scene we should have filmed!"

There were many other scenes we did film but mostly the 6th Photo Section kept itself busy doing aerial mapping and covering Army maneuvers.

And so the days sped by, highlighted by the unusual.

The Deacon in his curiosity wanted to find out what it was like to touch the bottom of a Loening amphibian on the surface of the water at top speed. He found out, stripping the aluminum keel off the plane. This ship happened to be General MacArthur's private aircraft and the Deacon had good cause to read his Bible.

Marge and I had a month's leave at the City of Baguio, the Army rest camp, which was comparable to having a lodge in the White Mountains free from mosquitoes, humidity, and poor living conditions.

I visited the Moro Island of Jolo in Sulu Archipelago, where I filmed the famous Sultan of Sulu and his forty wives. The native Moros called my plane "Devil Bird" and bowed their heads to the ground in fear. The wives, on the other hand, kept me under fascinated surveillance.

It had never been very safe for Americans to visit this area because of the "Juramentado," a Mohammedan religious fanatic, usually a criminal being sought by the authorities who, by physical abuse of his body, finally became crazed and ran amuck. Seizing his barong, a razor-sharp blade somewhat like a longitudinal cross-section of a banana, he raced afield in search of Christians, all the while yelling "Whoo-eee, whoo-eee," in blood-curdling tones.

Fortunately no "Juramentado" came my way, but the Sultan did come to Manila as the special guest of Camp Nichols. We had our new Douglas O-2H airplanes with the first air-cooled radial engines, and we really gave him a fine exhibition of acrobatics and a Cook's Tour of the Manila area.

Then finally in February 1929 I received orders that I would be returning to the States aboard the Army transport *Thomas,* sailing on April 10. With these orders came the best news of all—I was to return to Dayton, Ohio, to be Director of Research and Development of Aerial Photographic Equipment and Techniques. I would be reporting to Wright Field instead of McCook because the Air Corps had outgrown the latter, it being too small to accommodate the testing of new aircraft and also the townspeople had gotten fed up with the ever increasing noise and the dangers involved.

Sailing day was a festive occasion and I could not help contrasting it with our arrival. There were many goodbyes, all gay ones. The Army band provided the music and amidst streamers and confetti, the *Thomas* eased out into the bay escorted by a large formation of Army and Navy Aircraft.

The long voyage home by way of China, Japan, Hawaii, San Francisco and the Panama Canal was a joyful travelogue until about the time we reached the international date line. Then I was called to the ship's military headquarters and handed an official telegram. Its contents dropped my chin and my morale right into the ship's bilge. It read in Army order style: As of such and such a date orders sending you to Wright Field Dayton Ohio are hereby rescinded directing you to report for duty at Chanute Field, Rantoul, Illinois, as Director of the School of Photography, Air Corps Technical Command.

My immediate reaction was profound shock. I could not turn to General Patrick, for he had retired and the new Chief of the Air Corps was Major General James E. Fechet, whom I knew, of course, but not on the same terms that I had known Mason Patrick.

My two years in the Philippines, as General Patrick had predicted, had been extremely beneficial. However, the experience of working under tropical conditions in all kinds of weather had stimulated a good many thoughts on how to solve a number of basic problems. My thinking, even as the CO of a photo section, had never been far removed from the realm of research and development and my eagerness to return to Wright Field was not only natural but from my point of view in the best interests of the Air Corps.

I wanted to work on the development of waterproof paper to eliminate drying problems in a climate where there was high humidity.

I wanted to see developed an emulsion on film pre-hardened,

so the film could be dried in less time and scratching could be minimized.

I wanted to improve on our flash bombs, to develop a more positive release mechanism to eliminate the chance of what happened to Don Bruner and me over Manila.

A small but important change I wanted to bring about was in the packaging of chemicals. I wanted them put in small cans to avoid the mistakes often made in mixing the wrong chemicals taken from poorly marked barrels.

Finally, I wanted to develop a method by which we could hermetically seal chemicals to protect them from dampness and solidification. All of the chemicals we received in the Philippines arrived in barrels. When opened we would more often than not find them solidified. And this meant we had to chisel out the material and then pulverize it. Naturally, the process was time-consuming. In a war in the tropics there would not be such time available.

Now I saw these plans and others put in cold storage for at least the next four years. I would, of course, recommend my pet projects be brought up for consideration, but I knew that in the Army unless you had rank or were in the driver's seat, outside suggestions were generally for filing and not much else. I was enraged and sick at heart.

The good thing about the voyage was that it was a long one. It gave me time to simmer down, time for reflection. After about a week of glaring at the Pacific I began to cool off and perceive that maybe being the director of a school for a while wasn't such a bad idea and might prove to be quite a challenge.

In retrospect, my sudden transfer from McCook to the Philippines had not been expected or to my liking, and yet, I knew that the two years of aerial photographic work in the tropics had been an education in themselves. They had helped to broaden my knowledge. They had shown me firsthand the problems of working under adverse conditions. I had always considered myself resourceful but two years in the field had sharpened that quality.

Considering my twelve years of military service I could not argue with the thought that perhaps I *was* well qualified to take over as Director of the School of Photography, and if I could instill within my students the kind of resourcefulness which I knew was so essential to the trade, then I would indeed be serving a useful role in the Air Corps. From another angle, I saw that in the job I would have more time to devote to my own studies: electronics, photography, chemistry, optics, and other subjects. I began to see also that with the personnel and facilities available to me, I might on my own be able to conduct a certain amount of research and development. Doors would be open at Kodak and other photographic and optical laboratories. Transportation would never be a problem, for I would have a fleet of aircraft under my command.

So, in a manner of speaking, I dried my tears and by the time the lights of San Francisco finally reached out to welcome us back to the good ol' U.S.A., I was more or less looking forward to my new assignment.

## 14

Chanute Field was the Air Corps center for technical training for both officers and enlisted men. Its photographic school had been established in 1917 and as operated in 1929 it graduated approximately 144 enlisted men a year, a new class entering each succeeding month for a 24-week course.

The course for enlisted students covered a varied curriculum of subjects ranging from mathematics to mosaic making.[1] There was also a nine-month course for a class of officers. Their curriculum was basically the same as that of the enlisted men, but in addition, they studied practical aerial photography, the military use of photographs, photographic interpretation, and aerial intelligence. Included were approximately 150 hours of air time divided equally between piloting and acting as the photographic observer.

In the training of officers to become photographic pilots and observers the utmost care was taken in selecting men who had an aptitude for navigation, engineering and endurance flying— rather than the spectacular fighter or attack types. Bomber and transport pilots generally made good photographic aviators, particularly for mapping operations. With our limited number of navigation instruments, it required months of practice and study to become a good photographic pilot.

In June of 1929 when I reported to Major Leo Heffernan,

[1] The basic photographic course included mathematics involved in photography, the principles of photography, negative making processes, lantern slide making, photographic optics, cameras, practical ground photography, newspaper and commercial photography, copying, filters, the work of the field photographic section and mosaic making.

the CO at Chanute, the old work horse, the DH, was finally being phased out. The Douglas O-2H brought forth in 1927 was for our kind of work a step in the right direction. A bi-plane with a 450 hp radial engine, its performance was in every respect an improvement over the DH.

However, sometime around 1930 Sherman Fairchild, who had entered the aircraft-making business in the mid-'20s, came out with his C-8, and, like his original K-3 camera, it was the best of its kind. The C-8 was especially designed as a small transport and for photoreconnaissance and was the first aircraft built specifically for that purpose which the Air Corps purchased. Actually an improvement over an earlier model, the C-8 was a high wing monoplane with a 450 hp Pratt & Whitney Wasp Junior engine. The enclosed cockpit was a real greenhouse with excellent all-round visibility. In the cabin area there were two specially cut holes in the floor for the placement of cameras taking vertical expanses. On either side of the fuselage there were glass doors with special camera fittings for cameras filming oblique photos. The C-8 had a ceiling of around 25,000 feet, a range of 500 miles, could carry five passengers plus the pilot, and was a real pleasure to fly.

A long time dream of mine had been a plane designed especially for aerial photographic work but because of the money problem I had known it was out of the question. Now, Sherman Fairchild, wishing to provide his own cameramen with such a plane had provided us with one and in time we acquired five for the school to go with our fleet of nine O-2Hs.

One of the first things I did in taking over the directorship of the school was to add night photography to the officer training course, including the most promising of the enlisted men. It became mandatory that before an officer could graduate he must be able to take night photographs of four different locations indicated on an Illinois map. These target areas were so chosen that in case of a bomb malfunction no damage would be done to property on the ground. One target was a quarry, another an abandoned bridge over a small river. For extra safety, we installed triple igniting fuses in each bomb and during the years that followed we never had a failure.

Since some of the officer trainees would go on to command photo sections and, both officers and enlisted men alike were required to be proficient in the demanding work involved in every aspect of aerial photography, I stressed innovation in all training. Resourcefulness became the watchword of the school.

For example, in the dead of winter a group of students would be dumped out beside a frozen river. They would have portable laboratory equipment with them. At some point in the next twenty-four hours a plane would fly over and drop rolls of exposed film. Processing the film required cutting a hole in the ice to get fresh water. When the film was developed it was sent back to base by motorcycle. During the exercise the men not only worked under difficult climatic conditions, they also lived under them.

Mosaic map making was emphasized among the enlisted trainees. A special six-month course was instituted in which the students learned how to rescale existing maps, how to rectify errors in photographs taken when the plane was thrown off course by rough air, and generally how to make mosaics. This course actually helped to contribute to the growth of the business of aerial mapping. Civilian companies were springing up all over the U.S. and many of the graduates joined these companies, getting excellent jobs and a lot better salary than the Air Corps could offer. In the long run, the Air Corps benefited by this exchange because when war did come, most of these men were recalled to duty and their expertise was of great value.

One recruit, Mr. James Deeg, a Texan with two years of college, had read about our enlisted mapping course and he went through with flying colors. From there he went to Brook Field and completed the flying course. He spent his entire time in aerial mapping as an Air Force Civilian Engineer. At the time of retirement he received high government honors.

During the depression years our school graduated some outstanding enlisted personnel. Many young men didn't have the

money to attend college and the Air Corps recruiting advertisement "Learn While You Earn" attracted them.

I was so impressed with one enlistee, Private "Red" Nelson,
that I talked him into going to college. His parents couldn't
afford to send him, so I stuck my neck out and loaned him some
Air Corps cameras and lab equipment on the proviso that he
take photographs as a means of working his way through school.
He did just that and graduated from Franklin as an honor
student, later going on to a successful career in military and
civilian aviation.

Another brilliant student was John Morse of Hudson, Ohio.
Following his graduation from the course he was assigned to the
camera repair department. One day he asked my permission to
redesign a hand-held camera he didn't think was "worth a damn."
The result was he came up with the most efficient hand-held
camera of the time. Johnny went on to found his own photographic equipment company and built it up to a multimillion-
dollar business.

There were, of course, may others who went on to high
ranking commands in the Air Corps and the civilian world.

While my job was the over-all running of the school, I did a
considerable amount of lecturing, some of it outside the school to
ROTC students at the University of Illinois and Purdue. I was
also asked to lecture on a yearly basis at West Point. However, as
a lecturer on aerial photography I was in fairly constant demand
by clubs and civic organizations. In this regard, I had met Gail
Borden, a columnist for the Chicago *Daily Times,* when he had
had a forced landing in his private plane in bad weather at
Chanute. We got to know each other and he invited me to
address the Chicago Tavern Club. The club was one of the
swankiest in the country. Adlai Stevenson was a member as were
many other social and political luminaries.

At the conclusion of my talk, the president half jokingly asked
if it would be possible for me to take a night photograph of the
club from the air at their next meeting. They would all gather
outside on the roof of the skyscraper and I could catch their

smiles from three thousand feet. I allowed how it might be possible.

Well in advance of the club's next meeting, Gail Borden gave me the date the members would assemble. In preparation I had a special 50-pound bomb made up. Then on the designated night with my assistant Lieutenant "Pedee" Weikert as pilot, we took off and circled over Lake Michigan waiting for the appointed hour of ten o'clock when the members would be waiting for the big blast.

For the drop we selected the east side of the Tribune Tower, a building adjacent to an unoccupied warehouse area on the lakeside away from Michigan Avenue. We made the drop from 4000 feet and the bomb exploded with the usual bang.

The next morning the Chicago *Tribune* appeared with the headline GANGSTERS BOMB TRIBUNE TOWER. There was a great mystery because the police couldn't find any trace of damage or blast marks on the ground, although some of the windows on the top floors were cracked. Neither could the police find any reason for the "gangsters" act and so far as I know no one enlightened them.

As for gangsters, Chicago was not their only haunt. Payday for the hundreds of enlisted men at Chanute was always a big occasion. The money was shipped from a Chicago bank in a baggage car on an Illinois Central train. It generally arrived at the Rantoul railroad station in the morning and every precaution was taken to keep it safe. Machine guns were mounted on several Army trucks and overhead two aircraft circled with their guns mounted for and aft. Alas, one day as the planes circled over Rantoul, the wily gangsters were stealing the money out of the baggage car at Paxton, Illinois, a small town ten miles north of Rantoul. After that our planes circled the train all the way down from Chicago.

In June 1931 I flew to Rochester to see Dr. Kenneth Mees about improving some of our photographic materials and laboratory processes. While at the Kodak plant I saw George Eastman again and asked him if he would meet our Regular Army photographic officers' class which was going to visit Rochester a few days before graduation. Despite his advanced years and ill health, he graciously accepted the invitation and, in a few days, a formation of photographic airplanes landed at the field and was met by Mr. Eastman.

After talking to the students and inspecting the various camera installations in the airplanes, he asked if I would take him for an airplane ride over the city. He wanted to see the expansion which had taken place at the Kodak works, the new buildings at the University of Rochester, which had his financial support, his home on East Avenue, and the office buildings on State Street. I called the Chief of Air Corps in Washington and obtained official permission for the flight in the C-8 with the proviso that Mr. Eastman and his aide sign a form releasing the government from any claim in case of an accident.

The two of them donned parachutes and we placed Mr. Eastman in an easy chair from where he could look out through the glass doors on both sides of the aircraft. He thoroughly enjoyed the comfort of the plane, and the experience of having his secretary wave to him from the 19th floor of the Kodak Building as we circled it.

After we landed Mr. Eastman talked with the officer students at the field and back at the Kodak offices. He asked them numerous questions about their flying experiences and details of the aerial photographic course. Before we left he promised to visit the Air Corps school. He was never able to keep that promise, however, for he died four months later.

The question of funds in running the photographic school was just as acute as it had been in the research and development department, only aggravated by the depression. Many new items of photographic equipment in the commercial field could not be purchased by the school, but I suddenly got an idea of how to put more pennies in the kitty. We had many darkrooms where the students developed films, made contact prints and enlargements, and dumped the hypo down the drains. The hypo had silver in it, and we made arrangements with a Chicago firm to reclaim the silver from the used solution and reimburse us for it. Through this silver mining operation we were able to purchase some of the material we needed.

In 1932 we enlarged our officer school to include Naval officers as well as those from several Latin American countries. The Navy came to us because they had no comparable school nor, of course, did students from Colombia, Guatemala, and Venezuela.

As noted, I had hoped that while at Chanute I might do a bit of research on my own, and in the area of quick work photography I was successful. I was able to foster the development of an inflight laboratory. Our previous quick work operations had been restricted to a few photographs taken and processed in the air and then dropped to those waiting below. Now with the increase in aircraft size, I was able to enlarge the laboratory and to increase the output enormously.

At the Century of Progress Exposition in Chicago we gave the first demonstration of the unit. In a C-8 we photographed a 25-mile-square area, developed the film, and mounted it on a board to form a mosaic map of the Exposition and the surrounding territory. The total time of the mission was two hours and twenty minutes from  take-off to presentation of the finished article to Major General Frank Parker, Sixth Army Corps Area Commander. Chicago newspapers carried a large spread of the event.

The inflight laboratory was of importance to the students because it was another innovation that taught them how to operate under difficult conditions. Formerly, we could develop photographs in the air but they had to be printed on the ground. In the "flying darkroom," as the newspapers called it, we could conduct the entire operation from filming to printing. Our students got plenty of experience using the equipment on maneuvers.

In early 1934 an historic aviation event with both tragic and beneficial results for the Air Corps had a direct effect upon my activities.

Shortly after President Franklin D. Roosevelt took office, a number of independent airlines charged that the outgoing Republican Postmaster General, Martin F. Brown, had awarded mail contracts by favoritism to the bigger airline operators. An investigation into these charges was launched, chaired by Alabama Senator Hugo L. Black. It appeared at the outset that the charges were valid, and the new Democratic Postmaster General, James A. Farley, under the President's instructions, canceled all mail contracts with private operators and turned the flying of the mail over to the Air Corps.

Major General Benjamin D. Foulois was Chief, and he accepted the opportunity, believing that flying the mail would give valuable experience to Air Corps pilots. He had just ten days to set up operations which entailed maintaining fourteen routes, connecting eleven major cities with daily flights of 41,000 miles. During these ten days three pilots were killed in blind flying and radio beam familiarization flights, and when the actual mission began on February 19, 1934, the worst of the winter storms were raging over a large portion of the routes to be flown.

Neither our planes nor our pilots were prepared for the kind of pilotage that was required. Airline pilots had been flying their routes for years and knew them intimately, knew radio beam flying as well as visual, and flew planes that were specially instrumented for blind flying. In three weeks' time, nine Air Corps pilots died in crashes. In March, General Foulois called a ten-day halt to try and improve on equipment and safety measures. It was at this juncture that I was called into the picture.

A blind flying school had been started by the Air Corps at Rockwell Field in San Diego, California. It needed a training film to better illustrate the details of the course and I was ordered to make it. The assignment was given top priority. Minus the usual lack of funds and red tape, I was authorized to purchase the latest sound motion picture equipment plus a $15,000 movie camera.

The only motion pictures I had ever made were the silent variety and it had been purely a matter of photography. But with the aid of a knowledgable movie specialist, Master Sergeant Schneider, I bought the necessary camera and equipment, loaded them into my C-8, and with the sergeant headed west for San Diego.

At the school, I immediately saw that I was in over my head, that the sergeant and I were mere babes in the woods when it came to going Hollywood. But it was to Hollywood I quickly went to get some much needed help.

Jack Arnold, chief cameraman for Metro-Goldwyn-Mayer, was an old friend and when I unveiled the project I had been assigned he couldn't help but laugh at the thought of a lieutenant and a sergeant trying to tackle such a difficult production. He told me I would need an organization of specialists composed of script writers, an announcer, a man with a good recording voice, an electronic specialist, a film editor and the usual background music.

As we were talking, Arnold suggested that we try to get an Air Corps lieutenant stationed at March Field to do the voice recording. A short time before we arrived in California there had been an air show at March Field and Lieutenant Hal Bowman, the announcer, had impressed the movie people. They also knew of a Captain Jack Upton, who would be qualified as a script writer; and a noncommissioned officer experienced in movie sound recording.

We flew to March Field to see its CO, Colonel Henry "Hap" Arnold. I had been on good terms with Hap for many years and he was quick to say "yes" to my request for the three men. In short order our crew was at work at Rockwell. Jack Upton promptly prepared an excellent script and we started shooting the film in the classroom and in flight.

We had set up a sound studio and film processing laboratory adjacent to the school where we kept Hal Bowman busy dubbing in his voice and the crew members explaining the details of their particular jobs during an instrument flight. The project was completed in six weeks, and we went back to Wright Field to finish the final details.

The film *Blind Flying* was the first sound motion picture ever made in the Air Corps. It was shown to the Army staff in

Washington and, while it was not on a par with Metro-Goldwyn-Mayer productions it did meet the requirements and was used at all Air Corps fields for training purposes.

In May 1934, after Senator Black's committee investigation had found that there had been no favoritism in the awarding of airline contracts, Postmaster General Farley quickly restored the flying of the mail to the airlines. However, despite the tragic loss of life, the Air Corps, unprepared as it had been for the difficult requirements of its assignment, had by force of circumstances moved swiftly into the realm of regular night and instrument flying. This hard step forward had a major effect in that it improved the quality of our pilots; it broadened the range of our flight activities; and its benefits were fully realized during the war years.

The year 1934 was a notable one in other respects for the Air Corps and for myself. The Martin B-10 a twin engine, all metal bomber made its appearance on the scene. The B-10 was a real breakthrough in bomber design. It had a speed in excess of 200 miles per hour, a ceiling of 28,000 feet, enclosed cockpits and was vastly superior to anything that had preceded it. It was the forerunner of true bombardment aircraft soon to follow.

In the summer of that year the B-10 was put to a widely publicized test in which I participated. Ordered to Washington to meet with a number of other officers, I was informed that I had been selected by the Chief of Staff to take part in a round-trip flight of a squadron of B-10s from Washington, D.C., to Fairbanks, Alaska.

The purposes of the mission were to test the practicality of dispatching an air force to Alaska should the necessity arise; to photograph strategic landing sites in the formulation of plans for frontier defense; and to investigate the possibilities of photographing large areas in a minimum time for mapping purposes. My job was to handle all the photographic details and to develop a plan to utilize six of the B-10s on a mass mapping flight from a point north of Fairbanks south to Seward. The squadron was to be organized into two elements of three aircraft and one of four. It was to be the first mass flight of bombers over so great a distance, 8290 miles, and the whole thing sounded like live adventure to me, just my cup of tea.

Hap Arnold was to be commanding officer and in flight command of the first two elements. Major Hugh J. Knerr was executive officer, and in command of the third element. Altogether the squadron was made up of thirty officers and enlisted men.

I had a reserve seat in one of the bombers—that is until unexpectedly Hap Arnold called me in to see him.

"George, we've got a problem," he greeted me, turning on his famous grin. "The longshoremen on the West Coast have gone on strike and refuse to load our gasoline, oil, aircraft parts, and what have you."

"Nice of them."

"They won't make any exceptions, so I want to make you transportation officer. You'll go to San Francisco by rail. By the time you get there we'll have a ship lined up for you, and we'll use our own people to load it. You'll come up on it to Seward, and then bring the supplies the rest of the way by train. We'll see you in Fairbanks."

He sent me on my way with a clap on the shoulder, a grin, and "Good luck."

Never having been a transportation officer before, I figured I could use all he had to offer, but I went west excited and eager to take on the longshoremen and anything else that got in the way.

On my arrival in San Francisco I had luck of another kind. It was the Fourth of July, the best date in the world to receive the telegram for which I'd been waiting for fourteen years. The clerk at my hotel handed it to me and nearly did a double back flip at my howl of delight.

It read: AS OF JULY FIRST, NINETEEN HUNDRED AND THIRTY FOUR, YOU ARE HEREBY PROMOTED TO THE RANK OF CAPTAIN, AIR CORPS, U.S. ARMY. It was indeed the Glorious Fourth!

The fifth wasn't quite so glorious even with captain's bars weighting my shoulders. The Air Corps had been trying to get me a mine sweeper to carry our supplies, but the Army turned thumbs down and gave us an old flat-bottom tub the Quartermaster Corps had been using to take fresh water to an Army base in the San Francisco Bay area. It was aptly named *El Aquario* (*Water Carrier*).

I took one look at *El Aquario* whose dimensions were little larger than a fair-sized tug boat and whose age put it somewhere in the Roman trireme class, and sent a wire to Hap Arnold informing him that the ship wasn't fit to ride the open seas. Arnold tried to get the minesweeper, but in those days he was only a lieutenant colonel and the local brass said, it's *El Aquario* or nothing.

We had 32,000 gallons of gasoline and oil plus spare engines, wing and tail surfaces to load. Ordinarily the gas in fifty-gallon drums and the oil in five-gallon cans would have gone in the hold below decks, but I was worried about fumes from the fuel causing an explosion, and so I insisted it be loaded above deck, the other parts going below. This naturally made the old *El Aquario* top heavy, but it was a damned if you do, damned if you don't situation.

The Army hired a civilian captain to pilot the ship up the coast to Seattle where he would be replaced by a pilot familiar with Alaskan waters. I still didn't like the look of the old scow so I went back where I belonged and flew to Seattle in an Air Corps plane from Crissy Field. There I awaited the arrival of *El Aquario*.

I read about her before I saw her again. A newspaper story under the heading "Storm-tossed *El Aquario*" told of her misfortune. She had gotten caught in a storm and had taken refuge in the Columbia River at Astoria, Oregon. The paper said she had been in great danger of capsizing due to improper loading.

In spite of that about a week later, she staggered into port. There she took on two new captains, one to pilot the ship and the other a pilot who would rather have gone by air. We then proceeded north up along the inland sea through British Columbia.

The country was so spectacular, full of deep thick timbered fiords, that I soon forgot my nervousness. We couldn't make

Doc Burka and I prepare for a "Quick Work" photographic mission. The camera is a Fairchild K3, the equipment is for in-flight film processing. *U.S. Army Air Corps*

Dr. George Eastman gets ready to take his first flight in a military aircraft, with the author. 1931. *U.S. Army Air Corps*

Alaskan aerial mapping results, shot from B-10 bombers and being pieced together at Chanute Field, Illinois. (Inset) Martin B-10 bombers over Alaska being led by Colonel H. H. Arnold, 1934. *U.S. Army Air Corps*

We find the liner *Rex* 700 miles out, proving the superb navigation and
military value of the Boeing B-17 as a long range strategic bomber.
September, 1938. *U.S. Army Air Force*

Lorenzo Del Ricco at work atop his
magnificent camera tower; the first step
in the development of the stereo strip
camera. 1938. *U.S. Army Air Corps*

I discuss the merits and progress of aerial photography with President Franklin D. Roosevelt during his visit to Wright Field, 1940. *U.S. Army Air Corps*

"No cares have I to grieve me!" At the controls of a Northrup AT-7, 1942. *U.S. Army Air Corps*

more than ten knots an hour and when we encountered high-speed tides we'd actually back up. It reminded me of the early days, flying a Jenny against too strong a head wind. We anchored in beautiful bays and snug coves and the fishing was excellent. Slowly we made our way north to Ketchikan, Alaska, then Juneau, then past Cape Spencer. There the old *El Aquario* outdid herself as we sailed across the open sea of the Bay of Alaska. By the time we reached Seward, scow or not, I'd developed a fondness in my heart for her.

When we tied up at Seward we were greeted by a jeering crowd of longshoremen who stood between us and a line of waiting freight cars.

"Soldier boy," one shouted, "you ain't unloadin' that cargo here!"

This was Alaska, wide open, rough, frontier, and while we had the same attitude with longshoremen in California, I felt maybe I could get some of the frontier spirit on my side. I went to the local Chamber of Commerce and explained the situation, stressing the importance of not only our mission to Alaska but also the nationwide publicity Alaska would gain from it. It didn't take long to prove my instincts had been right. A force of about two hundred patriotic citizens joined by local law-enforcement officers followed me back to the dock, and the longshoremen, badly outnumbered, saw that perhaps it would be a far better thing if they backed off in their demands.

Two days after Hap Arnold had brought the squadron to Fairbanks from Washington, I arrived with our bulging train load of supplies.

My mass mapping plan was to use six of the B-10s flying at 19,000 feet at five-mile intervals. Our Bagley cameras were to be installed in the B-10s bomb bay. However, aside from myself and two very knowledgeable sergeants, Sam Bush and Tony Hansen, we lacked trained photographers. So I immediately had to find three likely candidates among the other crew members. On August 3, Captain Edward Bobzien, with Master Sergeant Bush on board, had a forced landing on take-off and put their B-10 down in the waters of Cook Inlet. The sergeant suffered a broken leg, and though the plane was ingeniously retrieved using air-tight steel drums as pontoons and a railroad wrecking crane, the camera was damaged by salt-water erosion. This meant our flight was reduced to five planes, but I still had to find three photographers. I had plenty of time because the weather turned sour and we got nothing but overcast skies and rain. It did give us a chance to practice some dry runs. Also we set up our rubberized, pressurized darkroom but in a hangar free from dust kicked up by the planes on the dirt field. The darkroom had no wooden or metal supports, and we kept it inflated by using an electric blower which pumped air into the tent faster than it could escape. It was like being inside a rubber balloon and it gave us plenty of room for processing and loading our five-lens cameras.

Every morning and evening I haunted the Fairbanks weather station along with our meteorological officer, Captain Harold Mc-Clelland, and every day it was the same wet story. But then one evening the forecaster dashed over to Hap Arnold's hotel and declared, "Tomorrow's your day! Get everything ready."

Sergeant Tony Hansen and I spent the night preparing the five cameras. They were extremely tricky to load, each having five separate chambers with six-inch film having to be threaded through rollers. But by dawn we were ready and the weather was just what the man had predicted. We took off, lined up at 19,000 feet, and flew the strips from north to south until all the film was exposed. Instruments kept us at the correct altitude and the navigators kept us on the proper course.

The next day we repeated the performance, and on the third day we completed the mission, filling in areas we had missed. We made it just in time because weather moved in and that was the last cloudless day of the summer. In all we had mapped approximately 30,000 square miles and had made mosaics of Fairbanks and Anchorage.

The planes were now committed to photographing prospective landing sites scattered throughout the territory, and in making a series of photographs of points along the Yukon River. I had Major Hugh Knerr as my pilot. Knerr, who had long been a Billy Mitchell advocate, was one of the prime leaders in the fight for the development of aircraft designed specifically for long-range bombardment.

When the job was done Hap Arnold called me in and said, "George, I want you to know what a fine job I think you've done. You've helped to make this mission a real success. Now I have a question for you." He grinned while I waited. "Do you want to fly back to Chanute or would you like to take the steamer down to Seattle and the train the rest of the way?"

He knew the answer before I could give it, and I went home in leisure and style, trading sleepless nights in a rubberized darkroom for a deck chair. When I arrived at Chanute the mass of exposed film was waiting, having been flown back on the B-10s. I put the school and laboratory to work in shifts, developing, transforming, and making the composite prints. We used the wooden floor of a hangar to lay out the photographs and match up the flight strips on a large map of Alaska. It was all excellent training for the students.

The Alaskan venture highlighted the need for additional photographic field operations, a real on-the-job training mission. As a result, I added a new requirement to the course. All regular officers would complete a one-day aerial mapping mission directly under their own command. An enlisted photographer and a mechanic would accompany the officer. Using a B-10, K-3 camera, darkroom tent and allied equipment, they'd take off on a 250-mile flight up into Wisconsin. The mission, conducted between sunrise and midnight, consisted of photographing a fifty square mile area, processing the film on the ground, making the prints and then orienting them into a pasteboard mosaic map. Then they would return to Chanute and the work would be evaluated. It was in essence the final examination for the course, and it gave us a fairly good indication of the officer's ability to handle a photo section under field conditions.

At Chanute, particularly in winter and spring, we had one

kind of weather—bad. Following heavy rains we would have floods. We even had a time when a flight of migrating ducks mistaking a low hanging fog blanket over the field for land came in and crashed in great numbers. But mostly the bad weather set our work schedule back and kept our students from their flight training. I had often discussed with my superiors moving the school to a better location. On one of my flights to the West Coast I had stopped in Denver at Lowry Field. There I had been regaled by flying personnel on how wonderful the weather was practically every day of the year.

At my suggestion, some of the people I had talked to at Lowry approached the local Chamber of Commerce. Soon thereafter I received a visitor at Chanute from the Chamber who wanted to get information about the school so he could learn what would be involved in having it moved to Lowry Field.

At the time of our last flood I had taken a picture of Master Sergeant Gilbert standing in the water up to his waist. In some mysterious fashion one of the pictures got into the hands of the Denver group and a month or so later, during Congressional hearings in Washington it was used. In a hot debate concerning the transfer of the school from Chanute to Lowry, the Rantoul Congressman accused me of doing a crude job of faking or exaggerating the picture of Gilbert standing in the water, charging that I had Gilbert on his knees when the picture was taken to make it appear that the water was very deep. How could anyone claim I would resort to such tactics?

The Denver group ultimately won the battle, and it was good-bye to the old World War I wooden hangars housing the school. Congress approved funds for the construction of a large brick laboratory at Lowry, one of the most modern in the country.

My four-year tour at Chanute had been up in 1933. At that time I had gone to Washington to see what my chances were of getting back to my chosen field. Because of some dramatic and well-regarded high altitude stratospheric balloon photography that Stevens was engaged in, I found my chances were not very good. Nor did they improve the next year when I made another attempt. But by the spring of 1936 the balloon work had been long completed, and I decided it was high time I tried again. The seven years at Chanute had been beneficial in many ways, but not in the particular way in which I was anxious to proceed. I could go on lecturing about my experiences in the Philippines, telling what it was like to photograph the volcanic eruption of Mount Mayon; I could instill resourcefulness in photographic students, but very little of what I was doing was in any way advancing the state of the art. My labors at Chanute would not improve night photography; they would not improve long-range photography or a host of other long neglected aerial photographic components from film to chemicals. I had had my seven lean years away from research and development. Now I was determined to take action.

Late in the spring of 1936 I wrote a letter to Major General Oscar Westover, Chief of Air Corps, outlining the work I had done previously at McCook Field. The most important accomplishment during that period was my patented electronic flash and shutter night photo system. Also outlined was the development of quick-work photography in flight, the transmission of aerial pictures over telegraph lines, the K-7 camera which took 9×18-inch photographs, and the development of the first long-range 36-inch optical system for high altitude long-range photography. I wound up my letter stating I had taken the bitter with the sweet and would now appreciate being given the opportunity to make further contributions to research and development.

By return mail General Westover informed me that he had looked into the matter and that he was taking immediate action to order me to Wright Field as director of photographic research and development. Until then I had never received orders that cheered me more. I was full of beans and rarin' to go!

# PART III

*The War Years 1936–1946*

## 15

In retrospect, 1936 marked the military prelude to world conflict. More than Mussolini's African adventures, the Spanish Civil War, which began in July 1936, was the opening gun. At the time neither I nor anyone with whom I associated recognized the forewarning. Billy Mitchell died that year and while so many of us had supported and fought for his ideas concerning air power, few had really listened to his predictions of wars to come. And so it was not until the catastrophe was nearly upon us that we awoke to its proximity and many of those in high command were forced to put away their concepts of yesteryear. For example, as late as 1939 officers attending the Air Corps Tactical School at Maxwell Field, Alabama, were required to know the answers to questions such as how many bales of hay and how many bushels of oats it would take to move a company of cavalry from point A to point B.

I found in June 1936 when I again took up the cause of aerial photographic research and development, the entire budget for the fiscal year 1936–37 was fifty thousand dollars. This was an increase of only twenty thousand dollars, spanning a decade. The amount included *all* of the money that was available for the development of new cameras, optics, and laboratory equipment.

Colonel Augustine W. Robbins, Chief of the Matériel Division, and the CO at Wright Field broke the news to me and compounded it by adding: "George, because there is so little in your budget, I want you to do all your buying from Fairchild."

"All of it, Colonel!"

"All of it, George. The Air Corps can't afford to keep more

than one company in business. It would be wasteful to retain new inexperienced companies, particularly when we know that Fairchild is tops."

I couldn't argue with that, but I had always believed in spreading the work because I felt that competition helped to stimulate new advances.

As for advances, I had other realities to face. Steve in his tenure of office had again concentrated on getting up there, this time via stratospheric balloons. In so doing he broke the world's altitude record in 1935, reaching a height of 72,000 feet, and, of course, he nearly broke his neck, too. In a high speed descent the balloon disintegrated, and he wasn't able to bail out of the gondola until it was less than 2000 feet above the ground.

In his ballooning, which was done in cooperation with the National Geographic Society, Steve came up with some remarkable long-range oblique and vertical photographs—the first to clearly show the curvature of the earth. These photographs were taken with experimental infrared film developed by Dr. Mees and his staff at Eastman Kodak, and they made it possible to take pictures of great clarity at great height, cutting through the haze with the use of special filters. Of equal value to the Air Corps and later to NASA Steve's stratospheric pioneering brought information pertaining to cosmic rays and the intensity of solar radiation. Knowledge was also gained concerning pressurized cabins in our bombers, electrically heated suits, two-way long-range aircraft radio, and lightweight aircraft metals. However, because the budget was so small, little had been done on progressing night, quick work or any other aspect of aerial photography. Some improvements had been made in existing cameras, but no one had come up with anything new and different. This was also true of chemicals, film and photographic paper, including the recommendations I had forwarded as a result of my experience in the Philippines.

On top of that my buddy and compatriot Doc Burka had gotten tired of the whole thing and had gone into the development of navigational instruments where he was in great demand and

I couldn't pry him loose. Only Bill Oswalt, Bob Feight, George Magnus, and Benny Thomas remained from the old crew. It was a much smaller crew than it had been when I'd left in 1927, for personnel had been reduced from fourteen to seven. I decided right then and there the first order of business was more money. This I knew only too well took salesmanship, and it was the kind of salesmanship that necessitated coming up with a new idea that would grab the attention of the "powers that be" in the Chief's office charged with operational planning.

It was not long after I had returned to duty that opportunity did come slithering my way. For as long as I had been in the Service aerial photographic R&D had come under the command of the Equipment Section. That had always meant that unless I sneaked around left end and got support from higher up for some project, it had to first be approved by the Chief of the Section. And all too often, for lack of funds, it had not been. And though I had become fairly proficient at left-end sneaking, having to be under the thumb of a Section on which there were many demands was, to my way of looking at it, a deterrent to progress. Then all at once I was confounded by the ironic.

Colonel Robbins summoned me and announced: "George, I want you to take over as Chief of the Equipment Section. Borum is going on nine months TDY to take the tactical course at Maxwell. While he's gone, I want you in charge."

Major Fritz Borum was an old colleague with whom I had served at Chanute. In his sly fashion he had taught me a trick or two on the never-ending study of how to get what you can't get without violating orders. Now officially and legally I had suddenly been placed in the driver's seat. But where to drive?—that was the question. I couldn't appropriate more money for aerial photography; the amount was fixed and I had no new project set up as yet to justify an increase. And then using the Fritz Borum theorem, plus a thought or two of my own, I foresaw the way to a golden tomorrow. To me there was something regal in it. As Chief of the Equipment Section, I would recommend that because the work load was such, and the potential growth of aerial photographic R&D was such, the laboratory and all its endeavors should be divorced from the Equipment Section and made a separate entity.

This dream-thought needed strong support and after a few sessions with Major Oliver Echols, Chief Engineer at Wright Field, and his assistant Major Frank Carroll, two gifted officers on whom I would have bestowed golden wings if I'd had any, I received benediction and approval. With their concurrence I succeeded in breaking the chains that had bound the aerial photographic laboratory for so long. The shackles were off. No longer would we have to take the drippings, no longer would we have to knuckle the forehead to the equipment boys before trying to sell our wares at the top.

And it wasn't long before I began to do just that. In all aerial photography there are three major barriers to overcome. They are speed, distance, and insufficient light. By 1936 we had in some measure surmounted all three, but from the point of view of greater clarity, day or night, longer range, and swifter resolution, we had many and many a mile to go. However, between my return to Dayton and the beginning of World War II, in September 1939, a number of major breakthroughs were accomplished which not only were to have a direct and beneficial bearing on our war effort, but also—and even more importantly—have had their effect upon the development of all aerial photography since.

The first was color. As early as 1926 I had become interested in the potential use of color photography as an instrument of aerial reconnaissance. Once in use it would show things as they were; it would show things as the eye perceives and in so doing reveal to a far greater degree the true character of what was being photographed. Conversely, from a military aspect, it would also show that which was hidden or camouflaged. Thus color photography in every respect was a means of offering greater clarity, and investigation into it became my first new project.

In my quest it was natural that I would turn to Dr. Mees and his colleagues at Eastman Kodak. This was true because of past cooperation but also because in 1935 two of Dr. Mees' scientists, Leopold Godowsky and Leopold Mannes,[1] had invented a process called Kodachrome. However, in discussing my needs with them I found there were two principal drawbacks to the process for use in aerial photography. The laboratory work in the developing of the film was time-consuming, complicated and could only be accomplished at Eastman Kodak installations. Further, although the company was then producing film for use in 16 and 35-mm cameras, it was not interested in producing it for our standard aerial cameras. One reason was that while Kodachrome took excellent ground photographs, there was a serious problem in the air created by haze. Air Corps requirements demanded film that could be easily processed in fixed bases or field laboratories. On top of that, of course, we needed film that could overcome the haze factor. So I smacked my lips and shook my head and said, "Boys, I guess I'll have to look elsewhere."

Elsewhere was Hollywood, California, where I had got wind of a subtractive color process invented by two brothers named Hesser. Investigation showed it to be as complicated and time consuming in printing as Kodachrome. It required the use of three negatives to make one print plus a laborious laboratory routine involving different colored dyes. Its single advantage was that the speed of the film was faster than any others.

I had George Magnus modify a standard Fairchild K-3 camera by removing the magazine and placing a plate holder over the focal plane. The plate held two exposures where what I was really after was a camera that would hold one hundred. Nevertheless, in experimenting with the Hesser process I took some excellent aerial shots of colorful flower beds around Hollywood. Some of these were published in magazines, which was fine, but I was basically interested in stimulating Dr. Mees, with whom I kept in close touch, so that he in turn would stimulate the powers of Eastman Kodak to become more sympathetic to our needs.

There were a number of other companies coming up with

[1] Leopold Godowsky is also a noted violinist and Leopold Mannes a noted pianist.

color developments and to run tests on all of the most promising I had our laboratory make up a series of felt panels which were spread out on the field. The felt panels were 40 by 20 feet long each and were non-fade red, green, blue and three different shades of gray. To conduct our tests we had the use of a Douglas B-18 twin engine bomber which had a greenhouse nose where the photographer-physicist could do his work.

I wouldn't claim that our testing was a piece of cheese that caught the mouse at Eastman Kodak, but it certainly tickled his whiskers. That and a fat cat called competition finally brought the kind of involvement I had known with Dr. Mees in the early days.

Both Leopold Godowsky and Leopold Mannes became intensely intrigued with overcoming the haze factor and also conjuring up a film that could be swiftly processed. Dr. Mees also assigned a delightful English-born physicist, Dr. Walter Clark, to work with us. "Nobby," as he was called, was as brilliant a conversationalist as he was a scientist, and he reminded me in appearance and manner of the noted actor Leslie Howard.

He, Godowsky, and Mannes were particularly pleased with our color panels and the use of the B-18, which they all got a big kick flying in. Working under dense, medium, and light haze conditions, they made many photographic tests. Their combined efforts greatly aided in the final development of a fairly fast, properly balanced color film called Kodacolor Aero Reversal Film. The exhaustive research that went into it, the Hesser process, and others did not take place in a day or a month or a year. But in 1939 when Hitler marched, color was fast becoming a usable tool of aerial reconnaissance. During the war years the quality of color film improved tremendously. Kodacolor was the forerunner of today's Ektacolor and Ektachrome film used in the exploration of space as well as home photography.

The development of aerial color photography stands as a milestone whose influence in war and peace would be difficult to measure.

The second major breakthrough occurring in this same time

span was the strip camera, equally as important in its military application.

It was actually horse racing that led me to the strip camera. On a flight to California in connection with color photography I met with General Thomas Milling, one of the Air Corps' real early birds who had been taught to fly by the Wright Brothers. Tommy had retired from the Service and when he invited me to go to the races at Agua Caliente, I had no idea he had business in mind.

At the track he introduced me to his friend Lorenzo Del Riccio, who at first glance appeared to be a rotund loquacious type with an effervescent manner and a ready smile. Behind the manner and the smile I detected a sharp and inventive mind, and Milling's purpose in bringing us together was predicated on more than betting on "a sure thing in the fifth." He wanted Del Riccio to show me the newly invented race track recording camera.

The camera was located at the finish line and as the horses crossed it, the camera took a continuous panoramic picture, the film moving across a one-four-thousandth of an inch open slit in the center of the focal plane. The film was electronically synchronized to move at the same speed at which the horses charged past the slit. Immediate processing followed, so that in a neck-and-neck finish the film would determine the winner.

Driving back to Del Riccio's shop in Hollywood, I asked him if he could modify a 35-mm camera in the same fashion as the track recorder, and we'd try it out in my photographic plane hangared at Griffith Park. I was excited and impressed by what I had seen, for I believed that it might be possible to use such a camera to excellent advantage in high speed aircraft flying at low level. I could see that the design concept would depend on the speed of the film moving past the camera focal plane governed by the aircraft speed, its altitude, and the focal length of the camera lens.

Del Riccio quickly modified the camera as requested and with the aid of a National Guard pilot, I flew a test at 200 feet along a straight and level highway.

The result was a sad disappointment. The film was blurred and I threw it in the waste basket in disgust. But just as I was leaving the lab a very strong something prompted me to retrieve it, and I took it back with me to the Roosevelt Hotel where I was staying. That evening, using a magnifying glass, I went over every inch of blurred footage and, lo and behold, among all the nothing I was startled to spot a farmer's truck on the road. Inside the bed of the truck I could see with maximum sharpness five or six pigs with small black markings on their backs. I realized that the truck must have been traveling at the correct speed to match the speed of the film. What was needed was a way to synchronize the film's movement with the movement of the image in the camera.

Before rushing back to Dayton to announce my new find—a shutterless camera with an unheard of potential for low level aerial reconnaissance—I gave the whole concept some serious thought. I could envision that the development of the strip camera would mean a new and different way in which to take aerial photographs. And that was what bothered me. It was difficult enough to sell that which was proved; it was harder to sell that which was not proved and almost impossible if it was not understood. The strip camera would not be understood.

Any soldier knows that often it is better to carry on without asking approval from higher headquarters, so that you don't risk being ordered to desist. I wanted to carry on by getting enough money for Del Riccio to produce a workable model of the camera for aerial use. I talked it over with Tommy Milling, and with his enthusiasm where it counted most in Washington, I was quietly able to get the project underway. To carry out his testing Del Riccio constructed a kind of Rube Goldberg contraption outside his workshop. He set up two wooden drums that cranked and clanked a continuous belt of aerial photographs taken of the ground. Thirty feet above the traveling picture belt he mounted his camera on a scaffold, and there he would perch, his bulk making the scaffolding tremble, laboring to perfect a stabilizing mechanism. The state of the art of gyros had not progressed to the point where he could go out and buy the one he needed; he had to try and make it himself. And so day after day wooden drums rumbled, belt traveled, and swearing softly in rich Tuscan, Del Riccio clinging to his scaffold sought to reach a distant star. He had determination and he had flare, and in time I was able to supply him with additional funds, but I realized if the strip camera was going to get off the ground in the foreseeable future, others would have to start working on it.

Eventually, through the press of world events, I was openly able to let competitive contracts to Russell Vought of Beverly Hills and Fred Sonne of Chicago Aerial Survey Company, assigning them to come up with individual strip camera designs. At the same time my laboratory engineers began conducting tests on our own improvised "cellar mechanics" model, and it was my old compatriot Andy Matos, the little fellow with the big smile, who developed a most valuable feature by using twin lenses to produce stereoscopic shots in black, white, and color.

We then turned this model over to Sonne's company, instructing their engineers to produce a light metal production model. It was to have an automatic electronic image synchronizing device which would accurately set the film speed to the speed of the plane over the ground. However, the vital synchronizing device was not developed by Sonne's Chicago Aerial Survey but was subcontracted to the Hammond Organ Company. There the intricate machining was accomplished under the astute direction of Herbert S. Minema and David Hancock. Finally, we had a camera that automatically stopped motion regardless of aircraft speed or altitude.

Like color photography the strip camera had to go through a long and laborious metamorphosis. Unlike color it met with the resistance I had feared in both its development and operations. Some failed to see its potential, others refused to see its value. There is no doubt that of all the many battles I had to fight in the cause of research and development, the battle of the strip camera was the most bitter and difficult and at a later date played a part in an attempt to discredit me and ruin my military career. Ironically, as will be revealed, it was not my own Service that first saw the enormous benefit of the strip camera but the Navy.

Today some of the features of the strip camera are out in space, used as a vital adjunct to exploration and helping to provide a keen and watchful eye in defense.

Within the 1936–39 time span another milestone we reached was in night aerial photography. Over a decade had passed since I had taken the first night aerial photograph, but the problem of dependable flash bombs was still a source of constant concern and my experience in the Philippines with Don Bruner was a good case in point.

The flash bomb as a tool of aerial photography had several disadvantages; it was dangerous because powder can be exploded easily; it was limited because we could only carry a few bombs which meant we could only take a few pictures; and it was inflexible because with time fuses on the bombs we could only operate at one altitude. If there were clouds beneath that altitude, there could be no pictures.

While my photoelectric cell system automatically opened the camera shutter when the bomb went off and therefore assured greater photographic dependability, the disadvantages remained and even though the Ordnance people worked long and hard at overcoming them, I began looking for a better method by which to light up the sky. I found it at MIT in the electroscopic laboratory of Dr. Harold E. Edgerton. I knew that Dr. Edgerton and his assistants had come a long way in methods of generating bright light using electricity. I reasoned that if an electric flash device could be developed for use in reconnaissance aircraft, the disadvantages of the flash bomb would be eliminated. An electric flash would be safe, you could use it for as many exposures as required, and at the lower altitudes as desired by the Observation squadrons.

Dr. Edgerton and his staff were not very optimistic. They had succeeded in producing an electric flash system for nothing larger than a small hand-held Graflex camera, and what I was asking for was a jump from candlelight to sunlight. To create the kind of light I wanted would take heavy generators, which would have to draw their power from the aircraft's engines. Unless the engines had extremely high horsepower they wouldn't be able to stand up to the need. Knowing at that time the kind of aircraft we would have at our disposal, I was not deterred. I could see the feasibility of an electric flash system, and I knew with the proper engineering, it could be achieved. Once achieved it would open an enemy's activities under cover of darkness to far greater exposure.

In this case I had the Air Corps' understanding and approval and more important to Dr. Edgerton in his small laboratory—not unlike my own—I had money in my pocket. When the MIT boys learned that, they became electrified, and in short order we were off and running with tests going forward at MIT and at Wright Field.

Like color and the strip camera, night reconnaissance using the electric flash system was of vast importance during the war. As one illustration, on the early morning of June 6, 1944, a night aerial photograph of an important highway junction in Normandy taken under a low deck of clouds showed that the junction was empty of traffic and thus proved the Germans were not aware of the Allies' intended landing.

Today the electric flash system, far advanced from what it was when we first tried it with a single shot in a B-18, has gone from the sky to the world under the sea. It is the way in which light has been brought to the vast darkness there.

During the 1936–39 period, color film, the strip camera and the electric flash system heralded new break-throughs in aerial photography. However, in the drive to improve existing operational equipment, some notable advances were also made, some of which fortuitously were ready for immensely productive use when war came to us.

One of these was the long range lens. In 1936 I had found that the 36-inch lens camera that Eastman Kodak had developed for us in 1926 had been dismantled and put on display in the

Wright Field museum. I immediately set to work to revive the project, for long range and high-altitude observation were obviously important methods of aerial reconnaissance. If you could fly high enough to be out of range of the enemy's antiaircraft fire and at the same time get photographs that were as clear and detailed as those taken at lower altitudes, you'd have a built-in safety factor. The same applied to being able to take oblique photos of a far distant point too heavily protected by fighters to get vertical shots.

The money powers in Washington, assisted by the persuasion of the engineering team of Oliver Echols and Frank Carroll, provided enough funds so that I was able to let several contracts in pushing for a 40-, then a 50-, then a 60-inch lens. Providentially the project was perfectly timed for coming war usage. When a great demand followed for telephoto lenses the technology had advanced to the point where it was possible to use American glass instead of the German upon which lensmakers had depended for so long.

By 1938 we were able to put a 40-inch Bausch & Lomb lens into a standard K-7 Fairchild camera. In running high altitude color tests with it, we demonstrated its practicality for observation, proving its capacity as a telephoto infrared haze penetration camera. At the same time we asked Bausch & Lomb to develop for us a 6-inch focal length 120-degree aerial mapping lens. This move was taken on an official recommendation I had made with regard to aerial mapping. In my report I said:

This development [aerial mapping] has always been considered the major project of the Aerial Photographic Laboratory. Ideas gained during the development of cameras for military and commercial mapmaking purposes have been incorporated in practically all types of cameras in use in the Army Air Corps. The development of mapping cameras progressed quite rapidly from 1920 to 1928, but since that time, probably due to the reduction in personnel, the development has been rather slow. This condition has reached a point whereby the making of precision mapping cameras is lagging behind the production of equipment used for turning out topographic charts. The widespread interest manifested in the use of aerial photographic maps by the various arms of the Service during the past year clearly indicated the need for speeding up this development.

And speed it up we did. Bausch & Lomb, prior to World War II, was closely connected to the famous German optical firm of Carl Zeiss. In producing the mapping lens we sought, they no doubt utilized a Zeiss design. The finished article was called a metrogon lens, and it turned out to be one of the most important ever developed for the Air Corps.

By using three of these lenses in three cameras we were able to get tri-lens pictures from horizon to horizon which greatly simplified the making of aeronautical strip maps of the world. Once we were in the war these maps were invaluable in helping green pilots fly long distances over unfamiliar territory. Before the end of the war 13,000,000 square miles were photographed with cameras using metrogon lenses. Today the same technique is used in mapping, aided by great advances in both cameras and electronics.

Another development which I had been pushing in 1926 and which had been left to languish was a remote controlled telephoto camera. I had first worked on the idea back in 1919 and it had led to my original meeting with Billy Mitchell. In 1926 we installed such a camera in the observer's cockpit of a CO-5 high altitude experimental ship and at 27,000 feet I took the pictures from my cockpit. The results looked promising, and then suddenly I was off to the Philippines. During my tour at Chanute I had tried to stimulate interest in the idea at Wright Field. When I had no luck I passed it on to a young friend of mine, Jim Piersol, aviation reporter for the Detroit *Daily News*. Jim, who was also a pilot, was constantly complaining about the fact that the newspaper's photographers could never seem to get the kind of aerial shots he was after. In 1932 the Detroit *Daily News* put my idea to work on the paper's Lockheed Vega, and from then on, Jim Piersol at the controls had no more complaints and the

*News* received much attention for the quality of its aerial photographs.

In 1938 the Air Corps started using this installation by placing the camera in the nose of a Douglas B-18. But where the remote controlled camera really came to pay off was in our twin-engine fighter, the Lockheed P-38. During the war reconnaissance pilots flying the P-38 (F-5) became noted for their "dicing" missions. They would dive down out of the clouds on the target, or come in on the deck, get the pictures and be gone. In this fashion the strategic Moselle Valley was photographed by one pilot in one sweep.

By 1939 my budget had been increased from $50,000 to $250,000. While I knew that some of this increase was due to my sales efforts there is no doubt that the major portion was prompted by the last minute awareness that war in Europe was imminent.

In retrospect, there is no way of measuring the importance of the technical advances made in aerial photography between 1936 and 1939. It is enough to say, had they not been inaugurated until war actually began, the conflict would have been longer, bloodier, and more costly in lives and material. It was General Werner von Fritsche of the German General Staff who had predicted before the war that the side with the best aerial reconnaissance facilities would win the conflict. It was a correct prediction.

## 16

Within the three year time span between my return to the
Photographic Laboratory and the beginning of World War II, my
activities as a pilot and an aerial photographer not only kept me
busy in the area of technical advances, they also took me far
afield in other Air Corps pursuits. They did, that is, after I had
the shock of my life.

When I arrived at Wright Field in June 1936, I reported to the
flight surgeon's office to take the routine pilot's physical examination. Having taken these examinations for eighteen years without any trouble, I wasn't at all prepared for the flight surgeon's
serious look and devastating words, "I'm sorry, Captain Goddard,
but I'm afraid your days as a pilot are over."

"W-what! What's the matter? I never felt better!"

"It's your eyes. They're in very bad shape."

While I stood listening to him, numb with disbelief, he explained and none of it made sense to me. It seemed that I had
weak eyes, poor vertical muscles; I was internally farsighted, had
protruding eyeballs as well as poor color and stereoptic vision.
He practically had me blind, and my eyes felt fine.

After he grimly repeated he knew of no way to correct the
condition, I left his office in a daze. Staggered as I was, I suddenly recalled hearing Major Junius Jones, the CO at Chanute,
tell of a wonderful doctor in Philadelphia who had helped a
fellow pilot over some serious eye trouble.

I immediately got in touch with the major. The doctor, I
learned, was Carroll F. Haines who had formerly been a flight
surgeon with the Naval Aviation Reserve. I telephoned Dr. Haines

and as a result of our conversation, I applied for a month's leave of absence and went to Philadelphia.

Dr. Haines was a small, sharply perceptive medico who was in love with flying machines and was anxious to do anything he could to progress the cause of aviation. After he'd examined me, he cheered me up by saying he'd put a number of pilots back in the cockpit who were in worse shape than I. Then, under his care and direction, I began three weeks of intensive eye exercises in which I had to merge rotating images through a stereoscopic viewer. At the end of that period, the good doctor found my eyes to be perfectly normal. I could have kissed him, but I restrained myself. When I asked how much I owed him, willing to pay anything I could beg, borrow or steal, he shook his head and said, "I've put you back on flying status, George, and that's payment enough."

I returned to Wright Field with the kind of feelings that must come to a prisoner reprieved from execution. When the flight surgeon found my eyes were normal, he couldn't believe it. But they were and thanks to Dr. Haines they stayed that way for the rest of my military career.

Once returned to pilot status, I took up the cause of meteorology. All Wright Field pilots were required to make weather gathering hops, and it usually meant that your name came up for such duty about once a month. Take-off time was 3:00 A.M. and, during the winter months, having to rise from a warm bed into the shivering pre-dawn darkness, followed by rising into the congealed air in the open cockpit of an O-2H was strictly no joy. In this bitter ascent to 16,500 feet, the pilot made notations on turbulence, icing, temperature changes and other meteorological data—most of it unfriendly. The plane was equipped with the latest blind flying instruments and a baby buggy hood could be fitted over the cockpit to insure blind flying proficiency.

The instruments were fine . . . when they worked.

For example, Lieutenant Frank Klein had the duty one wicked morning. Ten minutes after take-off he ran into a violent thunderstorm and decided it was time to head for the barn. Returning on instruments, his altimeter indicating 2000 feet, his plane made contact with something solid. Thinking it was another aircraft with which he had collided, he instinctively moved to bail out. The next thing Frank knew he was looking up in the darkness at a sepulchral figure, robe flapping in the wind and rain, lantern in hand. Old Frank was sure for a moment that the pearly gates had opened and Gabriel or one of his pals had come to fetch him. That is until the figure called out: "What in tarnation hell happened! Are you all right?"

What happened was that Frank had hit a few trees in a farm orchard not at 2000 feet but at about 50. As to the farmer's query, the answer was "Yes," although the plane wasn't even respectable scrap and, as for the altimeter, it still had a long way to go.

The same could be said of flash powder bombs. While I was pursuing the possibility of an electric flash system, we recognized at the laboratory that even if such a system could be developed, flash bombs would still be needed for night reconnaissance at higher altitudes. Therefore, I continued to push the Ordnance people at Aberdeen, Maryland, to come up with a more positive and reliable fuse and more efficient flash powder.

On the plus side, George Magnus and I made the world's first night mosaic map. We took twelve overlapping photographs at 4000 feet of the building area at Wright Field and the Huffman Dam along the Mad River. The results were on a par with daylight photographs of the same area.

But it wasn't all cakes and ale, for soon after this success, I was ordered to participate in night Army maneuvers at Mitchel Field. The purpose of the exercise was to test the effectiveness of the Army's new high-powered antiaircraft searchlights and to see if Air Corps observation planes could locate antiaircraft artillery units.

Again George Magnus, my chief engineer, accompanied me. George was a tall big-boned Viking, with a forthright manner, a pair of determined blue eyes, and a fine ability to improvise swiftly when the occasion demanded. He spoke with a faint trace of accent and whatever he had to say was direct and to the point.

On the second night of the maneuvers our plane was to drop four flash bombs along the edge of Mitchel Field bordering the Jericho Turnpike; our purpose being to photograph antiaircraft installations. It was a fine clear night, and our four bombs were equipped with the new Ordnance fuses and fifty pounds of new high-efficiency powder.

At five thousand feet I wheeled the C-8 in over the suspected target, and right on the button George released the first bomb, timed to explode at 2500 feet. We began the 20-second count-down and at its end . . . nothing. Twenty seconds later, we saw the flash of the bomb as it hit the ground on the wrong side of the Jericho Turnpike. I observed the immediate result through the glass window in the floor of my cockpit. Cars in the vicinity began to move along the Turnpike as though they had all heard the starting gun at the Indianapolis speedway.

George leaned over the back of my seat and said, "If that's the best they can turn out for us they'd better get somebody besides the janitor to work on the thing."

"We'd better go find out who we blew up," I said as I circled the area, trying to get the point of impact on my map.

"That'll make a great picture. Thank God for long fuses is all I can say," George grunted.

We quickly landed, grabbed an official car and drove to the general area. Close to the Turnpike, George spotted a house in which we could see a woman leaning out of an upper window. It looked like a good place to start searching, and it was, for we quickly noted that all of the windows in the front of the house had been blown out, the curtains flapping in the breeze.

The lady of the house was elderly and shaken. She spoke with a heavy accent: "My Franco and me we are in bed when comes a terrible crash! Terrible! Terrible! All the windows go poof and the glass she flies all over the house! My Franco he sick, he say airplanes go smash in the sky, he go to the Field to get help, but no airplanes fall down. All my windows broken! All the glass in my porch!"

She was right, too, but since most of the broken windows were on the south side of the house, we realized that the bomb must have exploded across the Turnpike where there was a golf course.

George and I took to the fairways and it wasn't long before we found what we were seeking, a bomb crater about six feet deep and twenty feet in diameter.

The next morning we got maintenance people from Mitchel started on replacing the windows while we tackled the manager of the golf course.

"I'm sorry about the-ahh—hole we made in your fairway."

"There's no need to be sorry at all, Captain," the weathered manager in plus-fours grinned. "I'd been wanting to put a sand trap just there for a long time, and like the angel of the Lord you did most of the work for me. Now all I need is a load of sand."

George and I decided that the best that could be said for the new fuses was that one of them at least would help to ruin somebody's golf game.

After the completion of the maneuvers, George and I stopped in to see Captain Froggy Reed, the Ordnance representative at Wright Field. There were two basic problems in the development of a reliable clock-timed fuse. The demands upon the Ordnance Department were such that aerial photography had a very low priority, and from a technical point of view Ordnance people were used to having their bombs go off on impact, not at some predetermined point in the air. Over the years they had gotten pretty used to my lean and hungry look, but they couldn't help but wince every time they saw me coming. Still, they kept at it for us with generally improved results.

The Mitchel Field maneuvers were axiomatic of a general quickening in the efforts of the Air Corps to establish itself as something more than a support arm of the Army. This was a continuation of the same old battle initiated by Billy Mitchell. It had never ended, of course, and a handful of air power proponents had, over the years, pushed for the goal of greater autonomy, always with the accent on the role that heavy bombardment would play in any future conflict.

In 1935, a partial victory was won when a separate General Headquarters Air Force was set up as an independent organization co-equal to the Army Air Corps, but directly responsible to the Chief of Staff of the War Department. GHQ Air Force had three tactical wings under the command of Brigadier General Frank M. Andrews. These wings were located at Langley Field, Virginia, which was also headquarters, Barksdale, Louisiana, and March Field, California. General Andrews' Chief of Staff was Major Hugh Knerr, who had piloted me in Alaska, and Major Robert Olds was his Executive Officer. The three of them fought long and hard for air power and the development of heavy bombardment aircraft. That the famous flying fortress, the B-17, was airborne as early as 1935 was in part due to their efforts and others of a like mind. Long before Pearl Harbor the B-17 proved its worth on numerous test occasions, flying great distances at record speeds. But in May 1938 it was given its most dramatic test, which turned out to be one of my most thrilling flights. It came shortly after I was promoted to the rank of major.

At that time maneuvers were being conducted by more than three thousand officers and men concentrated at nineteen airports in the New England area. Two hundred military aircraft were involved in the most realistic air exercises that had ever been undertaken. It was a war game in which our fleet was deployed in the Pacific and with only sufficient naval forces in the Atlantic to patrol the coast. It was the Air Corps' job to intercept an enemy fleet escorting troop transports from Europe preparing to attack New England.

Out of the blue, I received orders to report to General Andrews. Arriving at Mitchel Field for the meeting, I found him surrounded by the principal members of his staff, some of whom were old friends such as Mike Kilner, Ira Eaker, Tony Frank, and Hugh Knerr. Present also was a big dark-haired, good looking West

Point type who was introduced to me as Captain Cornelius Cousland.

The General didn't waste much time on the amenities. "George, we're planning an important mission that up until now few people have been let in on."

"The Italian liner *Rex* is presently headed for the U.S. Tomorrow morning she'll be about eight hundred miles off the coast. We're sending out three B-17s to intercept her. For all intents and purposes she represents the attacking fleet. Our point is to prove we're capable of intercepting any attacking force while it's still far from our shores. Another is to prove the ability of the Air Corps to find that ship in a vast ocean area and then to return to base in fair weather or foul."

There could be no doubt about the latter, for as the General went on to explain the details of the mission, the rain pelted against the windows and the wind whistled around the rooftops in fine nor'easter fashion.

"Captain Cousland will be piloting the number two ship, and we want you on board with your camera. This time one picture has got to be worth a thousand words and then some." The General gave a tight smile.

"And George, we want you to photograph more than the *Rex*," Hugh Knerr put in quickly. "We want the other two planes in the picture, too."

"Right," General Andrews chuckled, "Hugh doesn't want any skeptics. Now we've been figuring the best spot for you to take your pictures will be from the co-pilot's seat. You'll be able to tell Cous where to fly, and it will give you a clear line of vision. Isn't that correct?"

"Yes, sir, but I'll want to open the window a bit."

"Make it a small camera, Major," Cousland said.

"Just big enough to get the picture you want," I grinned.

"Suppose it's like this when you find the *Rex*," Ira Eaker said, nodding his head toward the window. "Can you get pictures, George?" As Air Corps Chief of Public Relations, Ira was the author of the whole idea of intercepting the *Rex* and his question was natural enough.

So was the General's reply. "Ahh, what's a little weather, Ira? George could photograph the eye of a storm at midnight and you'd see it winking at you." As every military pilot knew, Frank Andrews would fly when the birds were grounded. People close to him said one day it would kill him. Tragically, they were correct.[1]

But that day was far distant and in his office we made plans for an exciting tomorrow. The Executive officer for the flight was Major Vincent J. Meloy, and the pilots of the other two planes, bearing numbers 80 and 82 (we were 81) were Major Caleb B. Haynes and Captain A. Y. Smith. The chief navigator, who would be flying in Major Haynes' aircraft, was a serious-faced, cigar-smoking lieutenant named Curtis LeMay.

Dawn of the all important day came on, soggy and gray. The weather officer offered no comforting news. The low-pressure system influencing much of the eastern seaboard was moving rapidly out to sea, which meant we'd have to fly through it to find the *Rex*. And when and if we found her, we'd then have to turn around and come back through the mess again. No one could deny that the mission offered a certain amount of challenge.

To prepare for my part of it, I chose a 4×5 Graflex camera, installing a light meter on it and fixing an aluminum cone over the leather bellows for protection against the wind blast when I opened the co-pilot's window. I decided on the Graflex because the window could only be opened wide enough to shoot through with a small lens. I set the camera's range at infinity, and joined my compatriots at the officer's club to do some judicious speculating on the flight to come.

It was about eight-thirty the next morning that we rumbled down the Mitchel Field runway and Cousland lifted us off into the scud of the rain-swept skies. On board aside from the regular crew of co-pilot, navigator, radio operator, and crew chief there were two aviation writers, C. B. Allen of the New York *Herald*

[1] General Andrews was killed in a crash of his B-24 when it struck a mountain in Iceland in May 1943. The weather was not considered flyable.

*Tribune,* and Lieutenant Harris Hull, Air Force Reserve intelligence reporter. We were number two in the flight and took up
position to the left of the lead plane.

There was voice intercom between the planes, and this was the
first time I'd heard it used. Because we could not tell how high or
thick the overcast was, but knew that it was both, we did not
wish to try and penetrate it in the hope of getting on top into
clear air. It was essential that we stick together and keep visual
contact, and so the decision made in the lead plane by Haynes
and Meloy was to stay low. With the ceiling sitting in the treetops,
this meant very low. In fact, once we left Sandy Hook behind and
headed eastward out to sea, we were practically skimming the
wave tops. Being so close to the water, the impression of speed
was sharpened. Even though we were slowed down to conserve
fuel, we seemed to be hurtling into a gray swirling incubus, in
which sometimes forward visibility was non-existent as the rain
trip hammered against us and coated the front cockpit windows in
a watery glaze. Sometimes it suddenly ceased and permitted us to
see a short expanse of blended sea and sky ahead.

Perfect navigation was the only chance we had to make the
mission a success, that and three pilots who knew their business.
The *Rex* wasn't standing still. There were no helpful check-
points along the route, and if there had been, we wouldn't have
seen them. I was glad I wasn't Curtis LeMay.

Cous Cousland, smoking a cigarette through a long ivory
holder, was the soul of confidence. He divided his attention between his instruments and the lead plane whose right wing was
just off our nose.

Ordinarily a four-hour flight under such conditions would have
been considered a long, wearing trek, but as each minute clicked
by, we all became more excited and keyed up. Without having to
say so, we believed that finding the *Rex* was going to prove a
long contested point. It was going to wake a lot of people up. It
was going to be the culmination of effort begun by Billy Mitchell
way back when. We knew no matter how foul the weather we had
to find that ship.

When we were three hours out, the real tracking began. Visibility had improved a bit, and it appeared that we were finally outdistancing the storm. We climbed up to five hundred feet and spread out in a line of flight, then we got up to a thousand. Then all we could do was wait and hope that LeMay had gotten a bearing off a seagull or a white cap and had us locked in.

The minutes clicked by. We were four hours and around 700 miles out. We were looking for a speck in a watery wasteland. And we found it, dead on!

It was Cousland who spotted her. "There she is! There she is!" he boomed out, gesturing with one hand and then it was shouts and cheers as we headed down toward her, the most beautiful ship I ever hope to see. In formation we circled her and saw her passengers come flocking out on to the decks. We radioed the news to Mitchel Field, and we contacted the *Rex*'s skipper to pay our respects. With fine Italian courtesy, he invited us to lunch and we were sorry we had to decline the offer. Then it was picture taking time. I directed the other two planes to circle the *Rex* at smoke-stack level and while Cous held a straight course off to one side, I went to work.

When word came through from GHQ at Mitchel to proceed back to base, we circled the liner a final time. On the afterdeck we could see a small group of passengers set apart and waving furiously. Later we learned they were Americans, and though we couldn't hear them, or the *Rex*'s whistle over the sound of our engines, they were singing *The Star-Spangled Banner*. In those days, no one scoffed at patriotism; one was proud to be an American.

The excitement was not over by a long shot. In returning, there was no need for the three aircraft to stick close together, so each of the pilots determined to try and get above the weather. I had known rough flights in my day, but never one to match that long flight home.

The turbulence at times was so violent that the B-17 would drop sickeningly, hit what seemed to be solid cement, and then

shudder and shake from stem to stern, the props of its four cy-
clones chewing impotently at the air. It did not seem that any
altitude afforded us relief. We went through three wind shift lines
and, at one point, while hailstones the size of golf balls hammered
deafeningly against the plane's metal structure and made us fear
they'd smash the Plexiglas cockpit windows, lightning cracked and
spat along the wings. Pilots often say that flying can be hours
of boredom and a few seconds of pure terror. We were experi-
encing the few seconds.

I did not believe that any aircraft could withstand such a
structural beating. Inside, white faced and taut, we had the weird
experience of trying to secure a large gaggle of golf clubs that
were scattered from the bomb bay to the cockpit. They were
Cousland's, who never traveled anywhere without them. They'd
been in a bag behind his seat and when we hit the turbulence,
they and the bag had taken flight. No one could have painted
such a scene, and I only wished I could have photographed it,
but I was too busy trying to pluck a niblick out of the air before
it clouted me for a hole in one.

Insult was added to near fatal injury when the right inboard
engine developed a bad cold and quit. While Cousland and his
regular co-pilot diagnosed the problem as carburetor ice and
worked to overcome it with heat and mixture controls, I couldn't
help noting that the bird seemed to manage as well on three
engines as it had on four. We all gave a cheer as Cous brought the
ailing Cyclone back to life.

When we finally broke free of the weather, we emerged into
the fine clear air of a late spring afternoon. The far distant rim
of land, smoky in its curtain of haze, welcomed us home . . .
it was not the sailor but the flier home from the sea. We had
been airborne for nearly eight hours; we had covered close to
1500 miles. We had located our target, and in returning we had
proven that a B-17 was tremendously rugged in adverse weather.
In fact one of the other ships had suffered cracked windows from
the twisting of the fuselage.

But what we were really out to prove appeared on the front pages of most American newspapers the next morning—a photograph of two B-17s flying alongside the *Rex* at smoke-stack level. The headlines were thick, the congratulations long and plentiful.

General Andrews, when he first saw the pictures I had taken, predicted, "This is really going to show what we've done."

Ira Eaker wrote me a letter telling me I had made a great contribution of historic value to the flight as well as giving the General a tremendous sales tool. He concluded by saying, "If there is anything I can ever do for you, George, don't hesitate to call on me."

Later I did have occasion to call on Ira . . . frequently.

Unfortunately, however, enlightenment was not the watchword of the day, and the congratulations, the predictions, my photograph reprinted in 1800 newspapers, magazines, and periodicals around the world boomeranged.

Directly following the event, an agreement between the Chief of Staff and the Chief of Naval operations limited all Air Corps operational flights to within a hundred miles off the coast. Displaying equal visionary zeal, Secretary of War Harry H. Woodring ordered the Air Corps to purchase no more than the forty B-17s already on order. This was the eve of Munich, and not only did Frank Andrews and Hugh Knerr fail to get the go-ahead to develop long-range heavy bombardment for which GHQ Air Force had been organized, but they were given the Mitchell treatment. Less than a year after the flight, Andrews was sent to the exact remote post to which Mitchell had been sent in 1925 and like Billy his rank was dropped to Colonel. Knerr quit in disgust and spoke out so loudly as a civilian that in order to silence him he was later recalled to active duty. It took war to bring both men back into positions of responsible command, equal to their abilities.

Some months following the *Rex* flight I was witness to a tragedy of another although not unfamiliar kind. It was September and I was on one of my frequent California flights, testing the

Hesser-color process. My pilot was a lieutenant who had been a student of mine at Chanute and was at the time chief of the photo section at Bolling Field. As we were flying toward the Lockheed terminus I saw a black plume of smoke rising into the sky with flames flaring beneath. Its proximity to the airport indicated a crash. We landed quickly, ran for my car and raced to the scene.

We arrived just as the ambulance sped off, siren wailing. Even so, it had come too late. I was sickened and stunned to learn that Major General Oscar Westover had been the pilot and both he and his mechanic had been killed in the crash. Coming in on final approach in his A-17 attack plane, the General had stalled the aircraft and plowed into a house short of the runway. The remainder of my tour in California was saddened beyond words, for Oscar Westover filled the description of an officer and a gentleman in every respect.

The man promoted to take General Westover's place as Chief had been his former assistant, General Henry H. Arnold, and shortly after the turn of the fateful year of 1939, he summoned me to Washington for an important staff meeting. There I was asked to present my views on future photographic equipment and aircraft developmental matters.

By hindsight it was a crucial meeting. At it I fought for the development of a special high-performance photo reconnaissance aircraft. It must be fast, it must fly high, it must have long range, and it must have defensive armament. I ran into a solid wall of flak. Twenty years had changed nobody's mind, at least in the aircraft planning group. They were interested in bombers, fighters, and transport aircraft. They were dead set against the development of a combat photo reconnaissance plane for strategic and tactical use.

In large measure Wright Field aeronautical engineers backed them up, maintaining that my requirements went beyond the present state of development. It was suggested instead that slow, low flying observation type aircraft were adequate for aerial photography, and if needs be, existing bombers and fighters could be modified to handle the job.

The only okay I came away with was to proceed on the development of single wide angle lens mapping camera. This was the metrogon lens with a six-inch focal length. Even in this there was attempted interference from a mapping zealot in Washington who wanted to change the lens to a five-inch focal length. With the support of the Corps of Engineers detachment at Wright, I stuck to my guns. Time proved the decision to be the correct one. However, time was also to prove that failure to go ahead on a photoreconnaissance plane was an incorrect decision that cost lives, time and equipment. It required our going through the war using makeshift aircraft and doing our missions the hard way. But as one is often heard to say—them was the conditions that prevailed.

My wish for a special aircraft was not a total defeat thanks to Hap Arnold. I had taken some rather dramatic color shots of a squadron of pursuit ships stacked up in echelon formation, making it appear as though the wheels of each were resting on the wing of the plane beneath. I took the photographs to Washington and presented them to the General. Having served four years as General Patrick's Chief of Information, Hap knew something about public relations.

"George, these are just what the doctor ordered. We'll get them into every magazine we can that can reproduce color. Also I'll want enlargements made so we can use them for exhibitions."

"You know, General," I said, "I nearly didn't get those pictures. When we were pushing my C-8 out of the hangar the landing gear just folded up and died."

"No kidding! Retractable, hey?"

"Yes, but not intentionally. We've been flying those birds for over eight years, and they're getting really worn out. Our photo sections need something better. The plane's no longer suited to the equipment, and if you can crack it wheeling it out of a hangar, I hate to think of what's ahead."

"Yes, so would I," the General smiled. "I tell you what, George, you make a survey of the aircraft industry and select what you think will be a suitable photographic ship. You report back to me, and if it sounds feasible, I'll see that you get the planes you need."

At Wright the chief engineer studied our requirements for a plane to be used by our eighteen photo sections and the photo school for non-combat use and suggested either a new twin Beechcraft or Lockheed. After a series of tests, we chose the Beechcraft and Hap, true to his word, gave us the go-ahead to order a fleet of eighteen.

This was the first substantial procurement by the United States government of Beech aircraft. The timing of this procurement turned out to be perfect for, after debugging, the Beech offered excellent possibilities for uses other than photography. Just prior to World War II General Arnold was in the market for a good reliable twin-engine plane to use for training pilots, navigators and bombardiers. The Beechcraft met most of the requirements and was readily available, and the General authorized its immediate procurement.

The Beechcraft Company built and promptly delivered thousands of these trainers which cost much less money than the planes the crews would be using in executing their military bombing missions. Aside from the value of the airplane for training bombardiers and navigators, our fleet, which was later increased, did a tremendous job of aerial photographic mapping of airways in North and South America during the war.

Shortly after Hitler had marched on Poland and war began in Europe, I was assigned to take a three month course at the Air Force Tactical School at Maxwell Field in Montgomery, Alabama. This was an important requirement for all officers as they advanced in rank. Normally the course was nine months but because of the international situation it had been cut to three.

In one of the classes the discussion centered around the movement of troops and equipment, and the instructor was pointing out the value of movement by night.

Up popped a fellow student to announce, "There isn't going to be any darkness to move troops by if ol' Goddard's night photography is as good as he says it is."

The instructor called on me to explain, and after I had done so, he said, "Major, I appoint you a committee of one to fly to Dayton, return with the proper equipment, and put on a demonstration for the whole school."

That suited me fine and several days after I was back with a B-18 and a crew of night photo experts. The night we selected found us competing with an unexpected thunderstorm. At 4000 feet our flash bombs got all mixed up with streaks of lightning and crashes of thunder. The lightning actually gave us some extra pictures by triggering our photoelectric mechanism. On top of this we nearly got bombarded out of the sky by a deluge of hailstones. To make the evening complete, as we were touching down on the dirt strip the wind shifted. I've ridden through some unusual landings but that was the first one in which the entire event took place sideways. Luckily we came to rest in a rainfilled ditch with only minor damage to the aircraft.

The pictures, however, proved to the instructors and students alike how aerial photography could rob an army of concealment by night. This was 1939, war was on in Europe, and yet for many it was their first proof of what aerial reconnaissance could do. Others were more knowledgeable, for during the evening of the test the officers' wives were holding a bridge party at the club, and as the flash bombs and lightning were booming and flashing overhead, one woman asked, "What's all that noise?"

Another wife who had just moved to Maxwell from Wright Field, replied emphatically, "It's either God or Goddard."

Aerial photography got another boost while I was at Maxwell, this time via Hap Arnold. Previously, I had tested some of Eastman Kodak's new Kodachrome film and made a series of autumn color pictures of points of interest across the country.

The General thought these pictures should be reproduced by the *National Geographic Magazine* and so I received the following letter from him:

Dear George:

It is desired that you furnish me statements covering the following in connection with Kodachrome photography, as illustrated by the pictures you have so far taken: speed of airplane, altitude, range of exposure time, diaphragm openings, type of camera, lens and developing process. Also a short paragraph covering the history of it, military advantages, prophecy for the future, etc. Don't make it too long, about 1000 to 1500 words will suffice.

Knowing your tendency to procrastinate, at the same time I am writing this letter to you I am sending a copy of it to the Commandant of the school and directing that you answer it without delay by dictating it to a stenographer. I must have it not later than Monday morning.

    Kindest regards.

                          H. H. Arnold
                          Major General, Air Corps
                          Chief of the Air Corps

P.S. Written because I must have this reply by Monday. Don't get all mad.

The General received my answer early Monday morning and the last paragraph of his letter of thanks read: "Again, thanks a lot, and I must confess you called my bluff on this procrastination business I was accusing you of."[2]

Not everything we photographed was the result of a new piece of research and development. In the spring of 1940 I was conducting tests of a sixty inch and forty inch lens of German manufacture that had been used in German balloons during World War I. When I received orders to photograph the eclipse of the sun, coming up in early May, I decided to use both of these cameras. They had little value in aerial photography of the earth from

---

[2] The article, "Aerial Color Photography Becomes a War Weapon," by H. H. Arnold, Chief of Air Corps, with illustrations from Kodachromes by Major George W. Goddard was published in June 1940 in the *National Geographic Magazine*. This was the first country-wide coverage of color photographs published by *National Geographic*.

fast moving aircraft because the aperture of the lens was too small, but in the light of the eclipse using fast film and long exposures, I knew they'd work fine.

We were not overanxious to film the event because it had nothing to do with the sudden workload under which we had begun to labor, but a group of astronomers from leading observatories had as usual exerted pressure through Congressional channels, and that was that.

We were able to borrow a B-17, which was undergoing high altitude tests of a new General Electric supercharger. Major Stan Umstead, chief test pilot at Wright, was in command and Fritz Borum went along as co-pilot to test some of the instruments he had been developing in the equipment section.

In 1939 I'd been able to have Master Sergeant Andy Matos transferred from Bolling Field, where he had served since 1921, to my laboratory at Wright. Andy in my estimation was the best all-around man in the aerial photographic business. He was dependable as a rock, and fiercely loyal, and I asked him to come along on the mission to operate the forty-inch camera while I handled the sixty.

In preparation we installed two large oxygen tanks adjacent to the waist gunner's openings where we'd be working in the after-section of the aircraft. Leaving nothing to chance we also hung a small oxygen tank from the top of the fuselage near our camera stations.

We took off in poor weather and climbed steadily through one layer of clouds after another. At 33,000 feet where we had planned to take our pictures, we were still in the clouds being tossed around. Since we didn't have our full load of fuel aboard, Umstead kept on climbing and at 35,600 feet and 34° below zero, we broke out on top in perfectly clear atmosphere. At that time the sun was already partially obscured and we did not have to wait more than twenty minutes before we started shooting our pictures.

Heavily clothed as we were in fleece-lined flying gear, the cold was nevertheless intense and every movement took extra exertion. My oxygen mask suddenly felt overly uncomfortable and I recalled thinking that I wanted to take it off.

A moment later Andy saw me slump down against the side of the fuselage. Even with my mask on he could see that my face was turning blue. Swiftly he grabbed the hose on the emergency oxygen bottle, forced it into my mouth, and gave me a blast of what I needed most. In a few seconds I was back among the living, but if it hadn't been for Andy, more than the sun would have been eclipsed.

As it was, the mission still had a long way to go. Since my oxygen tank wasn't working properly, it was necessary that I use the small emergency tank. The supply was good for only about ten minutes, and when we tried to communicate with Umstead and Borum on the intercom we found the system didn't work. We couldn't get the small oxygen bottle out of its fittings and walk up to the cockpit, so I grabbed a hammer and began beating a tattoo on the fuselage floor.

It seemed like a small forever before we saw Fritz Borum stick his head around and look back through the long length of fuselage where we gestured emphatically to descend. Despite the fact that the descent and landing was in weather that even ducks avoided, I was perfectly agreeable.

Once on the ground, Andy and I borrowed the laboratory facilities of a local newspaper, and thereupon developed our films and made pictures until the wee hours. Newspaper coverage of the results was widespread, and from the standpoint of photography and the test of the airplane the mission was a success. As for the reliability of oxygen and aircraft intercommunications, it left something to be desired; it also left me with sore cheeks for weeks due to the life-giving blast of oxygen with which Andy had restored me.

A few months later Andy and I were on another mission which in many respects proved that history does repeat itself. It was in the summer of that year. France and the Low Countries had been overrun and occupied by the Wehrmacht. Hitler and

Stalin were allies, and England stood at bay. In the U.S. the biggest Army maneuvers on record took place in Louisiana.

Our assignment in these maneuvers was to demonstrate the value of daylight color and night aerial photography and to drop the developed results to the staff on the ground.

In illustrating the former we located a column of cavalry camouflaged under the trees. The horses had been tied in a long row to a fence on one side of the woods, and we identified them, although we could not see them, by a long brown streak their shadows cast on the field. Ours was a demonstration of a new technique in warfare, while the horse cavalry was a throwback to the Civil War which took a long hard time to be put to pasture.

It was the night photography, however, in which the clock seemed to really turn back. Our mission was to photograph a river where the Army Engineers were constructing pontoon bridges. Lieutenant Whitmel Rison was pilot of our B-18, and, like old home week, Doc Burka was on board to test the latest navigational instruments. Andy was camera operator and Bob Feight of our laboratory was in charge of releasing the flash bombs on a signal from Doc. I rode along in the glass nose of the plane to keep him company.

Flying at a thousand feet we had found the river and taken two pictures right over the bridges. There was one more to go. Rison lined her up. Doc gave the signal and then all hell hit the fan. The immediate explosion blew me right back to a night in 1927. Only now we were pointed straight down, the bail-out bell was clanging, and neither Doc nor I could move. It wouldn't have mattered anyway; neither of us had on our chutes and we were too low to get out. Somehow Rison pulled the plane's nose up and, with bell still clanging, sought gingerly to gain some altitude.

I began scrambling around looking for my chute, muttering, "Where the hell is the damn thing!"

Doc was muttering, too, only his complaint was more direct. "Those dumb clucks gave me an experimental chute and it won't fit my harness!"

I finally located the object of my search behind the mechanic's tool box, but when I realized what Doc was talking about I turned to see if I could help him. At that blessed moment the bail-out bell stopped clanging.

Making my way to the cockpit, I found that Rison was flying low and slow back to the field at Barksdale. He asked me to take a flashlight back into the tail of the airplane and see how much damage had been done. Using my flashlight I could see that the blast had produced a pronounced dihedral in the elevator surfaces and had wrinkled the metal fuselage all the way from the tail to the nose section. At least this time neither Andy nor Bill had been blown through the roof.

The following morning the Douglas people received another wire to continue their study of the effects of antiaircraft fire on aircraft in flight. The Wright Field and Douglas engineers arrived and, as in the case of our near-fatal C-1 accident in 1927, they obtained some more valuable information without having to go through the standard laboratory static test.

As for Doc, Andy, and myself, we began to wonder if the hazards of a flying career were worth the late hours and low pay.

Several months after our explosive flight all the directors of the various research laboratories were called into the office of Major General George H. Brett, CO of Wright Field. We were advised that President Roosevelt would be visiting us and that exhibits were to be prepared describing the work of our respective laboratories. These exhibits would be displayed in tents along the roadways to the laboratory buildings so President Roosevelt could view them. They were to be placed in such a way that the President would not have to get out of his car. The General was very specific that the President was on a tight schedule and that none of the directors would keep him at an exhibit for more than seven or eight minutes.

Since the visit was to take place in about a week, I saw opportunity waving frantically at me, and the next day I was flying eastward to take a most important picture.

The big day arrived and right on schedule the official car began its tour of the Field. In the rear seat with the President were Orville Wright and Ohio's former Governor James M. Cox. Seated in the front was the chauffeur and square-jawed General Brett.

When the car drew up alongside my exhibit, I showed the President all my wares including night aerial photographs and dramatic color shots. He grew interested, and just before my allotted time was up I produced the *pièce de résistance*—a photo of the Roosevelt home in Hyde Park I'd taken from 1500 feet on my quick trip east. The President was so pleased he began pointing out to me where his mother had planted certain trees, new and old buildings and other salient points. Orville Wright and Governor Cox leaned over to see the picture, and we all got into a very chummy discussion about the photograph in particular and the merits of aerial photography in general.

All the while I could see General Brett giving me the "I'll hang you by the heels!" look, and the Secret Service men were reminding the President they were behind schedule. But old FDR wasn't the type to stop what he was doing until it suited him, and while we chatted the minutes ticked by.

Finally, General Brett managed to say evenly between clenched teeth, "Mr. President, I'm afraid if we don't move on, you'll miss *other important* exhibits."

They had spent almost half an hour in my company and just before the car started away the President said enthusiastically, "Major, that's a splendid picture and I want you to take one exactly like it in color."

Being behind schedule the official car breezed past several other exhibits and for a while the most unpopular officer at Wright Field was a man named Goddard.

General Brett was sure I had deliberately planned the entrapment, and one afternoon a short time after the visit he summoned me to his office and without preamble said: "Major, you've promised everybody and his brother in the Air Corps photographs and have never made good. Now I heard you promise to take a color picture for the President, and by God, you're going to make good on this one! I'm ordering you to take off right now and be in the East tomorrow, and don't come back without the photograph!"

I carried out the General's orders with pleasure, making a dozen prints from 500 to 1000 feet of Hyde Park dressed in its autumn foliage. At Rochester I had the film processed, and then it was back to Wright Field to give General Brett the pleasure of picking the best of the lot.

I felt that when the enlarged picture was delivered to the President he would want hundreds of them for his friends. Reprinting them was a laborious and time-consuming job for our laboratory, but I made a deal with a very good friend of mine, Walter Van Egidy, connected with *McCall's* magazine at Stamford, Connecticut. For the exclusive use of the picture, they agreed to give me two-hundred color reproductions properly mounted.

My guess had been correct. The President had no sooner received the framed photograph when he wrote a letter of thanks and concluded saying, "Please send me fifty copies right away." Then Eleanor and the President's mother put in their order, and in no time 199 prints found their way to the White House. The 200th remains the property of George W. Goddard.

## 17

President Roosevelt's visit to Wright Field had been in the nature of something more than a courtesy call. It was a manifestation of the sudden political and military change which had taken place as a result of international events. From where I sat it was almost an overnight change. Whereas the technical advances in aerial photography which had been inaugurated and were in the process of development during the 1936–39 period were for the most part undertaken with a limited budget, a handful of technicians and a few interested firms, now all at once the wraps were off and the sky was no limit.

In this sudden change of perspective we all seemed to awaken to the fact that our participation in the war was inevitable. As a result funds for my laboratory were only equalled by the onslaught of demands. In meeting them I had to have additional personnel, and Hap Arnold, who understood the importance of aerial photoreconnaissance, gave me his blessing. In late 1940 and early 1941 I went on a recruiting campaign in which I was able to offer commissions to a number of qualified civilians and bring back to active duty other specialists who were in the reserve. On this tour I managed to talk Dr. Mees of Eastman Kodak out of some of his younger research people. I also took Gail Borden, pilot and Chicago *Daily Times* managing editor, away from his paper, put captain's bars on his shoulders and in time made him chief of our aerial photographic flight test branch.

As our pace quickened to a run that was not to let up for five years, the need for additional facilities became all too apparent. One typical example was illustrated by our work with mobile photographic laboratories. We had to devise mobiles to be used in different parts of the world, and the equipment to be used in them under every kind of climatic condition. All these units must be capable of producing many thousand aerial photos daily.

To give those assigned to the project breathing room, I acquired some land at the edge of Wright Field, which we dubbed "the farm." The farm looked more like the Ringling Brothers Circus had come to stay, tents and trailer trucks all over the place. The acts going on inside conducted by Bill Richards, Johnny Ward, and Bill Whitaker, might not have thrilled the animal lovers, but the Army, Navy, and Marine Corps had my performers jumping through hoops day and night.

Getting the right people for the laboratory was difficult but possible. So was the expansion of facilities. However, under the multiplying weight of demands placed upon our laboratory I was faced by a fact I had long known but heretofore had not been required to surmount. In the all-important field of optics, there was no firm in the United States or Great Britain that was capable of turning out the precision lenses needed for long-range photography in anything less than two years time. Further, the lenses turned out were not of the quality necessary to meet the demands made on them under the swiftly varying conditions of altitude and temperature that tactical reconnaissance aircraft would encounter.

After a great deal of flying about the country looking for both people and facilities capable of designing and developing the type of long focal length lenses the Air Corps was going to need and need in quick time, I was about ready to admit defeat. Sorely troubled I went to see my old friend Dr. Mees and poured out my tale of woe.

He listened to me in silence and then said with a twinkle in his eye, "George, you should have come to me in the first place. I think I know the man you're looking for. He's young, very young, but he's a genius. I've studied some of his proposals, and we'd give our eyeteeth to get him here at Eastman Kodak, but—" he sighed, "we can't budge him."

"Why not? Who is he with?"

"You'll find him at the Harvard Observatory in Cambridge. He's an astronomer. His name is Jim Baker—Dr. James Baker, I should say. George, you make a deal with him so that you don't take him away from his telescopes and it will be one of the wisest moves you ever made. He'll show you optical systems that will make you loop the loop without your airplane."

"How is it you didn't tell me about him before?"

"Well," the doctor grinned, "I always had the hope we might hook him ourselves, but I can see the Air Corps needs him more than we do right now. But remember, don't try and box him in. He's poor as a church mouse but he won't give up the observatory for gold."

That night on Dr. Mees' recommendation, I wrote two letters —one to Dr. Harlow Shapley, Director of the Harvard Observatory, and one to Dr. James Baker. In both I suggested that Dr. Baker might come to work for the Research and Development Division of the Air Corps on a part-time basis, so that he would not have to discontinue his work at Harvard. And then giving the letters time to arrive but not to be answered, I headed for Cambridge, Massachusetts, and the ivied halls of Harvard.

It was not amidst the ivy that I first met Jim Baker, but in a dusty, cluttered little work shop located in what appeared to be the attic of the observatory. It was a proper setting in which to find an astronomer when he wasn't gazing through a telescope. But although Dr. Mees had said that Jim Baker was a young man, I was not prepared to find him all that young. Dressed in a faded pair of coveralls he turned from a battered drawing board, and for a moment I thought he must be an undergraduate.

"Dr. Baker?" I asked to be on the safe side.

"Yes, I'm Baker." His response was as cool and quiet as the steadiness of his gaze. He had almost classic features and in the dry clasp of his hand and faint smile on his lips I sensed a quality of self-containment and serenity.

I introduced myself and then we sat down to talk with a fine New England wind rattling around to keep us company. At once I realized that Dr. Mees had not exaggerated Jim Baker's abilities. He showed me some of the optical systems he had designed and others on the drawing board in the design stage. His interest in

Night aerial photograph taken at 8000 ft. over Bergen, Norway by RAF, using U.S. K-19 camera, showing dockyards and elements of the German fleet. 1942. *RAF*

Lieutenant Colonel Elliott Roosevelt, showing aerial photo results to officers of the Allied command at La Marsa, North Africa. General Carl Spaatz is to Roosevelt's right. 1943. *U.S. Army Air Corps*

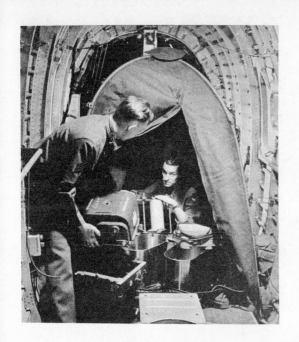

Developing film in porta
darkroom on return from m
sion in B-17, 1943. *LIF*
*photograph by Andreas Fe*
*inger*

Night aerial photograph over the Irrawaddy River in Burma, shows Japanese using pontoon crossing in place of destroyed bridge on an important military highway. *U.S. Army A.A.F. Photo*

A "dicing" shot along the Normandy beaches one month before D-day. German soldiers preparing defenses run for cover. *U.S. Army A.A.F. Photo*

D-day over Normandy, June 6, 1944. Landing craft make a dent in Germany's west wall. *U.S. Army A.A.F. Photo*

The entire German fleet (with the exception of the *Von Tirpitz*) gets caught with its anchors down in the harbor of Gyndia, Poland, August 1944. *U.S. Army A.A.F. Photo*

**Night** photo taken during the Battle of the Bulge, showing German tanks on the move near Houffalize, Belgium, December 26, 1944. *U.S. Army A.A.F. Photo*

long-range optics was similar to what I had in mind for long-range photoreconnaissance operations.

I could see that there was an originality to his ideas that was not bound to old concepts. When I mentioned that I was looking for a system whose lenses would be automatically corrective of extremes of altitude and pressure, he didn't bat an eye.

So far as I knew, no one had thought of or talked of this kind of an approach. We all recognized that up to a certain altitude a lens would offer a clear picture but then because glass contracts and expands under temperature and pressure changes, the lens would go out of focus. This was particularly true in large glass elements necessary to long focal length cameras.

Jim Baker had me hooked all right, and I knew I had to hook him. "How would you like to design a 40-inch optical system for our laboratory?" I asked matter-of-factly.

He smiled and it made him look about fifteen years old. "Yes, I'd like to but—"

"Do you think twenty-five thousand would cover the cost? You'd have to hire people to expedite the project."

"Twenty-five thou–sand!" His eyes opened as wide as his mouth and his smile became a mile long. "Twenty-five thousand, did you say?"

"Think that's enough?" The same offer had captured Dr. Edgerton of MIT. It was the kind of figure that in 1940 a scientist could only dream about.

"Why for that amount I can develop practically anything!" Retiring as he was, I thought he might do a dance.

"Great," I said, "let's get down to cases."

Later we left his workshop and he took me to see Dr. Shapley to whom I further outlined my proposal and the conditions under which his young protégé would set up an optical laboratory for us at Harvard. Everything was agreed upon, and I left Observatory Hill with a song in my heart and an astronomer in my pocket.

A few weeks later Jim Baker came out to Dayton for a brief indoctrination course and to get acquainted. He sat down with our optical technicians and we outlined a plan to expand his facilities.

The only area in which he felt uninformed was in camera shutters. As he said, "The kind of shutter problem we're used to in astronomy you could manage with your hat."

But I had the answer to that with another young wizard who had come to us in November of 1940 as a junior physicist via Civil Service examination. His name was Amron Katz. Amron had a round beaming face, a deceptive grin and a mind so sharp it emitted sparks. He nearly sent the camera manufacturing business into an inverted spin when he discovered that all indicated camera shutter speeds were incorrect, that the calibrations were in error. This meant on every single camera manufactured in the United States! The camera industry cried out in one collective voice: "You can't do that to us!"

And Amron, beaming, cigar in mouth, called back, "Boys, I didn't do it to you. You did it to yourselves. You'll have to make the changes."

Amron Katz taught Jim Baker all about camera shutters in jig time.

I also put him to work with my two top optical physicists, Ed Woodford and Clarence Kendall, and Hank Roganti my principal aerial camera engineer. Everyone in the laboratory soon recognized that getting Jim Baker associated with aerial photography was like a ball team signing up a Babe Ruth. As I was convinced he would do after our first meeting, he very quickly brought forth a design for two new types of advanced 40-inch lenses.

This was the first step into exotic optical systems; a step which went far beyond conventional formulas and methods by which the art had been guided for so long. What Jim Baker proposed and eventually produced in 40-, 60-, and 100-inch cameras was the forerunner of present-day optical systems we are using to explore space and to help safeguard our nation. Without his pioneering and leadership, such systems would not be at the stage they are today.

In my own mind, I know of all the decisions I made during my military career, my decision one gray autumn day in a dusty little workshop to ask a boyish twenty-four-year-old astronomer to go to work for me, was the most significant. He was a bright star in my life. I could not create what was needed. I could only describe to him what my own knowledge perceived would be necessary and then watch him translate the need into reality, feeling deep satisfaction in the results of his energy, his youth, his shining brilliance.

Although my evaluation and judgment of Jim Baker proved to be 100 percent correct, I have not always been so accurate in my assessment of people. In fact, such a wrong assessment made in the same period nearly ruined my entire career.

He was no stranger. I had thought him a friend. We had first met when he was an officer student at the aerial photographic school at Chanute and I was director. Later when I returned to the laboratory, he headed the photo section at Bolling Field and in Hawaii, and I had had occasion both to communicate and fly with him on many occasions.

In June of 1940 I wrote to Hap Arnold, concerning this young officer's future, stating in part:

I heard from him a few days ago regarding his photographic training program in the Hawaiian Islands. He is doing some fine work in photography and I hope when he returns to the States next fall that he will be continued in this work. He has always been one of the shining lights in this speciality and if it is at all possible, I hope you can have him assigned to my department, as I need him quite badly on the color and night photo development. If this is impracticable, then I hope you will seriously consider placing him in the Washington Office as Photographic Officer. There is a tremendous amount of planning details to be worked out in photography, particularly as pertains to procurement, organization, development and contacts with the using arms. I don't know of anybody in the Service more qualified to handle this job than he.

About a year later, certainly to a large degree on the strength of my recommendation, my young friend, he was fifteen years my junior, became Photographic Officer at headquarters in Washington. I sent my sincere congratulations, and shortly thereafter he put in an appearance at my office.

He was a rather tall man with full features, pleasant looking and pleasant seeming. Now he ignored my outstretched hand, and although I had recently been promoted to lieutenant colonel and he was a major, his manner indicated that he felt he was my superior.

"Goddard," he said flatly, "let's understand each other right now. I've been made director of all aerial photographic operations and that means I'm running the show, the whole show. I've got General Arnold's complete backing, and what I say goes."

For once I was speechless. I knew he lacked a sense of humor but even so I couldn't believe he was serious. However, he quickly convinced me that he was: "The fact of the matter is that I have been given complete authority to direct R&D, planning operations, and procurement. But more to the point I'm empowered to make any personnel changes I think necessary." He fixed me with a fishy stare. "I think changing you, Goddard, is necessary."

I was flabbergasted, but my blood was starting to rise, "Sonny boy, who the hell do you think you're talking to!"

"I know who I'm talking to, Colonel, but you'd better understand who you're talking to."

"A goddam fool from the sound of it."

"Yeah, well, I'm going to have you replaced here as director, and you can bet that as long as I'm in charge in Washington you'll have nothing further to do with aerial photography."

I held on to my temper as best I could, shaken by this totally unexpected attack, motivated by reasons I simply couldn't grasp.

"Would you mind telling me why this sudden change toward me?"

"Sudden, nothing. You'll never know how long I've waited for this day. My suggestion is that you look for a job in public relations or any other Air Corps speciality outside aerial photography."

I sat down and looking up at him with his set and serious manner, kind of puffed up like a he frog, I had to laugh. "Come on down, sonny boy," I said. "Your britches can't have gotten that full of hot air."

"You'll see what—"

"Now just a minute—" I held up my hand. "In the first place you don't have the position, the rank, or the authority to say boo about my work. I've known General Arnold a lot longer than you, and I know what he thinks about the job I'm doing here. Further, I'd be willing to bet and not immodestly that I've forgotten more about aerial photography than you'll ever know, but—"

"But nothing," he snapped. "I've got people in Washington who can replace you in a minute, and do a damnsite better job than you've ever done."

At this point his underlip was thrust out and he looked like a pouting child.

I laughed outright. "What is it they say about power? Power corrupts and absolute power corrupts absolutely. You sound like you're starting early. We're going to have to work together, Sonny boy, so you'd better get used to the idea. Shall we start over?" I smiled.

"Your days are numbered here, Goddard," he replied and then strode out of my office under a full head of steam.

I sat thinking about the encounter for some time. I was dumfounded, hurt, and concerned. There had never been the slightest indication of animosity. We had spent weekends together, our wives knew each other on very friendly terms. There had never been any sign of disrespect for my work. On much of the Hesser color testing in California he had been my pilot. All the unexpected scene had proved was how little at times one can know a person's true nature despite close association.

Later I recounted the meeting to Oliver Echols who laughed and said, "That pip-squeak! If he boots you out of here, George, it'll be over my dead body. I think you're doing a tremendous job. You're doing exactly what Arnold and his special boards want you to do. That boy had better come down out of the clouds or he'll find himself behind the plow."

And that appeared to be that for the time being, and while I couldn't dismiss the threat or the unfriendliness that went with it,

I decided to go along as though it had never happened and see if I couldn't change his attitude through cooperation.

An important part of this cooperation now dealt with Great Britain's war effort.

In March of 1941 the Lend Lease program had gone into operation. This meant closer ties between our Air Corps and the RAF. Shortly thereafter, an RAF sergeant major was assigned to our laboratory at Wright Field to act as liaison between the two services, concerning aerial photographic developments.

In this same time period General Arnold sent General Ralph Royce on an inspection tour of RAF installations in Egypt and the Middle East. Ralph, an old friend, had been a pilot since 1915, and there wasn't much he didn't know about every aspect of aviation. Upon his return he wrote a report which stated that most all of the British aerial photographs he saw in Egypt were of very poor quality, and that if they had been made for his use, he would have demanded that they be made over.

The British were using two cameras in their operations, the F-52 and the F-24. The F-52 with its 36-inch lens was used by Spitfires (and later twin engine Mosquitoes) in strategic daylight reconnaissance missions. The F-24 was used on RAF bombers on their night raids over occupied Europe and Germany. Since the RAF Bomber Command flew no daylight missions, the F-24 was used strictly for night photography. It was a recording camera placed in the tail of the aircraft. Its shutter was triggered by both flash powder and bomb explosions. It served two purposes—to show the degree and accuracy of the bombing and to prove that the aircraft had reached the correct target. This last did not endear it to the pilots and crews, but during the early years of the war at night under adverse weather conditions it wasn't all that easy for bombers to locate the correct target. In time radio navigational aids and radar eliminated the problem, but the F-24 remained the RAFs night camera. It took $5 \times 5$ photographs and could be hand held, taking oblique as well as vertical exposures.

It was natural that the British would prefer their own equipment to our own, and in spite of General Royce's report, it was recommended that we mass produce the F-24 for them.

In September 1941, I wrote to my late lamented Washington friend about the matter:

> We have made contact with the Eastman Kodak Company regarding the facilities for the construction of this camera. Yesterday they advised us that they would be willing to assign the greater part of their plant to rush production of this camera, and in order to save time on building an experimental model, they have agreed to build a production model and all the necessary tools and be in production inside of six months from the date of receipt of order . . .
>
> For your information, and also for General Arnold's, if you can get it to him, the optical people from Eastman and Bausch & Lomb inform me that they have A-1-A priority ratings on practically all Navy orders for camera lenses, and that the Army Priorities are very low. I thought you should know this as it may give you some idea of why it takes so long to complete Army orders . . .

The matter of priorities was his own responsibility and my observation was a placating gesture hinting that his office had better get cracking on it. Instead, from his office word drifted back that he was planning to use U.S. production of the British camera as proof that our equipment was inferior; and that, of course, was my responsibility.

I decided to get to the bottom of the British attitude, which I really knew was guided in large measure by their requirements and their strategy. They did no mapping, and in their critical defensive position, aerial photo-intelligence was of prime importance. The young man in Washington was so dedicated to the use of aerial mapping that he failed either to see or to understand the British needs.

On the strength of what I knew and what I wanted to find out, I dispatched George Magnus to England. He carried with him one of every kind of camera we then had in use, and his orders were to go to Farnborough, the British Research headquarters, and to bring back a detailed report on RAF reaction to what we had to offer.

He did so, and while the RAF found our equipment much to their liking, it did not, as I had previously understood, suit their immediate needs. Our daylight cameras had not been designed to fit into the nose of a Spitfire. Our tri-lens metrogon mapping camera was greatly admired but of no use to them. Our system of night aerial photography, while offering better resolution and sharper results, would have meant modifying every single bomber that carried it. With regard to film, Eastman Kodak had a large London plant which supplied RAF needs.

The strip camera, the strobe light flash system, and Jim Baker's work on long-range high altitude cameras were all in various stages of research and development.

However, with the return of George Magnus and his report I felt that the matter was well in hand. What I did not know was that my newly authorized nemesis had sent his own man to London about the time that George Magnus returned. He was a lieutenant bearing the nickname "Pictures," and he returned to Washington with an entirely different picture. The result was that I received orders from General Hap Arnold to report on the double.

I had no inkling of what awaited me. Only a few months previous I had received an official Commendation from him which read:

1. The undersigned, on recently observing Army maneuvers, was tremendously gratified at the excellent work being done by you and your photographic assistants. The results obtained indicate a careful planning, forethought, and initiative in the utilization of photography as a military agency.
2. I therefore take this opportunity to commend you for the most excellent work you have done in connection therewith.

However, as I entered Hap's office, I could see there was no look of friendliness or commendation on his face. He was furious.

"Goddamit," he swore, "I understand our camera equipment isn't worth a damn compared to the British. This report," he picked it up and slammed it down on his desk, "is from the Photographic Director's office. It details just how far behind we are."

"Why, General, it's not so!" I protested. "You're not getting the right story! I have—"

"Look, Colonel, I'm sick and tired of your guff! The information I've got is firsthand. It's on the best authority. The source is irrefutable!"

"General, I know positively that our equipment is second to none. We've got cameras for every situation known. We've got—"

"Listen, goddamit," he shut me off, "I haven't time to go into details. I accept this report, and I think it's about time you found out what the score is. Now I want you to get your tail over to England on the first available transportation. You'll report to General Chaney, and then, Colonel, you find out where you've fallen down so maybe we here can get things going in the right direction. Now take off!"

General Arnold's mind was made up. There was nothing I could say to convince him that he had been given incorrect information nor could I explain why.

I realized my nemesis had hoped that Hap Arnold would relieve me of my command on the strength of his derogatory report. Hap hadn't been ready to do quite that, but it had been a near thing.

Ironically, though I was thoroughly disturbed by being placed so firmly in the chief's well-populated doghouse by means which I considered vicious, I was elated about getting a chance to go to England for reasons both professional and personal. England had been the place of my birth; she was at war; my family lived there and I knew I wouldn't come back until I had a report signed by the RAF attesting to the quality of our camera equipment. On top of that I was going into a theater of operations where I would broaden my experience and add to my record. Young Major Nemesis in trying to down me had actually done me a favor.

## 18

In the latter part of October 1941 I arrived in Lisbon via a Pan American Yankee Clipper. Dressed in civilian clothes, I had made the crossing in style in the company of Britain's Labour Secretary, Clement R. Attlee, several Congressmen and a contingent from the State Department.

Lisbon was a city out of a spy movie. It seemed to be equally crowded by cloak and dagger types and refugees of every kind. Rumors came so fast and furious, one didn't have to read the papers to get the news. The Embassy advised that we leave all official papers in its care until departure. During my first day I came to understand why. Nearly every time I returned to my hotel I would find a plumber repairing a leak, an electrician working on a lamp or a fellow polishing the brass bed. In addition, it always took me awhile before I could make the key work the lock. Even though my bag was locked, it was obvious that somebody had been moving things around in it. Upon reporting this to the Embassy, the Air Attaché had me moved to the Avis Hotel, the best in town.

In a few days, we were taken to the airport for the flight to London on an old DC-3, or Gooney Bird. The skin of the fuselage had several small patches to cover the holes caused by bullets fired from German aircraft. All the windows were boarded up and our pilot and co-pilot were a couple of Dutchmen from the Netherlands Air Force who had escaped to England. At the front of our cabin was a large altimeter at least 18 inches in diameter and everyone kept an eye on it throughout the flight. Most of the time it registered almost zero altitude, and I got so curious I pried open the wooden board covering the window far enough so I could see that we were flying in a heavy rain just a few feet above the waves. We could not use our radio without giving away our position to German airplanes scouting the Atlantic, and the two Dutchmen navigated by dead reckoning.

On our way the steward told us that a few days before one of the planes on the run had been badly shot up. He said the reason for the delay in Lisbon was that they had been waiting for bad weather to hide in. As we rounded Land's End in England, we received word that both Bristol and London were socked in by fog, so while the weather had protected us on the flight now it forced us to come down at the RAF field at Barnstable.

I wouldn't have cared where those Dutchmen put us down just so long as it was somewhere on that little "realm of kings." The damp and wet were familiar, the smell of the sea was familiar. I was an American, but I was an American glad to be among his kinfolk again, present with them in their difficult hour.

The particular hour we landed was late, and I made my way to London by train where in the early light the Air Attaché from the Embassy was on hand to greet me and get me bedded down at Claridge's Hotel.

For the first few days I was anticipating an air raid at any moment, but in the fall of 1941 about two-thirds of the German Luftwaffe was engaged against the Russians and a good portion of the remainder was occupied in the Mediterranean. Nevertheless, the air-raid sirens did wail quite frequently, and for the first couple of nights I trooped down into the underground to take my assigned bunk amid a sea of bodies and a conglomerate odor that somehow reminded me of the stretch of village road between Manila and Camp Nichols. A strong desire for fresh air and no heavy bombing raids convinced me that I'd rather take my chances above ground.

The most difficult adjustment was the blackout. This was particularly true when on occasion I'd go down to Tunbridge Wells to visit my family. My mother had passed away in June, and my father lived alone in the old house. My two sisters, who resided in the town, took care of his few needs. Because of the proximity of the sea coast, the sky was crowded with barrage balloons, looking like a herd of fat sausages cluttering up the sky. Otherwise the nightly blackout and the scarcity of food were the two major reminders in Tunbridge Wells that a war was going on.

The poor food undermined my father's health and the blackout gave him a closed in claustrophobic feeling. Even so, advanced as he was in years, he kept his sense of humor.

"You know, George, living this way is really educational, it teaches us how our ancestors must have felt residing in caves. Also I've thought of a way we can all have a grand meal. Tonight you go out and shoot down one of those damned balloons and we'll roast it. I'm sure it will taste just as good as some of the things we've been eating, and there'll be a lot more of it."

My visits to Tunbridge Wells were, of course, brief interludes snatched at infrequent intervals.

Directly after my arrival in London I reported to Major General James E. Chaney, Commanding Officer of the Air Corps Observers Group attached to the Embassy. We had met previously several times, and because I didn't know whether he understood the conditions under which I was joining his small staff of about a dozen pilots, each assigned to study a particular phase of RAF operations, I gave him a completely frank briefing.

A number of years my senior he reminded me in looks and manner somewhat of General Patrick. He was the kind of staff officer who did his work quietly and efficiently, content to remain in the background, but there was something in his quietness, the dryness of his smile, and the way he chose his words that spelled understanding. And in our first conversation he proved the point.

When I finished he didn't say anything for a moment, then he looked up at me and with a twinkle in his eye said, "Well, George . . . welcome to the club. . . . There are others on my staff here for essentially the same reason that brought you. . . . Cummings bears the cross of inferior equipment. . . . Mc-

Clelland, communications . . . and so forth. . . . How long have you been in the Service, George?"

"Since nineteen-seventeen."

"Most of us old-timers have been . . . that and longer. It's simply a matter of perspective, George. Up to a year ago, it was years and years of famine, then suddenly a feast . . . only a feast in which all at once there is too much food and not enough cooks . . . and mind you when we actually get into this war it will be a lot worse. Most of the cooks they'll have to bring in won't know a frying pan from a fried egg. So pity the poor head chef, George. He's being hit from all sides at once. Lend Lease is going to drive us all up the wall. Orders and no facilities, and cries of inferior equipment. In your case it happens to be some nasty politics in Washington plus British pride and the fact they've been at war for two years and they know what they're doing a damnsite better than anyone in the Chief's office. But"—he sighed and stretched—"don't be too hard on the Chief because he's sore at you. He's got to trust the people around him, that or he'll simply become engulfed. I'll do everything I can to put you in touch with the right bodies here, George. Then you see what you can do about it."

I left General Chaney's office with my confidence somewhat restored and my perspective a little less blurred. It became sharper as I went on, particularly after I met and got to know Group Captain V. C. Laws, director of all aerial photography in the Air Ministry, in London. He had joined the RAF in World War I, and he had been the prime mover of aerial photoreconnaissance since. Short in stature, very proper in manner, he was just as wary and sensitive as I might have been had he come prowling around my laboratory at Wright Field out to prove his goods were better than mine.

"You chaps have developed some fine equipment, old boy, but frankly we've been at it for quite a spell, too, you know, and we're rather pleased with what we've got."

You can't argue with a man for liking his own product particularly if he's been busy refining it in combat operations and his manufacturing facilities are mass producing it.

On top of that there had been a major difference in camera design between the British and ourselves. They preferred the focal plane shutter and since 1921 we had specialized in the Fairchild between the lens shutter. Their type shutter was not desirable for aerial mapping and aerial mapping since World War I had been the be all and end all of Air Corps reconnaissance. Further, pictures taken with a focal plane shutter were to a certain extent distorted by elongation and exposures were uneven. As shutter speeds improved the disadvantages were cut down but not completely eliminated. Our design, on the other hand, lent itself perfectly to color photography. Although in pursuing new development into long-range telephoto lenses, I had turned again to the focal plane shutter, basically, at the particular time we preferred our standard design and they preferred theirs.

On balance, it could be said that the British F-52 and its 36-inch lens, used on high altitude daylight missions was a fine piece of reconnaissance equipment. I did not think it was as good as our K-21, but from every standpoint it did not make sense to suggest to the RAF that it put aside a proven product then in mass production for a product, while in some respects superior, could not at the time be manufactured in any quantity at all.

As Laws politely put it, "I say, old chap, why don't you offer your K— whatever it is, to the Russians?"

With regard to the British F-24 used for night bombing operations, its purpose was different from that of our comparable night camera. In the first place, the Air Corps strategic concept was daylight bombing, and so no night bombing camera had ever been developed. The RAF camera flew with its shutter open, its mission, as noted, to record bomb damage and also correctness of target. But in so recording, it also photographed tracers coming up from antiaircraft emplacements, revealing their location and giving the RAF a chance to bomb them on the next go round.

The night camera I had developed, the K-19, was strictly to expose the enemy's moving of men and supplies by land or by sea under cover of darkness and thus it was a reconnaissance weapon in the true sense of the word. To compare it and the British F-24 was not feasible. Thus it became apparent that nothing could be gained by arguing the relative merits of cameras designed for different purposes. Although I was on the scene to prove that all my years of effort had not been wasted, I knew that if one were to let politics as well as personal pride and jealousy stand in the way of cooperation, nothing was to be gained, and the end result would give aid and comfort to the enemy, who was located across the channel and not at Farnborough, Wright Field, or in Washington.

General Chaney had pointed out that Lend Lease might be a boon to our allies, but it was going to be a godawful headache to ourselves. Our industries were just beginning to tool up for what lay ahead. It seemed to me that any short cuts we could find through cooperation would benefit all, and I had the aim firmly in mind as I made my investigation. I also knew, although I made no mention of the fact, that once the strip camera was in production it would eliminate the need of either the focal plane or the between the lens cameras. What I didn't know, however, was that in my absence young Major Nemesis had put a stop order on all development and production of the strip camera then going forward at the Chicago Aerial Survey Company.

On the personal investigation front, I soon recognized that while Group Commander Laws and his colleagues at Farnborough were willing to show me all that they were doing and even run tests of the K-21 and other equipment at the laboratory, they were not particularly interested in pushing use of our equipment under combat conditions. Since I had authority to go anywhere in England on my own, I began visiting RAF reconnaissance squadrons to see if I couldn't get more enthusiastic cooperation from the operational boys.

Every day that the weather was flyable and often when it wasn't, the RAF "recce" pilots climbed into their specially modified Spitfires and took off on what they called their milk runs over Norway, France, Germany and Austria. In the place of extra armament, they carried extra fuel tanks; in place of machine guns they carried cameras. Generally flying above thirty thousand feet, they would photograph shipping along the coastal areas keeping track of German vessels, as well as airfields, military activities or plant installations under construction. Over Germany they would obtain up-to-date pictures of cities, camps, gun emplacements or industrial areas over which a night bombing raid was being planned. Where a bombing had been accomplished, they would photograph the damage done and the action being taken to rebuild. Similar missions were being carried out over France, particularly over the immense submarine pens at Brest, Lorient, and Saint-Nazaire.

Occasionally it was necessary for the RAF to dispatch a Spitfire to dive down to one hundred or so feet above the ground to acquire close-up photography. This was a dangerous job and the losses were relatively high because the enemy always had many antiaircraft guns well manned and ready to fire. However, the mission was absolutely necessary to substantiate the interpretation made from the high-altitude pictures. For instance, the interpreter might see certain unknown pieces of equipment on the deck of a battleship being built or repaired, however the detail was too small and not at the right angle to afford positive identification. This also applied to the identification of camouflaged equipment and gun emplacements.

All the vertical high-altitude photographs taken on the milk runs were made with a 60 percent overlap on the adjoining photographs. This made it possible to take two overlapping pictures, place them under a stereoscopic viewer and see objects in relief. Looking at a single picture there was no depth but viewed through a stereoscope it was possible to measure the height and width of anything of interest.

I found the RAF recce pilots to be a wonderful lot, and as to the importance of their work one example of their efforts in 1941 epitomizes the value of their hazardous assignments.

The German battleship *Bismarck* was the most powerful ship afloat. Her location was of first magnitude importance to the British Navy, spread thin over vast ocean areas. It was known that if the *Bismarck* could set out from some undisclosed port and reach the Atlantic shipping lanes, she would massacre troop and supply convoys with ease. At the time in question, eleven British convoys, one carrying thousands of troops, were either in the Atlantic or about to sail. It was RAF recce pilot, Michael Suckling, who found the *Bismarck* in a Norwegian fiord just as she was putting to sea. The photographs he took gave the British Navy the information it needed to intercept, and, after a hard-fought running battle, sink her. Of her sinking Sir Winston Churchill wrote: "Had she escaped, the moral effects of her continuing existence much as the material damage she might have inflicted on our shipping would have been calamitous. Many misgivings would have arisen regarding our capacity to control the oceans, and these would have been trumpeted around the world to our great detriment and discomfort."[1]

British recce pilots were back-stopped by a remarkable group of men and women at a place called Medmenham in the country north of London. Medmenham was the RAF photographic interpretation center. It was located in a sprawling country mansion on a large estate, secluded and inoffensive looking. Here some of the most important work of the entire war was carried out by a staff of experts. They were intelligence officers of a new sort, detectives who in studying aerial photos were able to reveal the enemies most treasured secrets. They knew the exact dimensions and the rate of production of the German submarine fleet. They knew what buildings were being used by the enemy to make strategic war materials. They knew what was camouflaged, what was decoy, what was real. Long before the Germans had launched their V-1 and V-2 missiles, interpreters at Medmenham had discovered the test sites of these secret weapons at Peenemünde on the island of Usedom off the Baltic coast. Additional discoveries were made of actual "launching shelters" along the French coast. All of these critical areas were bombed by the RAF and the Eighth Air Force for the first time in August 1943. As Medmenham interpreters uncovered new launching shelters, other attacks followed, and it was

[1] Sir Winston Churchill, *The Grand Alliance* (Boston: Houghton Mifflin Co., 1950), p. 320.

not until September of 1944 that Hitler was able to let fly his first V-2 rocket against England. Not only had the use of these *Vergeltung* weapons been delayed by at least a year, but also their numbers had been reduced from a planned downpour to a drizzle.[2]

In my travels about northern England, during what turned out to be a bitter cold winter, I did not find a soul who had anything but the highest praise for American aerial photographic equipment. However, while the RAF tactical people would exclaim, "Wizard!" and "Top hole!" over our photographic wares, it was combat testing I was most anxiously seeking and finally got.

Under my direction a K-19 camera was placed in the tail of a Blenheim bomber scheduled for a night reconnaissance mission over Bergen, Norway. Along with the camera went some of the latest flash bombs. The Blenheim and its crew returned from the mission with three perfect overlapping shots taken at 8000 feet, clearly revealing German shipping in the harbor, dock areas, and the city. "The Photographic results of the flight," the official RAF report read, "were of excellent quality."

This was the same camera we had used in the Louisiana maneuvers about which General Hap Arnold had written me a letter of commendation. The shots then had been taken not at eight thousand feet but at four. It was also the camera which young Major Nemesis had described as not being worth a damn.

In the midst of my investigation two events occurred which had a direct influence on it—one long range and the other, short. The Japanese attacked Pearl Harbor and the Philippines, and I caught the flu. I was not surprised at the Japs' attack or its catastrophic success. After all I had served in the Philippines. On hearing the news I couldn't help remark, "Well, it looks like the Japs paid more attention to Billy Mitchell than anyone else."

Someone suggested I get out of my civilian clothes and put on a uniform, which fortunately I had brought with me, and that was that.

[2] Constance Babington-Smith, *Air Spy* (New York: Harper & Brothers, 1957).

The flu, following soon after, put me in the hospital and gave me a chance to rest and think things over. Since we were now involved directly in the war I knew that the demands for aerial photographic equipment would be increased a hundredfold. I had made, and was in the process of completing, a thorough study of the RAF aerial photographic program, from supply to interpretation, and I believed the RAF could handle its own manufacturing needs. But until we could get such cameras as the 40-inch K-22 into mass production, it seemed to me that we could help to fill our immediate requirements by manufacturing the existing British F-52 for high altitude reconnaissance work.

Thus as a stop gap I decided to recommend the immediate U.S. production of between fifty and one hundred F-52 cameras, and on December 31, 1941, General Chaney dispatched the following cablegram to General Arnold and other interested parties including young Major Nemesis:

GODDARD IS FAVORABLY IMPRESSED WITH F-52 CAMERA, AND BELIEVES IT SHOULD BE CONSIDERED FOR U.S. STANDARDIZATION AND PRODUCTION. THIS MESSAGE FOR ECHOLS. THE 3RD PRODUCTION MODEL OF THIS CAMERA, COMPLETE WITH MOUNT, QUANTITY OF TEST FILM, AND DRAWINGS HAS BEEN DISASSEMBLED AND SHIPPED BY AM IN SEVERAL POUCHES ADDRESSED TO WD, G-2 FOR GEN. KENNY. JANUARY 10 IS EXPECTED DATE OF ARRIVAL OF SHIPMENT. PER ARRANGEMENTS, GODDARD ON RETURN WILL CARRY COMPLETE CAMERA DRAWINGS PLUS TWO ROLLS TEST FILM.

By the middle of February 1942 I had completed my four-month investigation. I wrote up my report and presented it to General Chaney for comment.

"George, I think it's just what the doctor ordered . . . and it should certainly ease you out of the old man's doghouse."

"Amen to that. Do you suggest any changes, sir?"

"No, you've made it clear. We're the aerial mappers of the world. Your R&D going on at Wright and Harvard is far advanced over theirs. They've got some good cameras in use, we've got some better ones coming along, and they agree they'll be anxious to have some plus a helluva lot of equipment. What else is there to say?"

"Nothing, I guess. I've tried to touch everything."

"It's quite a list of groceries," the General chuckled. "Portable processing machines, continuous printers, packaged chemicals, camouflage detection film—you name it, and old George Goddard's got it. All Hap can say now is get to work."

"I hope so."

It proved in part to be a false hope. After an exciting voyage home, ducking German U-boats all of the way from the Clyde to Halifax, I reported to General Arnold in Washington.

His outer office was mobbed with people, and it was two hours before I was ushered in. There was no smile of greeting, no extended hand.

"Well, what can I do for you, Colonel? What do you want?"

"You personally sent me overseas, General, to evaluate British aerial photographic equipment as compared with our own. You had heard stories that ours was inferior. I wanted to present in person my report on these allegations." I handed it across the desk to him. "You'll note, sir, it has been endorsed by General Chaney and a number of RAF officers. The stories you heard were not correct, sir, and no one in General Chaney's office or at Farnborough ever said our cameras were no good."

He held the report in his hand, head lowered. "Well, I'll look into it," he said and then glancing up over my shoulder at his aide, he ordered, "Show in whoever is next, please."

## 19

Upon my return to Wright Field I found, as I had expected, that it had become a real madhouse of activity. As the heart of research and development for the Air Corps, it was not only the center at which all new material must be tested and approved, it was also the place at which all demands were directed and most criticism from tactical forces was leveled. My laboratory staff which had numbered ten in 1936, numbered about four hundred by the spring of 1942. There was not enough space, not enough trained people, not enough administrative personnel, not enough industrial facilities for procurement or shipping, and above all, not enough time in a day, a week, or a month to accomplish all that must be done. We simply did the best we could to handle the tornado of demands and take them in our stride.

In addition to wrestling with the understandable problems galvanized by an all-out war effort, I had the extra joy of having to deal with a man who devoutly sought my removal. He was now young Lieutenant Colonel Nemesis, but the promotion had done nothing to deflect his aim. When I learned upon my return that he had stopped all work on the strip camera, I put the Chicago Aerial Survey Company back to work on it on my own initiative. In wanting to expedite its development and production, I went further and directed the planning on two different types of strip cameras and then awarded contracts to two engineering companies to proceed accordingly.

In the inaugurating of R&D on photographic equipment, I now had considerable leeway. With our involvement in the war, it was a different ball game, and not only were we supplying the Air Corps but the Navy and the Marines as well.

During my overseas investigation I had observed certain problems encountered by the RAF which I set about to correct. One was that in desert countries excessive dust in the air presented obvious difficulties in operating field laboratories. Another had to do with the difference between actual and anticipated light conditions found over the target. And a third, which was extremely important, had to do with film that caught fire when struck by bullets. I set up tests on both nitrate and acetate film, finding that the former caught fire when struck by machine gun bullets and the latter did not. We standardized acetate film, and no doubt we saved some lives in the process.

However, when it came to the production of existing equipment, this was young Colonel Nemesis' domain. No action was ever taken on my recommendation to produce the F-52 camera and a host of other items. To some degree the same could be said for the K-18 camera. I had actually begun development on it back in 1925 at McCook, and in my opinion it was in 1942 the best all-round aerial camera we had, both from the point of view of making mosaics and reconnaissance. The Navy came to use it almost exclusively in the Pacific, but its mass production was delayed by at least a year because no action was taken by the young colonel on my production recommendation. As to the reasons why, it is fair to state that the demands on the office of the Director of Photography in Washington were no less than those at Wright.

Along with R&D, priorities, and procurement there was at the outset the primary question of a suitable aircraft for reconnaissance. My desire for a special aircraft had long been rejected and while everybody in Washington seemed to have a different idea about the most suitable ship, we were instructed to consider the B-17 as the standard aircraft. We set to work with the Boeing people at once, and at our modification depot we began installing a complete complement of cameras and equipment for mapping, long range, and night photography. Two of these aircraft were sent to the U. S. Eighth Air Force in the summer of 1942. But it was quickly realized they would be sitting ducks for German Messer-schmitts without constant fighter escort and such escort at the time could not be afforded for reconnaissance missions.

As a result, our laboratory received orders from Washington to do what we had already recommended in September 1941—set up an aircraft modification center in Fort Worth, Texas, and modify the Lockheed P-38 twin-engine fighter aircraft to the F-4 photographic airplane.

The P-38 had a large nose compartment which was normally filled with four 50-caliber machine guns and ammunition. All of this equipment was to be removed, together with the heavy armor plate, and in its place we were to install a forward-looking camera. Back of that single camera was to be a tri-met camera system. Provisions were also made to install two vertical, long focal length cameras for high altitude operation.

The aircraft modification project had a very high priority and a short fuse. I had just the man in my laboratory to manage this job: Willis Harrison, project engineer, who had had years of experience working on aerial photographic mapping projects for the Fairchild Aerial Surveys in South America. He assembled a group from the laboratory, set up shop in Fort Worth, and immediately there was a stream of P-38 airplanes flying to Fort Worth from the Lockheed Aircraft plant in Burbank, California. The Harrison gang worked around the clock and, in a matter of days, many of the F-4s were on their way across the Pacific to our aerial photographic squadrons, operating out of Australia and Port Moresby. Later many of these modified airplanes were sent to North Africa for use by the 3rd Reconnaissance Group.

We had no sooner got this job underway when a very special modification job to install recording cameras in sixteen B-25 airplanes was received. This was one of those top-secret, around-the-clock, mad-scramble jobs and to make sure it was a success I appointed my trusty camera technician "Hank Roganti" project engineer. He had a habit of sleeping only when such jobs were finished so I wrote that project off in jig time.

Lieutenant Colonel Jimmy Doolittle was in command of organ-

izing the squadron for a mission so highly classified his pilots didn't
know where they were going until shortly before they got there.

It was not until we read in the newspapers about Jimmy and
his B-25s taking off from the aircraft carrier *Hornet* some 800
miles east of Japan and his daring bombing raid over Tokyo that
we realized our aerial photographic laboratory had played a part
in this historic mission.

Of course I was intensely interested in knowing how well the
camera installation had worked and was very upset when I was
informed cryptically by General Arnold that not one solitary
aerial photograph was obtained on the raid. Naturally I was
anxious to learn the full facts of the matter and later Jimmy
Doolittle gave them to me:

"George, do you know a lot of people have thought that
the Tokyo bombing flight—taking off from the aircraft carrier—
was my own original idea. I want to make it clear that was not
the case. As far as I can find out, a Navy officer—then Captain,
later Vice-Admiral, Lowe—conceived the idea, took it to his
chief, Admiral King, who discussed it with General Marshall.
General Marshall called in General Arnold, who thought it was
a good idea.

"General Arnold gave me the chore of preparing the aircraft
and training the crews for the mission. Later I asked if I might
command it and he granted the request. I selected the people,
trained them, using Eglin Field, Florida, as a base to do all the
preliminary work.

"I am sorry to have to tell you none of the cameras, as far
as I remember, was saved, the reason being that all of the
aircraft crashed except one, which went to Vladivostok and the
Russians confiscated it and its equipment.

"After the raid when we reached the China coast we were
all separated in order to conserve gasoline. You know how you
jockey the throttle in formation. Anyhow it was a very bad
night, heavy rain and solid overcast. We knew the hills were at
least five thousand feet and we didn't know how good the maps
were, so we flew as far as we felt we could fly to the selected field

on dead reckoning, and then, at about nine thousand feet, we bailed out. But my sergeant, who was a very good boy, went back in the tail of our plane before he jumped. He took one of the cameras and put it inside the front of his coveralls and when he left the ship he had that camera with him. Unfortunately, the camera was heavy enough so that when his parachute popped, with the usual severe jolt, it tore the front out of his coverall and we lost it. But that's how close we came to getting a few pictures."

The Doolittle raid, of course, was a one-time shot, but shortly after it, we began putting aerial reconnaissance squadrons into combat operations with exceedingly grim results. It was a combined matter of green pilots and green aircraft.

The performance of an airplane can only be determined through grueling daily flying operations, where the aircraft is flown by different pilots each day under various weather and climatic conditions. Unfortunately the modified P-38 as it went into operation in the Pacific and later in North Africa, showed up a number of serious deficiencies. It flew at speeds of 400 miles an hour and higher due to our removal of all the armor plating, which lightened it considerably. In spite of that, the 8th Reconnaissance Squadron, commanded by Lieutenant Colonel Karl Polifka, suffered such heavy losses that he was left with only one F-4 aircraft a few weeks after establishing his organization at Port Moresby, Australia. The unfortunate part was that pilots would take off on a mission and just disappear and no trace of pilot or airplane was ever found.

"Pop" Polifka flew his last remaining airplane on several missions to try to find a clue to the mystery. He discovered that the electrically controlled propellers were affecting the aircraft compass and apparently pilots were being steered out to the open sea instead of to their home base. He also experienced serious trouble with the tail surfaces which put the aircraft in a dive during sharp maneuvers with Jap fighters. The main source of trouble, however, was the Allison engine. In the tropics under severe operating conditions at high and low altitudes, they were troubled by thrown rods, lack of proper cooling, and other faults.

Of all our World War II recce pilots there is no doubt that Pop Polifka was the most outstanding. He had come to aerial reconnaissance in 1939 via cadet pilot training and the photographic school at Lowry Field. A heavy set, square-faced blond tiger with Slavic features and no visible nerves, he was at age thirty-three a pilot par excellence and a flight commander who inspired tremendous respect and loyalty from his men.

While at Wright Field we sought both to supply and improve reconnaissance equipment, Polifka and other boys who were trying to emulate him were out making use of our efforts under less than the best conditions. No one described these conditions in 1942 any more graphically than Polifka himself:

I'd be swell here if we could get the equipment necessary to fulfill at least ten percent of our obligations without flying bailing wire and rags.

We have not been up to strength with aircraft at any time, even including wrecks and aircraft missing. Our problems are only aggravated by this lack of equipment. We now have five flyables and two in depot. One total wreck and three missing in action. *That* is all the airplanes we've had. As you could guess, after we equipped the planes, trained the crews, both combat and maintenance, they took our B-17 flight away from us, complete! We have recently been presented with five old B-25s. They won't go as far as the P-38s.

Hdqtrs. does not believe in asking anyone who should know some of the answers, they ask some stooge. Name and serial number will be supplied on request. We'll have fun bombing at least. You have no idea how we sometimes long to personally do some damage especially after one of us gets badly chased or we find a juicy job and bombardment bungles, as usual. I won't mention which bomb outfit stinks but if you pick a number between 18 and 20, you won't be far off.

Refrigeration is, as you realize, indispensable in a photo outfit, but, here in the jungle of New Guinea, you have no idea how much you do need. We have eight boxes and three ice making machines and we should have more. If communications were better it would be okay, but they aren't better, they're worse. Camels are fast compared to this lack of system. Example: two trailers, A-2, left Brisbane Sept. 11, since that time all we've done is lose track of them. The Heavenly Father alone knows where they are. Chances are some Longheel has set up housekeeping in them.

Under the subject of power equipment, first, the generators on the trailers will not last a week until overhaul, after that the useable period becomes shorter. There's a generator put out by Ford . . . which we are finding to be what the doctor ordered. We have four of them due to some beautiful horse trading. Remember the Sketch Master that we procured for whoever was to do our compiling? We traded it for the generators, lots of other stuff and held out for first choice on the Aussio girls. They didn't know that we were going to give it to them anyway! But big, well built generators are essential if production is to continue unhampered by fluctuating current or none at all.

The sleeping bags, air mattresses, et al, are well worth packing around with a unit of this sort, if you can get them. If you decide to get rid of them, it would be easy enough, wherever you might be. We're the envy of this theatre.

Medical supplies. Start off with a *good* stock of all drugs, especially *all* sulpha drugs, vitamin capsules, anti-dysentery drugs including sterile salt and glucose solutions for intravenous. I kept flying with dysentery and finally fell on my face (right after a flight, fortunately) because so much blood had been lost and the osmotic balance so badly off that blood pressure was down around 40. It would have been bad had we not swiped some intravenous solution from the ship's surgeon of the *Coolidge*. That's one sin which worked well.

Your squadron commanders must fly. The morale, the work and the attitude of combat personnel in outfits where the CO doesn't fly is horrible. There is no respect for him as a man, as an officer or as a director or leader. As a result, shows go awfully sour. Example: the entire 19th Bomb Group, two sqdns. of the 22nd Bomb Group unless actually led by the group CO or "Shanty" O'Neill, CO of the 408th Sqdn. O'Neill flys and has a scrappy outfit. I fly and have more guts per cubic foot in my pilots than any other outfit in the world. Sometimes I think the boys have too much. I know that you all ordered me not to fly, but, when we got here with no trained mechanics, it was necessary that I fly, so I did. I now have 41 missions, all of which were to Rabaul from Moresby. Rabaul is outside our radius now because we're not allowed to operate over water from any distance. Suits.

On the subject of "Tactics," I could write all night and not scratch the surface, but, speaking in generalities, I'll try to sum it up fairly briefly. General tactics are fairly simple: (1) Don't approach your target from the same direction twice in a row. (2) Evade known spotting stations. (3) Inasmuch as you're necessarily high, use mountains, if available, to block news of your approach from reaching enemy radar stations. If range of plane permits, feint toward another known target at this stage. (4) Cruise slow on the outbound leg until outside radar range if you intend hitting another target, then cruise normally or fast. The slow cruise at first will bring your interceptors to your altitude late. After being intercepted 19 times in eleven straight missions, the above procedure was adopted and some refinements added for Tojo's confusion. Haven't been intercepted since but have seen many planes trying to without making it. By using the Nip radar (or equivalent) at Gasmata for the dissemination of false reports, Rabaul became pretty cush except when the Navy was in. The naval ack ack is not bad! We're doing short range stuff now and having the time of our lives. We have air supremacy right now but don't expect the Nips to lay off forever, just 'til the Solomon deal is settled. We're doing good training on our youngsters at this stage, looking into a shooting future.

When you're cornered by superior numbers, there are a number of things to do exclusive of being killed. (a) One is allow them to close into long range, chop *one* throttle, hands and feet off then break through directly into your attackers. They can't follow that one even with a zero—you don't know exactly where she's going yourself! Use only throttles on that one and you can't miss unless the Dutchman has more guts than the Nip. (b) The variation to be used when you're going to get yours anyway is simply to pick the biggest concentration and fly into them, nose to nose, with the proper fatalistic attitude, you'll win. So far, they've climbed off like flies off a burning latrine for me. I grant you that the above were used before we had proper maintenance, but the procedure is effective if you get caught sleeping and don't know you have company until you see tracers. The throttle job is most effective under that condition. (c) Then there is the race across the target, if the F-4 is cooking with gas, you're in, if not, use either (a) or (b) and get out. (d) Cloud coverage race, or race for home, is the same as in (c) except on the race for home descend slowly and nurse them along, calling for your own fighters to kill. If you're losing on this, use (a) or (b) and get close to the ground or water so they can only shoot from the top of you. A sick F-4 will outrun a healthy Zero at sea level if you can run in a straight line. Training the photo Sqdns. with adjacent pursuit with camera guns should be effective for all concerned.

If I'm going to my favorite area, it would be greatly appreciated if I were allowed four to six weeks in which to shake the dead wood out and train the unit into fighting form, to my own personal specifications; which are, I'm afraid, pretty tough for the country club boys.

. . . Speaking of twitting a Nip, we've worked out a beautiful method of cleaning ack-ack out of the dense jungle surrounding Nip 'dromes, they're hard to spot on pictures sometimes. Been keeping the youngsters off this, but the technique is to simply ride around above the 'drome at their bad altitude, fairly low, and plot their positions on old photos by the muzzle flashes; then the A-20's visit them with parachute bombs while you lead them by about 10 minutes in order to get the gun crews in the pits and shooting at a target up high. It really works. We've cleaned Lae, Salamaua and Buna out of ack-ack crews and some guns several times in the past month by this method. In a combined raid on Buna for their Air Corps supplies, the A-20's silenced every gun on the first pass. The B-26's set off seven gasoline dumps with 300 pounders and the A-20's and Beaufighters burned 18 airplanes on the ground. Eighth Photo got the credit from General Whitehead for the whole show. It was a beaut.[1]

In time Polifka's straight talk received action from Washington and he was the recipient of a fleet of beefed up debugged

[1] From a letter written to Colonel Paul Cullen, in charge of operational Reconnaissance Procedures, Hq., Air Corps, Washington, D.C., 1942

P-38s, designated as F-5s. However, shortly after the U. S. Army went into North Africa in November 1942, Pop was assigned as Deputy Wing Commander of the 3rd Photo Reconnaissance Group, stationed near Tunis, under the Command of Lieutenant Colonel Elliott Roosevelt.

I had first met Elliott in the fall of 1940, directly after his father had visited the Field. As a reserve officer the President's son had been called to active duty and was assigned to the Procurement Division. He stopped by my lab one day and I presented him with the famous aerial color picture of Hyde Park. He was delighted to receive it, and we had a long session on aerial photography both generally and specifically. I took an immediate liking to him not just because of his curiosity but because of his straight forward manner. Whether our conversation planted a seed that stirred his interest, I never knew, but soon afterward he transferred from Procurement to Aerial Reconnaissance. He did tell me that the sudden switch was in part stimulated by thousands upon thousands of letters that began coming in to him from all over the country, their general theme being—I didn't raise my boy to be a captain in the supply corps.

They just didn't know Elliott. After attending reconnaissance school he became one of the key officers in a big and vital chore. The Air Corps was then desperately in need of airway flight charts. They were for the locating of new airports and to help pilots in flying material to all parts of the world. Between November 1940 and September 1941, Elliott was based in Newfoundland out of which reconnaissance over Labrador, Baffin Island, Greenland, and Iceland was conducted.

Upon his return to Washington with photographs and reports of the northern route over which so much traffic was soon to flow, he was put in command of two B-17s. They were stripped down and equipped with the latest navigational aids and three wide angle mapping cameras locked together to form a single tri-lens camera. Under suitable weather conditions, Elliott's expedition could make photographic strips from horizon to horizon for hundreds of miles in a day. And they did just that, although one of the B-17s disappeared on a flight between Puerto Rico and Trinidad and was never found. The other, with Elliott on board, went on down the coast of South America to Natal, Brazil, then across the ocean to Liberia. From there they spanned the African continent heading for Cairo. Beyond Cairo lay the Near East, India, the Himalayas and finally China. They mapped it all, and did a marvelous job in gathering the material out of which our airway charts were made. In the days and years that followed these maps greatly aided our pilots in flying across unknown lands and undoubtedly saved many lives.

After the U. S. Army invaded North Africa, Elliott was made Commander of the 3rd Reconnaissance Group and, like Polifka, he had to put up with the bitter realities of untried equipment and inexperienced pilots. Of his first ninety-six planes, he lost ninety-three in a few weeks of operations.

As to the way Elliott Roosevelt felt about Pop and his fellow recce pilots, his own words tell the story:

"Polifka was one of the best pilots I have ever seen. He knew more about the technique of taking low-altitude pictures, particularly, and especially obliques. Some of the best pictures that came out of World War II were pictures that Pop took. He would go in at the assigned altitude of 28,000 or 30,000 feet and take his pictures, then he'd go down and get some low-altitude dicing pictures. Often his pictures brought out all kinds of things you couldn't pick out otherwise—things that were camouflaged from overhead came right out on his obliques.

"We had one low-altitude mission we had to fly in Yugoslavia and we had ordered Polifka specifically not to fly it. He promised us faithfully—after all he was the deputy wing commander and was only supposed to go in on certain missions, due to his value. He ignored the order, at the last minute he told the pilot assigned to go on back to his bunk, and he'd take the mission.

"We were to try to identify the headquarters of Tito in this valley prior to dropping some people to assist Tito, and also some extremely valuable supplies and messages. Polifka filled out the forms with the other fellow's name and then he took over the mission which made him liable for court-martial. We overlooked it, though. He flew 130-odd missions in the European theater and he had some 35 missions in the Asiatic theater. He was one of the most highly decorated reconnaissance officers —he and Leon Gray and Johnny Hoover.

"Leon Gray flew 146 missions in the European theater and Johnny Hoover flew 144. Johnny Hoover came to me as a boy of eighteen—a second lieutenant replacement pilot in North Africa—and Leon Gray came to me as a man who had been court-martialed in the Air Transport Command and was given the choice of accepting a very severe punishment or of going on combat duty. He thought he was going into the fighters or the bombers, but instead he found himself, much to his disgust, flying reconnaissance. He came to love reconnaissance when he found that it really wasn't very sissified and discovered that we had a higher rate loss than any other outfit flying in World War II. He became an outstanding reconnaissance pilot and added a great deal to the techniques, doing some of the best work of the war in night photography."

And so while we on the home front warred on the battlefield of red tape, shot at by priorities, bombed by complaints, blitzed by orders from above, the young pilots with cameras in place of guns played their hazardous role in the conflict, their valor and skill little recognized but vital to the total effort.

Toward pushing that effort, I sometimes received the kind of help the doctor ordered, and in one particular case the doctor was Vannevar Bush. He had been appointed by President Roosevelt to be director of the Office of Scientific Research and Development (OSR), which included the National Defense Research Council (NDRC). The purpose of these organizations was to provide R&D facilities and scientific aid to the military. I wanted both for Jim Baker. He was making great progress at Harvard but he needed more room and he needed more people.

I went to see Dr. Bush about the matter, and his immediate

response was that he was ready to leave for Harvard as soon
as I could get a plane.

I knew a general in Washington who had a plane, but I
didn't know how he'd feel about lending it to me. I decided
to take the phone by the horns. The result was Hap Arnold
almost smiled again as he said, "Okay, George. Just don't break
it."

It was a high-powered flight not so much from the standpoint of horsepower but horse sense. On board beside Dr. Bush
were some of the best scientific brains in the country—Drs.
Millikin, Compton, Johnson, Dunham, and Condon. We went
forth to surround and sell Harvard's President James Bryant
Conant. Our proposal for expanding Jim Baker's entire operation
received his immediate blessing.

Already Jim had accomplished a miracle or two. The 40-
inch optical system he had undertaken had been constructed
and test-flown in seven months' time. Ordinarily such a feat
would have taken two years or more. He had proved to Dr.
Bush and his colleagues that she was without peer in the field
of optics, and my aim was to give him everything he needed
so he could go into bigger and better things.

Sometime earlier I had coined a phrase—there is no substitute for focal length. At Wright Field and elsewhere it became
known as Goddard's law. It simply meant the longer you made
the lens, the higher your aircraft could fly and the photograph
still retained its close-up sharp detail. Great altitude to a reconnaissance pilot in World War II was money in the bank, it
meant he had a much better chance of coming home safely.
And that above all was the underlying purpose of Jim Baker's
inspired work.

## 20

In every respect 1942 was a year of hectic and ceaseless activity. I was promoted to full colonel, and after twenty years at year's end, Marge and I decided to call it a day. On the military fronts our armed forces began to make substantial gains in the Pacific and North Africa, but we all knew it was going to be a long hard war. Many of the ideas I had put on the drawing boards during the 1936–39 period had started paying off; others were reaching toward the production stage. The most important of these was the stereoscopic twin-lens strip camera.

In the summer of 1942 we installed one in an F-5, and tests were flown at speeds between 350 and 400 miles per hour at an altitude of 200 feet. A picture was taken of an old wooden bridge which actually showed the knotholes and the grain of the planks. On the windshield of a car parked close by, the letter "A" on the gasoline ration ticket stood out clearly. On this flight we had stopped motion for the first time with an aerial camera which did not have a shutter.

Everyone at the laboratory was sold on the product. But this was not the case in Washington and elsewhere. In fact, there was a powerful body of opinion dead set against ever letting the strip camera off the ground. Their reasons in some respects were understandable if not enlightened. With millions upon millions of dollars invested in the tooling necessary to produce shutter aerial photograph cameras, manufacturing firms were determinedly opposed to changing and, entrenched as they were, they were not about to welcome competition from companies that would be willing to produce the strip camera. These firms had their friends in official Washington and their tech representatives in the various theaters of war. Between the two they built up the myth that the strip camera was just no good. There were others against it because it was something new in the field, and their announced reason for opposition, swiftly passed on to the tactical squadrons, was that a pilot using it would have to fly so low he'd be a sitting duck for enemy ground fire. And finally there was the young lieutenant colonel in Washington who had the ear and trust of Hap Arnold, and was against anything Goddard had to offer for whatever his reasons.

Early in 1943 I decided one way to prove the value of the camera was to give it a test where it would count most. I called in the hottest test pilot on the field, Lieutenant Harry Trimble. He was from Alabama and he had a drawl that was like honey on bread.

"Harry," I said, "how would you like to take a little trip?"

"Why, Colonel, suh, I'd fly anywhere for you-all."

"Good. You know where La Marsa is?"

"Isn't that just a bit south of Birmingham, suh?"

"Nooo. I'd say a bit east, maybe about two thousand miles. You ever heard of North Africa, Harry?"

Harry's eyes bugged out and his drawl turned into a Cheshire cat smile. "Yes, suh, Colonel, suh! When do I take off?"

"Soon as we can put the strip camera in your plane."

Harry made the long flight to La Marsa in quick time. But quick as he made it, word of his coming and its purpose got there before him. His official orders read that he was to report to Colonel Roosevelt, but Elliott unfortunately had returned temporarily to the U.S. Instead Harry reported to the number two man of the third photo group; he presented a letter to him that I had written asking that he be permitted to test the camera over enemy lines.

Harry sent back the following message: "When I reported to the colonel in charge, he seemed to have some knowledge of my temporary duty order and its purpose. Also he was familiar with the continuous strip camera; familiar enough to decide there was no need for it there. There was, however, much need for the airplane I had brought it over in, and the strip camera came out in a hurry."

Although Harry managed to fly reconnaissance missions before he returned six months later, the strip camera was not granted the same opportunity.

However, opportunity did come knocking from another direction when a *Life* magazine editor and photographer visited our laboratory. They photographed and took notes on a number of our new photographic developments which were not in the classified category. Naturally one of these was the strip camera.

When the story came out in May 1943, *Life* made it a feature, covering nine pages, filled with black and white and color photographs, and a text which read in part:

> The Army Air Force for years has been testing the techniques of air photography as carefully as it tests airplanes and guns. It has developed extraordinary equipment which has made the Army's eyes sharper and surer than they have been before. Its latest photographic device is the shutterless continuous strip camera. Used on low-flying high speed planes, it takes not a series of snaps but one long, uninterrupted flow of pictures.

In the article the strip camera received the major coverage, and it was like waving a red flag in the face of young Colonel Nemesis (recently promoted) and his staff officers.

He indicated his displeasure by writing a scorching letter to Major General Charles E. Branshaw, the commanding officer at Wright Field. In it he maintained that the article and others like it were "misleading to say the least" and that "to prevent further dissemination of such misinformation" all information dealing with photography was to be cleared through his office.

Charlie Branshaw fired back a swift reply, the meat of which stated "this office has no intention of acceding to the request of the Director of Photography."

It had now been nearly two years since the angry young

man had begun his attempt to chop me down, and finally suddenly, without word or warning, he succeeded.

At work in the laboratory one fine spring day I received a call to report to the CO. Charlie Branshaw and I had been at Chanute together and we were old flying friends. When I entered his office I had only to take one glance at his face to know that something was unhitched.

"Well, goddamit," he swore, throwing an official order down on his desk, "I hate like hell to tell you this, George, but it looks like you've joined the crowd in Arnold's doghouse. You're being relieved of your command immediately."

News like that takes a while to set in. "Why? What's the reason?"

"Apparently you've been judged incompetent."

"I'll call the Inspector General." I rasped, "I'll get him to make an investigation!"

Charlie gave a sad sigh. "You can, George, of course. But this comes from the Chief of the Army Air Forces. I don't think it would help."

"Where am I being sent to?"

"It doesn't say, just that you're to await orders."

"Well, in the meantime, I want to apply for leave. There are some people I want to see."

"Right. Take thirty days. God, I'm sorry, George. I wish there was something I could do."

"I know . . . and thanks, Charlie."

I took the train that night for Washington. In a daze, I couldn't help but reflect that my career in aerial photography had started on a train and now it appeared ended. All the years . . . the world had been young and gay then. Now I was past fifty and my spirits were at low ebb. Others I had noted were as stunned by the news as I, particularly at the lab where we were deeply involved in so many programs. Generals Echols and Carroll had been furious and supported the idea of calling for the Inspector General, saying they would be glad to testify on my behalf. But the problem was, I really didn't know why I had been thrown out. I hoped to learn the reason in Washington and to have a chance to face Hap Arnold. I did not succeed in either aim and it was not until years later that I learned it had been a complaint submitted by the Corps of Engineers on my *failure to take the proper attitude toward aerial mapping!* which the young man had used as the weapon to shoot me down.

Upon my arrival in Washington I went first to see a high ranking friend in Personnel. He was anything but sanguine about my problem.

"The word's going around, George, that they were looking for an island to send you to in the Pacific without any palm trees."

"Were?"

"Yeah. The CO of the Fourteenth Air Force in Hawaii sent word back he had no islands with or without palms for a man as qualified as you. Too bad your friends aren't closer to home."

"If I could only get to see Arnold."

"Well, take it from me, you can't. Your name's a dirty word around here."

"Okay, then I shall request an official investigation."

"George, believe me, the cards are stacked against you. Don't do it."

"Well what the hell would you suggest, that I quit?"

"No, I've got a much better idea. Why don't you sneak down to see Billy Streett. He's an old buddy of yours and he's in command of the Third Air Force. I am sure he can use you when it comes to reconnaissance."

"Say, that's not a bad idea," I agreed.

"Just don't make any noise about it."

I hadn't seen Billy in a long time. He was a major general, and although his hair was a bit grayer, his eyes hadn't lost their sparkle, and he was glad to see me.

When I told him the news he said, "George, you need some action anyway. I'll fix you up with a helluva good job. I'll make you my Chief of Reconnaissance. You'll organize all the training for my recce squadrons, how's that sound?"

It sounded better. It helped to coat the ball of lead in my stomach, but I was still finding it difficult to believe that I had been kicked out.

So were others. The Dayton *Herald* in an editorial titled *SOMEONE HAS BLUNDERED* said in part:

To take the most charitable view of the transfer of Colonel George W. Goddard, one of the most brilliant research men to ever work at Wright Field, the switch is one of the most inept blunders on the part of Washington Army (authorities) which has yet come out of the present War Department Administration.

That such a man, acknowledged by photographic experts throughout the world to be an outstanding and tireless worker in a field in which he has specialized for 25 years, should be jerked out of his present post . . . is grossly unfair to the man himself and a serious blow to the nation's war effort.

Many letters were to follow and one from Dr. Mees at Eastman Kodak declared my removal "represents a disaster for military aerial photography."

He who had seen to my removal, having stuck the knife in deep, was determined to twist it. Somehow the word slipped out that I had been given a job by Billy Streett, and just two days later the young lieutenant colonel himself came winging into Tampa.

"I'm down here," he told Billy, "to inform you that Colonel Goddard will have absolutely nothing whatever to do with aerial photography . . . in case you're thinking of setting up a job for him. This order from headquarters is to be carried out in the strictest sense of the word."

Billy was both angry and sad when he gave me the bad news; angry that he hadn't been able to throw the message bringer out on his tail skid and sad that he had to tell me, "I'm going to send you up to Morris Field at Charlotte, North Carolina. That's our training headquarters. You're to report to Colonel Gates there as his executive. It's only a housekeeping job, George."

"However," said Streett, "before you report, I think you should continue your leave."

This I did and I went to New York City to spend some time with my bride-to-be. Friends in New York had introduced me to Elizabeth Hayes. She had been in on the beginnings of the restoration of Colonial Williamsburg, Virginia, as secretary to Dr. Goodwin, the "father" of the restoration. When we met in New York at Christmastime 1942 she was finishing her second year helping Mrs. Vincent Astor (the 1st), as secretary and as liaison with her Musicians Emergency Fund.

We decided there was no time like the present and scheduled our wedding for May 8th in Scarsdale. It was a beautiful home wedding attended by our closest friends. Out of the darkness the future began to brighten. We spent our honeymoon driving to Morris Field, Charlotte, North Carolina.

Bill had not exaggerated, it was a housekeeping job, but one for which a special campaign ribbon should have been struck; the kind of duty only a man with the highest technical abilities was qualified to undertake. From the depths of my despair it was to become my finest hour.

It didn't take long to convince me that Colonel Gates was suffering from battle fatigue. Florid and perspiring he paced his office with all the cunning of a Mack truck. "It's serious, damned serious, Colonel. I want you to know that. We are in a most difficult position." He stopped before a big wall map of the city of Charlotte and glared at it like any good strategist would do before launching a maximum effort. "We must attack! We must!"

"You're sure it's that bad, Colonel?" I asked.

"Bad, man! Bad!" He shook the official documents clutched in his hand. "Direct from the War Department, an in-depth study. This base, Colonel," he proclaimed, "has the highest venereal disease rate in the entire U. S. Army! . . . Perhaps the Navy and the Marines as well, although it doesn't say."

"Well, it's a distinction of some kind," I sighed.

"I want you to put a stop to it!" He thrust his finger out

boldly. "I'm assigning you full command. You're to attack it head on and wipe it out!" The papers in his fist became a sword as he raised his arm skyward. "Wipe it out!" he repeated.

And so on the express orders of Colonel Gates, I girded up my loins, polished my eagles and went forth to war . . . against VD. My only weapon at the start was the strip camera, which had departed Wright Field in my company.

Underlying everything, I suspected that it was the strip camera which might have gotten me fired, and underlying everything I knew that somehow somewhere I was going to put it in someone's hands who would see its worth. At the time, although its name might sound like it had some connection with the wily foe I was about to face, I was reconciled to the fact that it would be of no use in the highly technological encounter confronting me.

Looking at the problem vertically or obliquely, with or without shutters, I decided that my strategy must be based on a sound program of research and development, with which I had had some small experience.

I began my research with a visit to the city fathers.

"Waal, General," one of the fathers philosophized, "all I can say is that boys will be boys especially where you have these large labor battalions and there ain't a helluva lot you-all can do about it . . . unless you want to lock them up every night."

"I came to get your cooperation in—"

"You mean you want us to lock 'em up!"

The mayor broke in over the laughter. "Now see here, the colonel is asking for our help, and I don't see anything to joke about. We're all in this war together. What do you suggest, Colonel?"

With the aid of the mayor, the chief of police and other patriotic officials, research indicated there were two major points of contact where our troops were falling into the pitfalls of sin—in the hotels and in a large cemetery located in the center of Charlotte. This called for swift action along the entire developmental front. Signs went up in all the city's hotels reading:

ANY MAN IN UNIFORM CAUGHT TAKING A GIRL TO HIS ROOM WILL BE COURT-MARTIALED." I called upon the MPs to do the catching. As for the happy time cemetery, I had bright lights strung around and through it, so that at midnight, it looked like midday, and that cleared the ground of all but those who were there legally. As a mopping-up operation, I began establishing prophylactic stations in strategic spots such as the basement of the old Baptist church, the minister only too happy to contribute to my war effort.

I reported to Colonel Gates that I felt the tide of battle had been turned, and it would not be very long before we lost our dubious distinction.

Alas, it was not so! If anything the VD rate rose even higher, and the old Baptist church remained empty except for Sundays. And then when it appeared that all was lost, that I had been badly defeated in my first tactical campaign, research charged up and won the war. I learned that through a military stroke of wisdom an order had been issued in days past which said that any man caught in the clutch of a venereal disease would not be permitted to serve overseas for the glory and honor of his country.

It was the kind of order that quickly made men out of boys, and I just as quickly revised it to read that any man now possessing or acquiring VD would *immediately be sent* overseas. This stroke of penmanship had three sudden effects. It swelled the ranks of our forces going overseas; it made the basement of the Baptist church look like Macy's basement on bargain day, and the VD rate at Morris Field plummeted like the October '29 stock market.

Colonel Gates was proud of me, a good many of his men wanted to shoot me, and I was very anxious to be about my chosen business.

After my departure from Wright Field, high-ranking officials in and out of uniform had been working on my behalf to get me reinstated in some phase of aerial photography. I had not dissuaded them, and I had supplied some with background material on my past record. I felt down, but not out and the encouraging letters I received from so many helped to keep my spirits alive.

The sun finally broke through the grayness in October 1943, and there was a wonderful touch of irony in it. Hal Roach of Hollywood fame, whom I had brought into my laboratory, along with Gail Borden and Merrill Meigs who was chief of Aircraft Production and others, convinced Secretary of the Navy Frank Knox that if the Air Corps couldn't use me the Navy certainly could. Orders were swiftly issued, and I went north to join the Naval Photographic laboratory at Bolling Field singing "Anchors Away" all the way.

Throughout the years I had kept in close contact with my opposite numbers in Naval aerial reconnaissance, and despite the intense rivalry between the two services, my relationships had been based on mutual respect and cooperation. Thus when I arrived at Bolling I did not come as a stranger, and I was received in a very friendly manner. Captains Larry Pope and Bob Quackenbush welcomed me aboard. My basic job was to advise the Navy on the selection of aerial equipment and new techniques.

Commander Thorne Donnelley was director of the Naval photographic laboratory at Bolling, and I quickly brought forth my strip camera and gave him a thorough briefing. At once he grasped the potential. "My God, Colonel, if that camera does what you say, we could determine the depth of water along invasion beaches before the landing force goes in."

"Also the height of obstacles on the beaches . . . tide levels and beach gradients," I added.

"We've got to give this thing a test, like yesterday!"

"Now you're talking my language, Commander. I don't know why I didn't join the Navy in the first place," I grinned.

"You're a little late, Colonel, but we're glad to have you."

Through Admiral DeWitt C. Ramsey, Chief of the Naval Bureau of Aeronautics, tests of the strip camera were immediately authorized. Over the next few months, operating out of

Palm Beach in a Lockheed Hudson, we put the strip camera through its paces, and it lived up to all I wagered on it. The Navy was excited by this new rapid method of making water-depth measurements. Its potential in the Pacific was tremendous, for the Japs had never permitted any peacetime mapping of their islands. With the strip camera our attacking forces would not only know the best location to come in with landing barges, but also what to anticipate once on the beach.

When the tests were completed, and we did many in stereo color, Thorne Donnelley and I were called to Admiral Ramsey's office to exhibit our results. Directly after the exhibit the Navy ordered a hundred of the cameras, on a top priority basis. This order established the Chicago Aerial Survey Company as a prime manufacturer of aerial cameras. It also established me as a fair-haired boy with the Navy. As an indication of his appreciation, Admiral Ramsey invited me to take his ticket to attend a gala celebration of the 40th anniversary of powered flight. The affair took place at the Statler-Hilton Hotel in Washington, and I found myself at a table reserved for top Navy brass. Seated above us on the speaker's rostrum were such luminaries as Orville Wright, Henry Ford . . . and Hap Arnold.

Hap was engaged in an animated smiling conversation with Orville when his wandering eye must have caught a touch of olive drab surrounded by blue. Never had I witnessed a more thunderous double-take. The eyes went wide; the smile congealed and fell off; the mouth snapped shut. I could read his dumfounded thoughts: "What's that goddam Goddard doing here with the Navy!"

I smiled and gave a little wave. The greeting was not returned.

Directly after the celebration, I decided something had to be done to break the log jam that had prevented my own service from having the benefit of the strip camera. Navy acceptance had done much to restore my confidence and my equilibrium. I was not about to let one misguided young fool destroy me or prevent the use of equipment which if given a fair test would be as readily wanted by the Air Force as the Navy. I decided to storm the Pentagon and find someone of high enough rank and intelligence to at least look at the Navy test reports and film samples.

Walking down one of the Pentagon's lost corridors, I found Brigadier General Hoyt S. Vandenberg, and I couldn't have found a better man. We had gotten to know each other some years past when he was a pursuit pilot at Selfridge Field and I had been making color shots of fighter planes flying in formation.

Now he invited me into his office. When he saw what I had, he said, "This is important, George. Let's go see Arnold and straighten this thing out."

"No, I'm afraid he wouldn't listen, Hoyt. He's really been soured on me, and I understand the word is around that I'm a nut."

"Yeah, just the kind we can use. I've got an idea." He picked up the phone.

A few minutes later I was explaining the strip camera and the resultant tests to the Assistant Secretary of War for Air, Robert A. Lovett.

Mr. Lovett was not amused by my explanation of why I was working for the Navy, but he was immediately excited by the underwater test data I presented him. "We need this kind of camera for amphibious landings in every theater of operations . . . Goddard, how many do you think we should buy for the Air Force?"

"At least two hundred, sir."

He picked up the phone and a few moments later my old friend Major General Oliver P. Echols, Chief of Air Force Matériel in the Pentagon, entered.

Oliver grinned while the Assistant Secretary explained that he wanted the strip camera purchased at once by letter of intent. Then he thanked General Vandenburg and me for bringing the matter to his attention.

I picked up my test material and started across the room, walking on air. As I reached the door he said, "Where are you going, Colonel?"

"Why, back to the Navy, sir."

"You're doing nothing of the sort. I want you to go home and pack your bags. I'll have an airplane at National tonight at ten o'clock to pick you up. You're flying to England. Come back here in half an hour so I can give you a letter I want you to personally deliver to Elliott Roosevelt."

I left the Pentagon, knowing the Goddard luck was still in pretty good shape. The Navy was sorry to see me go and Admiral Ramsey had in fact asked that I be continued in my liaison capacity under his command. Later he sent a letter of commendation on my behalf to the Commanding General, Army Air Forces.[1]

One other was sorry to see me go, and that was my bride of nine months. I flew away knowing the ache of leaving a loved one behind.

[1] NAVY DEPARTMENT
BUREAU OF AERONAUTICS
WASHINGTON 25, D.C.

26 June 1944

From:      Chief, BuAer.
To:        Commanding General, Army Air Forces.
Subject:   Colonel George W. Goddard, Air Corps,
           Performance of Duty from 1 November 1943 to
           31 January 1944.

1. During the period that Colonel George W. Goddard, USAAF, served in this bureau 1 November 1943 to 31 January 1944, he provided many services which heretofore were difficult to obtain. Colonel Goddard was very enthusiastic in his work, which facilitated the cooperation required from the many agencies which he was required to contact. His close relationship with the Army provided the Bureau of Aeronautics with much-needed information.

2. Colonel Goddard's pleasing personality and cooperative manner have added to the relationship between this office and the Army Air Forces. He is considered unusually well qualified for any assignment in photography.

D. C. RAMSEY
Rear Admiral, U.S.N.
Chief of the Bureau of Aeronautics

## 21

It was February 1, 1944, when I reported to Elliott Roosevelt at his headquarters at Widewing. I had last seen him during the summer. Thus, on the basis of past association he had been one of those I had sought out in the hope of getting official assistance. He had been courteous but cool, and I later learned from him that at the time he had bought the "Goddard is nuts" theme. Moreover, he was deeply involved in fighting for the production of aircraft especially designed for photoreconnaissance. It was a long hard fight, and even as the son of the President he did not seem to be making any more headway than I had when I had fought the same battle.

When I walked into his office near Hampton Court he was, of course, surprised to see me. He read the letter I brought from the Assistant Secretary and then looked up frowning. "George," he said bluntly, "I wish you'd stop trying to sell this thing. Our people over here have no use for it."

"How can they know how much use they have for it when they've never had a chance to try it?" I was tired. I had been buoyed up, and now the old cold water was hitting me in the face again.

"I've heard a helluva lot about it," he snapped. "A pilot would have to fly so low he'd be mincemeat."

"Well, I'd sure like to have you give it one test."

"I leave these things to my pilots, and they just don't go for the idea."

"I'm glad the Navy doesn't feel that way." I was fed up,

and I began shoving the test results he hadn't bothered to look at back in my briefcase.

"Well now, just don't get yourself in an uproar, George," he smiled, but I was having none of it. I picked up my playthings and headed for the door.

"Hey, where are you going! Come back here," he called.

"I'm going back to the States," I said. "There's no point in my staying."

"Like hell there isn't. I need someone who knows his business, and with all your experience, you're the man. I've got a couple of top priority modification jobs for the Eighth Air Force. Will you take them?"

He was smiling, and I stood at the door not smiling back. It was on the tip of my tongue to say, "no thanks," but calmer judgment prevailed. His offer was for a job in aerial photography; it was far from the iron hand in Washington, and I did have the strip camera with me. Certainly the last in itself presented a possible opportunity. I nodded my acceptance to the offer.

The two modification programs were to be run simultaneously. One was located at Alconbury in north central England, and the other at Langford Lodge, the Lockheed Aircraft Modification Center, near Belfast, Ireland. The job at Alconbury entailed the modification of eight British Mosquito aircraft, equipping them with radar cameras. The project in Ireland required the installation of night photographic equipment in twelve mosquitoes. I began shuttling back and forth between the two points, overseeing the work and getting myself some much desired flying time in assorted aircraft.

And then lady luck in the guise of the RAF smiled again. I didn't go anywhere without my strip camera. I cuddled up to it every day and tucked it away in the hotel closet at night. On such a night I attended an RAF function and there met Air Commodore Bennett. A pilot who had also served in the First World War, he was intensely interested in reconnaissance. When I told him about the Navy tests of the strip camera he

Berlin, May 1945. The Reich Chancellery under which Hitler's bunker was located. *George W. Goddard*

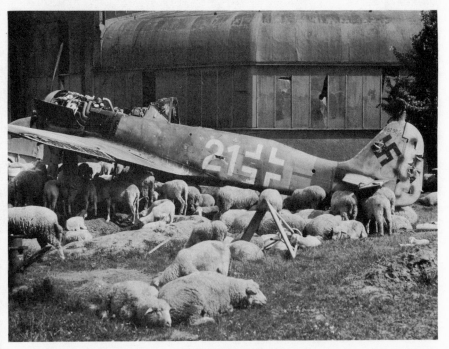

"Sheep may safely graze." Peace comes to Europe, May 1945. *George W. Goddard*

I met my daughter Diane for the first time. August 1945.

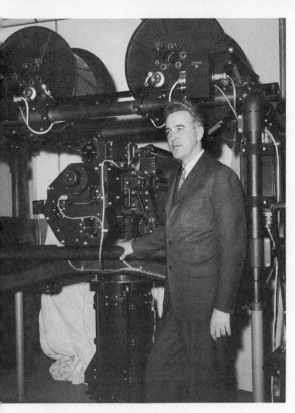

Dr. James Baker with experimental long range, high altitude camera, Harvard University. 1945. *Fred Wittner*

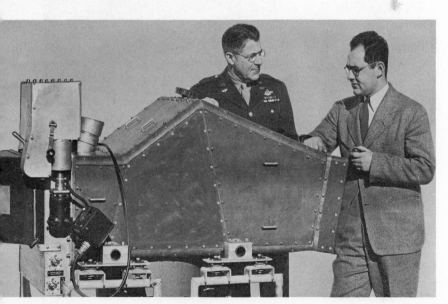

Dr. Duncan Macdonald and I strike a pose before the first camera with a 100 inch lens. 1947. *U.S. Air Force*

Installing stereo strip camera in nose of Lockheed P-80 for mission over Korea, August 1950. *U.S. Air Force*

"Dicing" shot of tanks along Korean road. *U.S. Air Force*.

asked if I would be willing to give a blackboard briefing to some top RAF reconnaissance staff officers.

The next day I flew with Commodore Bennett to the RAF photo reconnaissance center at Benson, and there I showed a group of some thirty officers the strip camera and the Navy test results. This was the first collective group of officers to whom I spoke on the subject who didn't have their fingers in their ears.

Since the camera operated best in super-speed aircraft, they wanted to test it in their latest and hottest fighter, the Typhoon. I helped them to install it at Farnborough and off went the pilot to fly several runs along the beaches of France, Belgium, and Holland. The results had them doing cartwheels.

"I say, how can we get some of these soonest, George old boy?" Commodore Bennett asked.

"I'm afraid, Commodore, it won't be soon," I said explaining why. "But I'll tell you what you can do. You can modify your F-52 so it has the moving film feature of the strip camera."

"You don't say! Well, how do we do that?"

"It won't be difficult. It's only a matter of an extra electric motor. I'll show your people how to rig it."

My assistance to the RAF was all carried out on the q.t., and they set to work to modify their F-52, making me feel that half a strip camera was better than none at all.

Meanwhile my work went on at Alconbury and in Ireland. At Alconbury we ran into tragedy. The first three planes to make tests using radar reconnaissance equipment were lost with their crews. The first two disappeared over Holland without trace and so the third test was conducted over Alconbury. A chase plane saw it blow up. Exhaustive ground tests showed that gasoline fumes from the wing tanks leaked back into the fuselage and when the radar electronic gear was turned on a spark did the rest. The danger was quickly remedied and Mosquitoes taking high-altitude radar pictures went into operation. They were the first radar reconnaissance pictures ever taken in war using an aerial camera expressly designed for that purpose.

When our first night photo Mosquito was ready for test at the Irish depot, Elliott Roosevelt invited me to fly with him to witness it. Climbing on board his B-25 the next morning I was amazed to see him sitting in the pilot's seat. He wore no wings, and I had never known he could fly. I wondered if he thought he was going to do so on the basis of being the President's son, but lo and behold, he fired up the engines like an old pro, taxied out to take-off. By the time we were airborne in one piece I began to relax.

The flight to Langford Lodge was smooth and uneventful, and Elliott made a nice landing. We watched the tests and then climbed back on board the B-25 for the return flight to London. It suddenly dawned on me that the aircraft had no life preservers or a raft, and we had a fair patch of water to cross.

As we were approaching the Isle of Man, I noticed a piece of metal cowling flapping in the breeze on top of the left engine and oil spewing out of it. I quickly went forward to the step behind the cockpit and called to Elliott: "You've got something wrong with your left engine!"

After a moment of glancing out at the engine and studying the instrument panel he called back, "Everything's okay from up here."

"You can't see it from where you're sitting, but you're losing oil. She's thrown a rod or something!" I insisted.

"No sweat, George. Relax, I'll get you to London."

I went back and had another look at the engine, and I figured it was the wrong time of year for swimming. We were just leaving the Isle of Man when I tapped Elliott on the shoulder and said, "Listen, I'm the command pilot on this plane, and I want to get on the ground and see what the trouble is right now!"

He didn't say anything but wracked the plane up in a tight turn and down we went to land at the Royal Navy Field near the town of Douglas.

We had no sooner touched the ground when the left engine let go with a bang. Elliott shut it down and we taxied in with a feathered prop. When he got down out of the plane, he was grinning from ear to ear. He thrust his hand out and said, "Well, George old boy, now I know why you've lived so long in the aviation business."

"When I see oil running where it shouldn't, I know enough to run, too," I replied.

That night the pub in Douglas rocked to our happy landing and the fact that the son of the President of the United States was standing drinks at the bar.

A few days after our impromptu visit to the Isle of Man, I received preemptory orders to report on the double to Colonel Roosevelt "in my office at 0900 tomorrow."

That old sinking feeling hit me again, and I thought, "Oh Lord, now I'm in his doghouse." The next morning I went down from Alconbury to London cloaked in an air of awful expectancy.

When I walked into his office, Elliott stood up scowling at me. Then his face lit up with a grin. "George," he said, "I want to shake your hand! And I want to take back everything I ever said about your strip camera." We shook hands and he laughed at the expression on my face. "Thought you'd pulled a fast one, hey? The 8th Air Force photo interpreters called and wanted to know why the latest RAF pictures were so much sharper than ours. Well, I found out why. All the work of a stubborn character who wouldn't quit. George, those are the best goddam pictures I've ever seen. I want to apologize for listening to the wrong people for so long, and I want you to get cracking on modifying our equipment with the moving film feature from that camera."

My smile reached around the back of my neck. "Those are the kind of words a man likes to hear," I said.

"I want a crash program. Start with the night cameras. Get the people you need to make it go. Things are in the wind, and what you've got is of tremendous importance to the whole works."

"Thanks, Elliott," I said . . . "for seeing the light."

"Don't thank me. I think you've done a great thing. I only wish I could do something to repay you for all you've been through to make your point."

Maybe I'd dreamt about somebody saying something like that to me because I didn't hesitate. "Do you really mean that?" I shot back.

"I surely do. Name it."

"I told you in Washington who was behind all my trouble. He's been a roadblock to progress for a long time. How about booting his fanny out to the Pacific?"

"You know," Elliott rubbed his chin thoughtfully, "you're absolutely right. He's a lousy director of aerial photography. He's not only snafued the war effort on the strip camera, he's failed me, too, a number of times. Where shall we send him?"

"Let's get out a map."

That night a courier took Elliott's letter to Washington, and a short while later, amidst a great gnashing of teeth and caterwauling in high places—but not high enough—young Colonel Nemesis, in a state of profound shock, was on his way to a post in India. The word trickled over that had he remained in Washington a few more weeks, he would have been promoted to brigadier general. As it was he remained in India for the duration.

Later I learned it had not been Elliott's letter alone that had brought the sudden fall of the young man, but also a complaint to the Chief of Air Force by the Corps of Engineers, the very service that he, no doubt, had used to discredit me. The irony had gone full circle, but perhaps the object lesson in this unnecessary game of dirty poker was that all unknowingly the young man's actions against me had in the long run been to my benefit. They had enabled me to work with the Navy; they had brought me back to a major theater of operations where I was dealing with combat problems; they had permitted me to cooperate with the RAF, and finally they had given me favorable recognition with tactical commanders. Had I remained at Wright Field, I would have continued in R&D but my breadth of experience would have been restricted and quite possibly I never would have been able to sell the strip camera and other reconnaissance developments, and it is a certainty that I would never have been able to win the Battle of Charlotte, North Carolina!

With my morale at peak altitude I made a hurried trip to the Air Force Modification Base at Warton, Lancashire to supervise the design and modification of a number of film magazines used with the Standard Fairchild Cameras, to incorporate the moving film feature similar to that used in the strip camera. Working around the clock with experienced instrument designers and machinists, we had a production line turning out moving film magazines within a two week period. Elliott Roosevelt used the first ones on his night cameras and quickly recommended the Distinguished Service Medal for me. Not only had the film magazines improved the sharpness of his pictures but they also allowed his pilots to fly at higher altitude out of range of anti-aircraft fire.

With the acceptance of the strip camera and the utilization of its moving film feature by the RAF and the Eighth Air Force, my personal problem appeared to have been resolved. Hap Arnold even broke down and sent me a letter of commendation for my work with the Navy. My old friend, Major General Hugh J. Knerr, Chief of Matériel for General Carl Spaatz, who was Ike's Chief of Staff for Air, put me in charge of all technical matters relating to reconnaissance equipment including aircraft modification.

In this regard, we had found that the nose of the F-5 was weakened when the gun installations were removed and the attendant vibration in it affected our photography. The new nose we built was more rigid and big enough to accommodate an extra crew member. We nicknamed the plane the "droop snoot." I was so pleased with it I wired Wright Field to send out Jim Baker's just completed 60-inch focal length camera. Wright Field maintained the camera would never fit, exactly as it had maintained the twin 40-inch Bausch & Lomb would never fit in a P-51, which it did with a bit of ingenuity.

The Baker 60-inch was shaped in the form of a U, and it went into the nose of the droop snoot perfectly with the aid of a shoe horn or two. On its first test, large scale pictures from thirty thousand feet showed remarkable detail, as clear as exposures made with our best cameras at a fraction of the altitude. Of even greater and more far reaching importance, Jim Baker's lens was the first to provide automatic facilities to compensate for changes in air temperature and pressures. This was the breakthrough I had been seeking when I had first described it to Jim on Harvard's Observatory Hill in 1941. The success of the 60-inch camera encouraged Baker and his cohorts to go on to a 100-inch and finally a 240-inch lens. To the recce pilot the greater the altitude the greater safety. To the photo interpreter it means a larger scale picture to study with no loss of critical detail. The 60-inch camera went into operation over enemy territory immediately.

In that swift moving spring of 1944 one could feel the quickening tempo of activity heading toward a day of climax we did not know, but whose development we could clearly perceive. The 9th Air Force[1] had been relocated in England and the reconnaissance pilots were flying thousands of sorties, photographing every square inch of French, Belgian, and Dutch coastal areas ranging far inland as well, getting exposures of everything that was to be hit before D-Day.

[1] Late in 1942 the Middle East Air Force was redesignated the 9th Air Force under the command of Major General L. H. Brereton. The Photographic reconnaissance operations of the 9th Air Force were directed by Colonel James G. Hall, a capable Air Force pilot from Texas who had been a World War I pilot in France with the French and American Air Service. When General Brereton started to build up his photographic reconnaissance groups he arranged to transfer Hall to his headquarters, promoted him from major to colonel and appointed him director of photo reconnaissance. Early in 1944 Colonel Hall was supplied with several newly organized aerial photographic units from the States which he formed into reconnaissance groups that were stationed at special flying fields in the central part of England.

Lieutenant Colonel Richard Leghorn, who had left Kodak in 1941 to work in my photo laboratory at Wright Field, was given command of the

Early that spring our Intelligence Staff realized the great importance of night aerial photography because it was noted that the Germans, fearing our vast number of fighter bombers, were constructing their fortifications, planting their mine fields and moving their troops, supplies and equipment under cover of darkness. Lieutenant Colonel Joe Gillespie's 155th Fighter Squadron was immediately converted to a night photographic organization to specialize in low altitude operations, generally at from 500 to 1000 feet, using the D-2 electric strobe flash equipment invented by Dr. Harold Edgerton and his group at MIT. Four A-20 airplanes were assigned for this installation and eight A-20s were assigned to photograph at altitudes up to 10,000 feet using the maximum size M-46 flash powder bombs.

Dr. Edgerton, whom I had baited with $25,000 at MIT in 1939, to design and develop the first aerial strobe system, was dispatched to the 155th Squadron located at the Chalgrove Air Base, north of London. His assignment was to install the latest D-2 strobe units in the four A-20 aircraft and to train the personnel in its operation and maintenance. Assignments of this nature were nothing new to "Doc," for since the start of the War he had equipped many U. S. Navy planes with his strobe systems. He had also equipped many U. S. Air Force planes during the African and Italian campaigns.

Doc Edgerton arrived at Chalgrove to find the Air Base so crowded that he could not find office space for his technicians and himself. He was a great improviser so instead of beefing to the Commanding Officer, he immediately went to the base dump and secured a number of large wooden airplane and glider crates. In

---

67th reconnaissance group. He was to meet the reconnaissance needs of General Pete Quesada, IX Tactical Air Command, and General Hodges' First Army.

Lieutenant Colonel Bert Smiley was made commander of the 26th reconnaissance group to serve Brigadier General Nugent's XXIX Tactical Air Command and the 9th Army. Lieutenant Colonel Russell Berg was given command of the 5th Reconnaissance Group work with Major General Otto P. Weyland's XIX Tactical Air Command and General George S. Patton's Third Army. Lieutenant Colonel Joe Gillespie was placed in command of the 155th night photo recce Squadron to work directly with Headquarters.

a few days he and his men were sitting in a comfortably equipped office containing stoves, desks, chairs, filing cases, and a nanny! This was typical of the Doctor for he was a man of action and always got the job done with distinction.

The men at Chalgrove marveled at his unbounding energy as they saw him in coveralls climbing in and out of airplanes and dashing to his machineshop and about the field on personnel training schedules.

In the training of the plane crews "Doc" and Lieutenant Colonel Gillespie were particularly concerned with pinpointing targets. At 600 to 1000 feet altitude the individual photographs covered a small area and in the blackness of night it was a big problem to navigate over England, across the English Channel, directly on for several miles into France, and then directly over the center of the target area which might not be more than 800 by 1000 feet. This problem of navigation had been bugging the RAF for several years, and they had finally been successful in developing the "Gee Navigational System." This system utilized chains of three ground stations, radiating high frequency radio pulses and were received on a Cathode-Ray indicator.

To further assist the pilots with their navigation "Doc" ingeniously installed a D-2 strobe unit on a tower at Chalgrove, pointing it toward the Channel, so that they could home on it to the Air Base. Today every important landing field uses rows of electric strobe units to guide pilots on to the runways in bad weather.

In a short time the 155th Squadron was doing an excellent job with this strobe equipment and cameras equipped with moving film magazines. However, they were not so successful with their high altitude flash bomb equipment. The M-46 bombs were not producing sufficient illumination, so an S.O.S. was radioed to the States requesting immediate assignment of a trouble shooter. On short notice Lieutenant Colonel Richard Philbrick reported to the 155th and started immediate investigation. Dick, a Harvard graduate in Astronomy, had completed his pilot's training in the Air Force and had specialized in Aerial Photography where he could work with optics and photography. His last assignment had been as Research and Development Officer in charge of testing equipment which was mainly the night photographic camera, bombs and strobe units. This Base was located at Eglin Field in northwestern Florida.

It did not take Dick Philbrick long to discover the trouble. The Ordnance Corps, without notifying the Air Force, had changed the chemical mixture in the M-46 bombs which were being supplied to the 155th Squadron. Barium nitrate had been substituted for potassium perchlorate which apparently was in short supply. In making the change, the photo-cell shutter tripping device was put out of phase with the peak illumination from the flash bomb. Dick, with the help of his assistant, Captain Joe Condon, readily solved the problem by re-phasing the shutter tripping mechanism. This required many air tests, exploding the flash bombs at the correct moment and position, and perfect timing of the camera shutter.

As had happened to me many times in the States, Dick and Joe occasionally experienced a malfunctioning of their bombs. On one test mission a bomb fell on a British ammunitions dump but luckily did not explode on impact.

Aerial photography was now being conducted on a twenty-four hour basis using every available photographic airplane in England, and many stereoscopic shots of the beaches and their defenses were made. From these photographs exact models were constructed so that our troops could be trained in techniques to capture the real thing.

Reconnaissance can be a two-edge sword, and in that moment of great preparation and high drama, it was used in one of the cleverest ruses of the War—to trick the Germans into believing that the Allied attack would come in the Pas-de-Calais coastal area. For several months the Allied Command had concentrated on convincing the Germans that Calais would be the point of invasion. As a final convincer, on June 5, a German recce pilot was permitted to fly over the harbor of Dover, the natural point of departure for an attack on Calais. Both the RAF and the antiaircraft units were cautioned not to shoot him down. He took some fine pictures of the harbor area teeming with troops, hundreds of imitation rubber tanks, and guns, and, in the adjacent fields, dummy aircraft gliders. Once the German recce pilot flew away, the troops left the area for Portsmouth and thence across the Channel to Normandy. In this case the pictures taken back to Von Rundstedt's headquarters did lie. The rest is history.

On D-day I visited two of our busiest reconnaissance activities and marveled at their tremendous activity. Recce airplanes were landing and taking off continually. The crews were dashing into photographic laboratories with their freshly exposed film magazines, and messengers were rushing to the Intelligence department with armfuls of aerial photographs. Around the clock thousands of photographs were being produced and without a hitch in the entire operation. I found myself wishing that General Arnold could have witnessed this vigorous and effective consummation of our plans. I am sure he would have agreed that our aerial photographic equipment was fully meeting the momentous requirements of D-day!

My own history was nearly terminated prior to the great day by an unexpected German air raid. Dr. "Nobby" Clark of Eastman Kodak had come over on a troubleshooting job, and we were taking our ease in my fifth-story room in the Cumberland Hotel when it sounded like all of London's air-raid sirens had cut loose at once.

Nobby was new to the sound and by the way he stood up suddenly I knew he took it seriously.

Being the hardened veteran, I comforted him, declaring, "Oh, it's just noise, pal. They exercise them every now and then."

He settled back slowly, but I could see he was not completely convinced. "George, what do we do if they do come over?" He asked.

"Ignore them."

"No, I mean if there really is a raid."

Because of the wailing we both had to raise our voices. "Well, the bath tub is the best place. It's almost big enough to swim in and it'll block anything that—"

A thunderous explosion interrupted my explanation. The whole building shook. It was quickly followed by two more detonations louder, closer and with more effect on the premises.

All at once I was running, and I knew I was in a race because Nobby was right beside me as we came down the stretch to the bathroom. I took off at the door and hit the bottom of the tub so hard, it sounded like Big Ben. The sound was snuffed out as completely as my breath as Nobby landed on top of me.

For the next few minutes while the uproar of exploding bombs in Hyde Park rocked the building and shattered the night, a rather poor grade of English was exchanged between us two victims of the storm.

Not until the all clear blew did either of us move from the porcelain safety of the tub, but then Nobby sat up and looking down at my crushed form said with hurt disdain, "Goddard, I thought I was your guest. You're a helluva rude host!"

Later we went out and looked at the damage which was very near and impressive.

I lived through another great day the following month with an historic event of a special kind. On July 27, 1944 I received a cablegram from Walter Reed Army Hospital in Washington telling me that I was the father of a daughter. After all these years I was at last a proud papa! Through an exchange of wires she was named Diane. I pondered on that mystical feeling that makes a man three thousand miles away love a baby he has never seen. I longed to fly home to see her but at that time the best I could do was to hope the end of the war would come soon, and to pay a prompt visit to the PX to start passing out cigars to our recce pilots who celebrated the occasion by smoking them over France and Germany on their daily recce milk runs.

## 22

Eleven months were to elapse between D-day and the German surrender. While the Wehrmacht was slowly crushed by the nutcracker of Allied and Soviet pressure, my job was to see that the reconnaissance equipment in operation was kept that way and given the best possible usage. The history of those eleven bloody months has been described in many dramatic ways, but aerial reconnaissance was the eyes of our ground forces and without it or without the best aerial photographic equipment in the world (which we had also supplied to the Russians, French and other allied Air Forces), or the highly proficient people who took the pictures, processed them and interpreted the results, there is no telling how long the war would have gone on. German missile sites were found by aerial photography as were secret German jet factories. Had the production of both weapons not been badly hurt by allied bombing raids, who can say what would have ensued? Even in our one major military set-back in Europe which culminated in the Battle of the Bulge, reconnaissance had not erred. Ten days before Field Marshal von Rundstedt's all out attack there was aerial photographic evidence of its development. Faulty intelligence and worse weather conspired to make the German advance a temporary success.

In the progression of things, once Paris was liberated I was ordered by General Hugh Knerr, Chief of Matériel, to make headquarters there. Specifically, my job was to study reconnassiance results in Europe and where necessary make modifications in cameras, aircraft, and processing equipment—all in an effort to improve the efficiency of the recce groups. When there were complaints from the field of operations—and there were many—we did all we could to respond. In so doing we were able to parcel out camera production assignments to the French camera industry. To aid and abet me in all my endeavors, I had hangar facilities at Villacoublay Airport, a complement of sixty-eight officers, enlisted men and civilian engineers and two of the best right hands anyone could ask for. They were Major Jo (Josiah) Child whom I finagled from ATC with the aid of Hugh Knerr, and Bill Tate, who left Lockheed in Ireland to join me, thanks to Elliott Roosevelt.

Jo had been a student of architecture at the Sorbonne and knew France and the French like a native. He had cool blue eyes and a cool unruffled manner, possibly a reflection of his Boston Back Bay antecedents. Whenever I presented a problem to him in which a knowledge of French industry, politics, or custom was involved, his response would be, "We can handle it all right." And we did despite the fact that Paris—not to mention France—after four years of Nazi occupation spent the next year doing little more than celebrating its liberation.

Bill Tate, by contrast, was small and dark with a hungry look. There have been notable scroungers in this world, but I'd put Bill up against the lot. He had one cardinal rule—"Never ask me how I get things done." He turned up things like two tons of coal to heat our quarters near the Eiffel Tower when no coal was to be had and tires for a liberated Mercedes Benz when there were none. One day when my old friend Alex Seversky came to my office out of gas and in a frantic hurry to get to an important meeting, Bill quickly fixed him up. This same talent was everywhere apparent in our work, and we accused him of being directly related to Beelzebub. Bill had no comment.

Between Jo and Bill our relationship with the French camera industry was superlative. We could get a production idea at 10 A.M. and two days later a factory would be making deliveries of the finished article. If management and workers were supplied with cigarettes and a Bill Tate truck came from somewhere with a load of cognac, it was Vive l'Americain! Vive la France!

and the wheels of progress rolled. In that period of friendly cooperation, red tape was something with which you decorated the Christmas tree.

As for Christmas, it came early for me in the guise of the first production model of my long-delayed stereo-strip camera from the Chicago Aerial Survey Company. We tenderly installed it in the nose of a P-51 Mustang, and Ham Wilkins, a Lockheed test pilot with a long drawl and no nerves, gave it its Parisian test. He buzzed the Champs Elysées at an altitude that made it necessary for him to pull up to clear the Arc de Triomphe. At 350 miles an hour his progress was as swift as it was startling. Gendarmes hit the deck. Pedestrians scrambled for shelter. On the sidewalk we had placed a copy of the service newspaper *Stars and Stripes*. The film results were as dramatic as the performance. You could read the headlines clearly. The next day we ran a similar test and the next after that and then suddenly headquarters at Saint-Germain became exercised. Fighter planes were ordered over the city in relays, trying to catch our elusive cameraman. But old Ham, flying an unmarked plane managed to escape them on every test. Finally when I saw how upset certain officers were becoming over our daily demonstration of street-level flying, I ordered Ham to desist. Instead, we shifted our tests to the battlefield where hedge-hopping was more in vogue. And then some months later from the battlefield itself, the Navy sent word of the strip camera's success in combat operations. Their confidential report read in part:

> Proved in combat, the low-altitude strip camera is scheduled for an increasingly important role in the Navy's photographic program. The continuous strip camera was first used extensively in the Okinawa invasion where its usefulness in determining underwater depths was a significant factor in confirming the selection of the so-called Hagushi beaches as the landing point. Throughout the ensuing campaign the Chicago Aerial Survey Company produced strip cameras mounted in Navy F6F-5P airplanes, operating from captured Youtan field, provided valuable intelligence photographs for the Tenth Army.

Used at Okinawa—In response to an urgent request for a means of obtaining vital hydrographic data on Okinawan reefs, the Navy dispatched a photographic officer and strip camera equipment from P.S.L. and a photographic interpretation officer from the Photographic Interpretation Command to Oahu. There the installation of the newly developed camera was to accompany the first January carrier strike on Okinawa. From then on, it was a struggle against chance. First the *Hornet* hit Formosa instead of Okinawa. Then when the *Hornet* took part in the second Okinawa strike in January the pilots originally selected to make the strip camera runs had been switched to another assignment for operational reasons. Two other pilots, hastily briefed and sent out to get the photo strips, failed to accomplish their mission.

Meanwhile, as plans for the invasion progressed at headquarters, landing sites were being studied with the aid of high altitude vertical photographs to discover a site long enough to permit the landing of four divisions abreast. As various possibilities were ruled out, the search narrowed to the Hagushi area on the west coast opposite Youtan and Kadena airfields. This location was finally recommended by photo interpreters, but there was still doubt as to the depth and character of the coral reefs. The best pictures available made it only reasonably certain that the landing barges would clear it at high tide. Strip camera photographs alone could eliminate the uncertainty.

The carrier strike in which the *Hornet* participated offered the last chance to obtain such coverage. Only one plane was used. The weather was good, the pilot had been adequately briefed and successful runs were made on the entire assault area, plus Ie Shima and Keise Shima where the Army wanted to land artillery if reef conditions permitted.

Near Disaster—The pictures taken, the pilot brought the plane in for the landing. On the approach, he was waved off and in circling for the second attempt, ran out of fuel. He switched to reserve tank, but it was empty. With the motor cut out, the plane dropped rapidly toward the sea, carrying with it the only strip camera photographs ever made of Okinawa. To the overwhelming relief of the strip-camera-trained photo intelligence officer who stood watching the results of months of preparation heading for the sea, the plane's engine caught hold on the second reserve tanks seconds before hitting the water. The pilot then came in for a safe landing!

From that point on, everything went well. The photographs, which were excellent, were rushed to Guam for interpretation by Interpron Two. Reports confirmed the judgment of interpreters in selecting Hagushi beaches from standard vertical photographs. At H-hour the photo intelligence officer watched the four divisions clear the reefs without trouble.

A short time prior to the Okinawa landing, our forces in Europe began moving into Germany and I received an additional important assignment in connection with the advance. All officers in the Air Force Technical Intelligence Group were issued special blue passes by Supreme Headquarters authorizing the bearer to go anywhere in liberated territory and do anything necessary in pursuit of his duties. In my case as Photographic Disarmament Officer, I was to gather all aerial photographic information, collect new photographic equipment, and to take as prisoners German military and civilian scientists who were in any way connected with photographic research and development. In such pursuits, I began operating between Paris and points ever eastward right behind General George Patton's hard-driving Third Army.

There were two primary areas of German photographic endeavor with which I was most interested—the well-known Schneider optical plant at Bad Kreuznach near Wiesbaden and the world famous Zeiss and Schott plants at Jena. Bill and I entered Bad Kreuznach hard on the heels of the Third Army and were disappointed to find the destruction our soldiers had wrecked inside the plant, the needless damage to machinery and much of the optical equipment.

When I ordered the management of the plant to meet with me, its twenty-five top people did so sullenly and uncooperatively. I put the reality of the situation to them quietly but firmly: "If you cooperate, you'll be treated well enough. If you don't, life will be rougher than it seems right now. There are two things I require. I want to see everything you've managed to hide in the research and development stage, and I want this plant put back in working order. The sooner you do this, the sooner you'll be back in business."

The sound of being back in business instead of the sound of gun fire had a rejuvenating effect upon those Germans. It appeared that business was the only thing that really mattered to them and in the hope of getting back at it again, they cooperated, almost eagerly showing me where they had hidden away their latest photographic secrets. Bill Tate had everything that looked new and promising carted back to Paris and once things were properly organized, the two of us moved on.

We stopped a few hours at the Wiesbaden flying field which had been taken over by the 9th Air Force. I was pleasantly surprised to meet Dick Philbrick and to know he had been made Commander of the newly organized 9th Provisional Recce Group which included the 155th Squadron. He showed me some remarkable night photographs that were made during the Breakthrough of the Bulge. Weather had grounded photographers during the daylight hours but on occasion it cleared around midnight permitting them to drop flash bombs and obtain pictures of great interest to the Intelligence Units.

In Frankfurt, Major General Stafford L. Irwin, commander of Patton's 5th Infantry Division, changed my mode of transportation and nearly got me shot. When he heard I was traveling in a jeep he said, "Goddard, a colonel should be riding in something better than that!" And the next day we were on our way in a large Mercedes Benz.

There is no uglier mark on the land than the mark of war. The scenes I saw in my travels, of gutted cities, of ravaged earth proved the point daily, but nothing could prove it like the sights and scenes of Buchenwald.

I arrived there almost at its liberation, with the first group of U.S. officers and newsmen. What I saw seared itself into my mind. No words could describe it accurately, nor for once could a picture do more than indicate the total horror. Nothing can describe the smell of starvation and death . . . the bodies of starved victims stacked like cordwood on a flat bed truck . . . the dying living with enormous eyes staring up from Hell, their skeletal hands reaching out in disbelief . . . And then from a vantage point of a hill in front of the main entrance, the grotesque and chilling sight of hundreds of figures all dressed in white walking, stumbling across the countryside; ghosts risen from the grave. They were the first wave of prisoners to be released and, stronger than the others, they had broken into a German Army warehouse and had put on the special arctic clothing they found there—white fur hats, coats, gloves. They and others who had the strength, smashed into shops, raided farms, taking horses, oxen, cows, anything that could pull a wagon to get them and their comrades away from the place and back to their homes.

The final touch was when a large group broke into a German Officer's Club in nearby Weimar and raided the wine cellar. Seizing axes they went after the rows and rows of huge wine kegs. They didn't just drink the wine. They waded in it, bathed in it, and went berserk in it, flailing about roaring and screaming. Had they found any Germans that day they would have torn them to bits. Instead, naked, and in drunken fury they attacked one another until enough MPs could be brought in to take control.

That evening as Bill and Jo and I were driving in the Mercedes through a village, I both heard and felt something *swish* past my nose. We ran a string through the two neat bullet holes in the windows, and it showed how close the sniper had come to me. I reported the incident to the MPs who informed me that I was crazy to be driving a German car on the highways. Several other officers hadn't been so lucky doing the same thing. Two days later back in Paris I sadly traded in my bullet-punctured chariot for a specially marked jeep. Also to facilitate our transportation I was assigned a C-47 aircraft which carried a portable ramp, allowing us to park the jeep inside. In this way we were able to fly to various cities and avoid the heavy military ground traffic.

The Yalta agreements of February 1945 designated that Jena in the province of Thuringia, was to be within the Soviet zone of Germany. My job was to get there before the Russians and remove everything of photographic value, including technical people—if they would agree to come.

Neither the Zeiss nor the Schott companies had suffered much bomb damage. This was because U.S. bombers were ordered to stay clear of them and in the one night raid the RAF conducted on the works their aim was faulty and they blew up the city's picturesque beer gardens and not much else.

Bill Tate moved into Jena with the infantry and I followed three days later. We set up offices in the Zeiss plant where I immediately called a meeting, by invitation of the Military Police, of the company's board of directors. There were about twenty of them and when I walked into the room the business manager, who was analogous to the chairman of the board, was seated in his chair at the head of the table. At the foot, a place had been left for me. He was a man in his sixties and I could see that neither he nor any of his fellow officers had come to the realization that they had lost the war.

I decided to inform them. "You move to the other end of the table," I indicated with my finger. "I'll direct this meeting."

Tears began to run down the business manager's cheeks. The others in the room stared at me in cold defiance. The Zeiss Company was more than a century old. Its people had been relatively untouched by the war, its management, research scientist and staff, highly favored. One official had refused to come to the meeting and my first act of business before these assembled was to order Bill Tate: "Find him. Have him thrown in jail."

Then I addressed the group. "In a short while the Russians will be here." I let that sink in. "You cooperate with me and you'll have nothing more to lose. If you don't you'll learn just how badly you lost this war." I've never been one to flaunt my authority but the scenes of Buchenwald were still fresh in my mind.

Having made myself clear, I then outlined our plans for moving the research and development facilities of the plant into the western sector of Germany and all those with their families who would like to continue working for the firm. By the time the meeting ended the gloom had lifted a bit. Fear of the Russians and the opportunity to continue working beyond Soviet clutches had the desired effect on some. Not on others, however, who had carefully hidden the Company's latest trade secrets and were damned if they were going to hand them over.

In his usual fashion Bill Tate smoked them out. One vice-president had buried some important blueprints under a schoolhouse floor. We recovered the documents in front of the man and then let him cool his heels in jail for a few days to reflect on his sins, reminding him that others would not have been so lenient and that he would have been shot for his pains.

In moving people and equipment from Jena to Munich, we used fourteen transport planes, sixty-eight trucks, and two freight trains a week. The operation also included the moving of top technicians as well as manufacturing items from the Schott Glass works, which adjoined Zeiss.

While rummaging around in the Zeiss underground storage tunnels, Bill and I learned of Nazi-Japanese cooperation dating from the mid-thirties when the Company had set up a school to train Japanese Naval officers. Evidence *proved* that Zeiss had actually set the Japanese up in the optical business—a business at which they have come to excel.

As the day of Russian occupation approached more and more of the top personnel of the two plants decided they wanted to go west. I flew one of the principal Zeiss directors to Munich and as we drove through the bomb-ravaged city he began to cry like a baby, sobbing, "Oh, my poor Munich! My poor Munich!"

"Listen," I said, "you ought to see what you people did to London."

The crying stopped immediately. "Like this in London?"

"Worse."

"Humm." The statement dried his tears, seeming to satisfy him.

He, like all the others I met in those days at war's end, was in a state of shock, but his attitude was one of hurt acceptance of something for which he bore no responsibility whatever. At times I found it difficult to remain civil. There was an air of unreality in the entire association. On the one hand in talking to most of the German scientists and managers of optical matters it was as though no war had taken place. They were dedicated to their profession, and they wished to continue working at it, and I could not help being stimulated by their talent and their enthusiasm. On the other hand, their mustached leader had led them on a six-year conquest that had laid waste to much of the world. True they had ground their lenses while others did the killing and blame for war can be cast in more than one direction, but . . . there was Buchenwald.

We were not so successful in moving the glass-making equipment from the Schott works. A great deal of effort went into loading it on a special train, but the Russians got wind of the move and stopped the train near the Czech border. In acquiescence to their demands, the State Department ordered the shipment returned to Jena to await Soviet occupation.

Two hours before the Russians moved in, we pulled out of the city in the chief of police's Mercedes—he didn't want it to fall into Soviet hands. To the last minute we tried to convince scientists and technicians of the two firms to accompany us. In the end, about 140 families from both firms made the move. Those who remained did so because they could not bring themselves to leave their homes and they believed because of their special talents, the Russians would not be too hard on them.

There is a footnote to be added concerning their fate. When the Russians arrived they ordered that the plants be put back in working order, but their treatment of the people was so poor that the workers began sabotaging the operations. In reprisal, the Russians had the entire machinery of both plants freighted to the Soviet Union as well as all the employees. Uprooted from their homes and shipped to an alien land, the Germans dug in their heels and refused to work. Their importance was such that the Soviets couldn't resort to the usual methods of force. Instead, they turned around and shipped the machinery and the whole kit and kaboodle back to Jena, which must have cost them a pretty ruble. The Germans were so glad to get back home they began to cooperate and today no doubt key aerial lens developments for Soviet reconnaissance emanates from the Zeiss and Schott works.

As for those who went west with us, they were first established in a plant near Munich and then later most with their families came to the U.S. continuing their work. Brilliant men, they have contributed much to the optical art.

The practice by U.S. military forces of setting up groups of German scientists to pursue various projects became known to the Soviets. They protested violently, and again the State Department bowed to their wishes and abandoned the idea, although here, too, most of the Germans involved emigrated to the U.S. and continued their work.

The war's end in Europe found me in Paris, and there wasn't any better place to celebrate the occasion, but it was a near thing, for I nearly celebrated it in jail. The day before, I had flown my C-47 to Munich to check on a report that the Germans had hidden away some advanced photo equipment there. Upon landing I switched from the pilot's seat to the driver's seat of my jeep and with four other officers set out for town.

We were sailing along when a siren wailed and an MP's jeep pulled along side. A burly sour-faced major in the right-hand seat, shouted, "Pull over! Get off the road!"

I did so and his driver skidded to a halt in front of us. The major came stomping back, a strong simian cast to his looks and manners.

"Where the hell do you think you're going?" he greeted me.

"To Munich," I replied. "What's the problem?"

"Not in that jeep you're not." He shoved a blunt finger at the offending vehicle. "It's against General Patton's orders for officers to drive jeeps."

I pulled out my blue Supreme Headquarters pass and handed it to him. It stated I was not to be questioned in carrying out my orders. His eyes bugged out as he read the fine print. "You're driving that jeep in strict violation of General Patton's orders," he rasped.

"Doesn't that pass mean anything to you?"

"Doesn't mean a damn thing in General Patton's area."

"Look," I said, realizing there was no reasoning with such a lump of authority. "I'll drive back to the field and get an enlisted driver."

He pondered that peace offering, then scowling, grunted, "Okay, but don't let me catch you again."

Back at the field I acquired the proper driver and then once more we were sailing along until the siren sounded, whereupon we were nearly run off the road.

"You're under arrest!" The major shouted as he came stalking back to us again.

"What the hell are we doing wrong now!" I was fast losing my sunny disposition.

"General Patton's orders are no more than five in a jeep!"

"Well, I happen to be on a job for General Eisenhower and—"

"Those orders don't mean a damn thing! You follow me. I'm taking you to the Summary Court!"

"He's nuts," one of my companions muttered. "Better humor him. We'll get help."

Shortly thereafter I found myself in an empty room in the Court building with a guard on the door so I wouldn't escape. I waited for my friends to take action, wishing that Bill Tate or Jo Child had been along. It was a fine end to the war. George Goddard had finally been taken prisoner by his own side. A number of frustrating hours passed before I spotted an infantry colonel through the open door. I hailed him and quickly explained the problem. He was aghast and at my suggestion quickly put in a call to General Hugh Knerr. Things moved after that. A staff officer arrived from General Patton's headquarters breathless and embarrassed. He was full of apologies from the General, quoting him as saying, "By God, I want that major fixed!" I didn't know whether that meant an execution, but if it did, I was ready to volunteer to carry it out.

A free man once again, I flew back to Paris, and the next day there was dancing in the streets and more champagne than a man could rightly drink . . . although we did our best.

The best celebration of all, of course, was that great day when I returned home to my family. I had been away for more than a year and a half, and I had a most exciting treat in store— meeting my year-old daughter, Diane, for the first time.

Earlier I had bought her an unusual collection of French dolls, intending to send them home via fellow Disarmament Officer and old friend, Colonel Harold Watson. Hal was a superb pilot and had been given the sticky job of flight testing all the latest German jets and anything else the Luftwaffe had that looked new and different. One such aircraft was a huge reconnaissance plane, the only one the Germans had produced. It was so big and unusual Hal planned to fly it across the ocean back to Wright Field where it could be gone over carefully. He agreed to take the dolls as passengers. However it seemed every time he was ready to take off, the big bird developed engine trouble. I became leary of the whole idea and decided I wasn't going to risk my daughter's dolls on such an undependable bird. Old Prince Hal, he just laughed and said, "No sweat, George. I'll get her there in one piece."

And he did, but after he'd landed and they began stripping the monster down, they found the Germans had booby-trapped it. Had it encountered severe turbulence or a bump on landing or take-off, that would have been that. Hal later wrote and said, "I didn't have your dolls on board, but I sure had the good Lord!"

And so in mid-August, 1945, I brought the dolls home myself and like millions of other soldiers came back to my loved ones. My arrival was in the best Air Corps tradition. When I landed at Dayton I had a silver B-24 which was scheduled for a training flight fired up for the last leg of the journey. Elizabeth and Diane had been living in my wife's hometown of Canandaigua, New York. All Canandaigua turned out for that low-level performance as I thundered around the house, dipping my wings in greeting— the soldier home from the wars.

I also returned, restored to glory, to my old job as Director of Aerial Research and Development at Wright Field. Hap Arnold had retired. Toohey Spaatz had taken over as Chief, and Hugh Knerr had written my orders. On top of that I had been awarded the Legion of Merit with Oak Leaf Cluster, several letters of commendation, the French Croix de Guerre and the Distinguished Service Medal. I'd gone away with a cloud over my head. I'd come back with the sun shining brightly.

# PART IV

———◆———

*Bikini Atoll and Beyond*

## 23

At the end of World War I the belief prevailed that there would be no more major wars, and it was no wonder that for a long time funds for military research and development were severely limited. At the end of World War II, in military circles at least, it was recognized we had defeated two enemies only to face the threat of a third. And so I knew I was not returning to preside over the dissolution of the laboratory. Its numbers would shrink, greatly, of course, but there was money and the resolve on the part of people in command to move ahead with aerial reconnaissance for they could foresee its critical role in the tense period ahead.

But if the importance of aerial reconnaissance was seen by some in the War Department, it was not seen by others outside of it, at least in the same context as it had been viewed during the fighting. I found this out with a vengeance when I went over to visit Jim Baker at Harvard.

His progress had been remarkable. With his staff of one hundred scientists and technicians, he had nearly completed the first 100-inch ultra-high precision lens ever to be used in an aerial camera. Baker's machine shop had made the barrel to accommodate the lens, and it was equipped with temperature and pressure compensation features. It was exciting for me to see this wonderfully efficient team operating so smoothly and effectively, and after a thorough review of their work, I paid a call on Dr. Harlow Shapley to discuss the continuance of the operation.

The doctor heard me out and then said, "I'm sorry, Colonel, but I can't go along with you. I want Jim Baker to get back to teaching as soon as he can. As long as there was a war on we were happy to do our part, and in an emergency we will be happy to help you again, but for now I'm afraid we'll have to close up shop."

I sat there stunned. "But Dr. Shapley," I protested. "While Jim has made wonderful progress, there's still so much more to be done! And the world situation is critical."

My arguments failed to register. "Jim Baker's job is teaching, so that we can produce more Jim Bakers. We have so few experts in the field of Astronomy and Optics."

Following this horrendous news, I held a meeting with Jim and his principal assistants in an effort to consider contingency plans, for I was fiercely determined that even without Jim or Harvard, the work must go on. At the meeting I became most impressed with Dr. Duncan Macdonald, a young scientist with a broad background in teaching astronomy and physics. Dunc, short, gregarious and pipe smoking, was also an outstanding administrator, I learned, and since there was no more chance of getting Jim Baker away from Dr. Shapley than there was of turning President Truman into a Republican, I decided that Dunc would be the ideal man to take over the management of the project.

In time through the good offices of Dr. David L. Marsh, president of Boston University, and Dr. Chester M. Alter, dean of the Graduate School, we were successful in making the move from Harvard to Boston University and in doing so, we were able to keep most of the top people with the operation. To further implement the staff, Dunc went to Germany and brought back some of the key German optical people who formerly had been with Zeiss and Schott. However, I realized that a special vote of thanks was due Drs. Marsh and Alter in agreeing to take on the Harvard optical facility. They did so mainly because they saw the need and were willing to assist the government in its fulfillment.

The formal opening of the Boston University optical research laboratory was attended by members of the photographic industry, faculty members and staff officers of the Air Force—including Lieutenant General Curtis E. LeMay, Chief of the Strategic Air Command, Major General Alden R. Crawford, Chief of Research and Development at Wright Field, and Major General Laurence C. Craigie, Chief of Air Force Matériel.

Assigned to deliver the opening address before such a mass of top brass, I could not afford to miss a few punch lines about the financial support required to carry out research on long range optical systems and its strategic requirement in the jet age.

The presence of LeMay, Crawford, and Craigie was without question most opportune for my cause. They got the picture. Afterward I never experienced any trouble in getting their financial support.

There is one simple way the layman can equate the critical importance of the continuance of this project during the decade that followed. Had it ceased with war's end, a U-2 would have been just another aircraft, and today's reconnaissance satellites, empty balls of metal chasing one another around in space.

At the time, one of Duncan Macdonald's first assignments involved the research and development of the largest and most advanced aerial camera ever flown in an airplane. The camera weighed nearly two tons. At thirty thousand feet it could take large detailed pictures one hundred miles distant or more. Its main purpose was for long-distance oblique photography. With jet planes coming into general use and altitudes of 100,000 feet predicted, our thinking was projected toward the development of lenses with focal lengths of over 200 inches. Dunc's camera was the forerunner of others whose need and usage became increasingly more necessary as the cold war set in.

Soon after Duncan Macdonald returned from Germany we were both ordered to the Pacific in connection with the photography of the Army Air Force and Navy atomic bomb tests at Bikini Island. Both services were anxious to conduct two tests of atomic bombs, aerial and underwater. About twenty special highly qualified photographers and laboratory technicians from my lab at Wright Field were assigned to do the filming and processing. I was to participate in the exercises to act as a consultant on aerial camera operations and especially on the camera installation work on the photographic airplane.

There was tremendous activity getting a special C-54 transport equipped to accommodate sixteen aerial camera operators and their mounted cameras. We removed the windows in order to fit in the cameras. Each either had a different focal length lens or was equipped with special filters to record specific details of the explosion. In addition, there were several special high speed motion picture cameras mounted to take pictures from the left side of the airplane.

I was able to locate a small window high up in back of the pilot for my observation point and I borrowed a welder's goggles to protect my eyes.

Our base of operations was Kwajalein Island not far from Bikini. Here the bombs were stored and other top secret equipment kept under close guard. On the morning before the test I arose bright and early and decided to walk around the island and shoot some interesting footage. I dressed in khaki but there was no insignia on my shirt, and I neglected to take my wallet along. All I carried was my trusty 16-mm motion picture camera.

A bit later I was concentrating on a nice angle shot of some of the installations when a voice snapped out: "You there! Drop that camera!"

I swung around to face a young Marine guard, rifle at the ready, bayonet pointed in my direction.

I said, "It's all right, son. I'm Colonel Goddard."

"Like hell it's all right! You're violating orders. No cameras are permitted. You move over there and get in that jeep." He gestured with his rifle, a most serious look on his face.

When I had obeyed, feeling slightly ridiculous, he said, "Okay, let's see your identification."

I reached for my wallet and then it dawned on me. " 'Fraid I left it in my quarters."

"Yeah, you can sure tell that one to the Marines. Put your hands on your knees and keep 'em there." I could see he was sure he'd caught a spy.

We rode in silence to the stockade. I figured there would be an officer there, but there wasn't and while I tried to explain once more he relieved me of my camera and into the barbed-wire enclosure I went. Well, I thought, it's a little better than being jailed for riding six in a jeep but not much.

I was not alone in my incarceration. There were others, assorted ratings from the three services who in some way or other had managed to get themselves locked up. One finally befriended me, a burly battered gob with a breath that he could have used to melt the barbed wire.

"Hey pop, what you in for?" he rasped.

"I was picked up as a spy."

"Yeah! No kiddin'." He looked me over critically. "You a spy?"

"I don't think so. How about you?"

"Me? Nahh. I ain't that bright. I busted Malone in the snoot. Rock pile for me. Suppose they'll shoot you, pop?"

"I suppose so," I sighed. "Just my luck."

"Yeah . . . tough on a guy your age."

Several hours passed before a very young but serious Marine first lieutenant came along to interrogate me. He was a bit more understanding and finally agreed that if I could take him to my CO, who was General Ramsey, he'd consider that maybe I wasn't a spy after all.

When the general's executive officer heard the story he nearly fell off his chair laughing. "Why, Lieutenant," he gasped, "you didn't get a spy, you just caught the best damn photographer in the Air Force!"

I don't think the lieutenant was fully convinced until I took him to my quarters and produced my identification.

"What about the film you shot?" he said, still not completely mollified. "Pictures aren't permitted."

I replied by taking the film out of the camera and giving it to him. "You Marines sure have real determination," I said. "Good hunting."

Free again, but dubbed Colonel Mata Hari by my gleeful colleagues, I prepared for the big event. The flight was conducted in the morning. Our plane leveled off at 12,000 feet about twelve miles away from the predicted area of the explosion. The Navy also had special photographic airplanes aloft but most of their valuable study pictures were made from special towers erected on islands nearby or on ships at sea. The test was well planned and all photographers were kept advised of the time of explosion through a radio countdown. The B-29 airplane released its atomic bomb on schedule from 25,000 feet. It exploded over the target at about 500 feet from the water.

The explosion, from our 12,000-foot perch above, was a terrifying sight. First the flash, then the white disc-shaped cloud that spread out rapidly like an umbrella, and then the tremendous round crimson inferno which seemed to boil and expand into a ball of fire at least a half mile in diameter. Still a boiling mass it started to rise, gradually changing from brilliant red to a dark red color. As it rose to six or seven thousand feet the fiery mass began to spread out rapidly and form a large round cloud trailing a stem-shaped white cloud all the way to the ground. We watched the cloud rise to thirty or forty thousand feet where another large white flat-topped disc appeared. This was referred to, by men who know their atomic bombs, as the "snow cloud"— the heat of the boiling cloud caused the heat to rise and the moisture to drop through the below-freezing level and freeze into snowflakes.

None of us observers nor, probably, the pilots, had ever given any thought to the effect the shock wave from the blast might have on our aircraft. We had seen and photographed the blast and the after effects and were about to light up a cigarette and settle down when we received a severe jolt which threw men and cameras up to the ceiling and almost turned the plane upside down. For weeks we had been figuring out all of the major and minor details of what we would do to accomplish our photographic mission but nobody ever gave a thought to the violent shock wave that had traveled the twelve miles to our airplane.

I had intended to stay a few days and witness the second

atomic explosion, known as "Baker Day," but I was asked by the Air Force to fly all the film made of the air test to Washington. Dunc Macdonald, Amrom Katz, and other photographic scientists were anxious to return to the States, so that evening we departed. It was very nearly my last flight.

There were eight of us besides the crew aboard the C-54 that left Kwajalein for San Francisco and points east. The pilot, Lieutenant Walter Ketron, looked to me to be about fifteen years old, but he soon proved that despite his youthful appearance he knew his aircraft which should have been named *Malfunction Junction*. First one engine then the next misbehaved, and while we stayed close to our chutes and eyed the plane's life raft with increasing speculation, our pilot nursed his ailing bird across what seemed an endless ocean between Hawaii and San Francisco. Somewhere in my mind was the question that if we went down in the drink and the film was lost would they have to do the test all over again!

Conversation on the last leg of the flight was minimal. One prop was neatly feathered and the other three engines didn't sound very healthy. I could see the headlines clearly and then finally Ketron cheered us immeasurably, announcing on the intercom "Land ho!"

At Fairfield Air Force Base near San Francisco our aircraft was given a new engine and the other three were purged of their ailments. Then it was on to Dayton. We took off early in the evening informed that scattered thunderstorm activity was reported east of Cheyenne. Why we were not informed that all commercial transcontinental flights had been canceled because of the severity of the activity which was in fact tornadic, can be left to the efficiency experts.

It was near midnight when we passed over Cheyenne, Wyoming. "Slide rule" Katz was peacefully snoozing in one of the plane's litter bunks. Several of us had been admiring his full-blown handlebar mustache, and one wag raised the important scientific question: "How do you think he'd look with only half a mustache?"

This question was carefully considered and a tentative but unanimous answer was "much better."

Since the answer was in the realm of the unproven it was decided that research and development would be necessary before we would be willing to stand on the postulation. A pair of scissors was produced from a kit bag. A suitable surgeon with steady hands and a good eye was selected and we gathered around silently to seek the moment of truth while our subject slept on in innocence and purity. Zeus came to his rescue.

A bright flash of light outside the plane distracted us. "What's that!" someone asked.

"Damned engine again!" came the reply, followed by a brighter flash of light. The plane gave an uneasy shrug.

"No," I said, peering out a window, "it's a thunderstorm."

Never have I come up with a better piece of understatement. In twenty-seven years of flying I had encountered my share of wild weather. The *Rex* mission of 1938 was a good case in point, but what followed on board that C-54 topped everything, for it is seldom that an aircraft has flown into a line squall of tornadoes and anyone has lived to tell about it.

Visually the lightning was suddenly incessant and blinding, the pounding of rain and hail on the metal fuselage thunderous, drowning out the engines but not the frantic clanging of the bail-out bell. None of us had been strapped in when Ketron penetrated the storm's edge and then, unknowingly, began angling along its front and not through it. As a result, in the bucketing turbulence we began flapping around the cabin like birds without wings, airborne and weightless one moment, slamming into roof or floor the next. The cabin was equipped to carry cargo with a short row of bucket seats which were located along one side. Everyone tried to grab hold of something to anchor himself. Coffee cups, sandwiches, loose baggage, anything that wasn't secured flew every which way. To add to the danger some of the heavy camera equipment tore loose and Dunc Macdonald, Amrom Katz and others on board threw themselves on the crates fighting to hold them down so they couldn't tear out the side of the plane. Despite the alarm bell there was no chance of bailing out, and I decided I'd better let Ketron know we were still on board. On hands and knees I crawled forward to the flight deck. Finally, I got my hands on the pilot and co-pilot's seat and slowly straightened up only to have my feet yanked out, my body horizontal as the plane dropped sickeningly. It hit solid air like it was cement, jarred to its rivets. Everything was shaking madly and momentarily standing still. On my knees again, I struggled to stand upright. Outside in the green and yellow lightning, the clouds were a swirling caldron.

"We're not bailing out!" I shouted. "Can't!"

"I'm going to try a one eighty!" Ketron grated through clenched teeth.

"No! Hold your course! You try to turn in this you'll put her on her back. Hold her steady, boy!"

All he and the co-pilot could do was to sit there at an altitude of 18,000 feet with a tight grip on the yoke and fight to keep the plane from turning turtle. They couldn't do anything to prevent the wings from snapping off or the engines from tearing out of their mounts. Prayer was about the only constructive action any of us could take. It worked because just as suddenly as we had hit the storm we broke free of it into a magnificent moonlit night. No plane could have withstood much more punishment without simply coming apart.

On very shaky legs I went back to the shambles of the cabin. The drawn white faces of Dunc and Amrom and the others could have been no paler than my own.

"We're out of it," I said. "We're in the clear."

"Wow!" Katz sat back with a trembling sigh. "That's enough for one flight!"

"What are you complaining about?" Dunc grunted. "That damn storm saved half your mustache."

Our ordeal made headlines in a number of cities because one of those on board was staff correspondent Alfred M. Klein of the Philadelphia *Record*. BOSTON SCIENTISTS RISK LIVES TO

SAVE BIKINI BOMB SECRETS was the way the Boston *Herald* had it.

Unfortunately not all perilous flights end on such a happy note, and several days later I was witness to the start of one whose inception went back many years.

Throughout the major portion of my career I had fought unsuccessfully for the development and production of a plane designed for reconnaissance and nothing else. During the war through bitter losses suffered by recce squadrons using modified combat aircraft, Elliott Roosevelt had taken up the cause. Even with his prestige and tactical experience, it was a long hard fight before the powers in Washington reluctantly agreed to go ahead on the R&D of such an aircraft. As it was we ended the war using the B-29, and the British Mosquito for high altitude long range photography, also the P-38, Mustang P-51 and the twin engine Douglas A-26 for medium and low-level work.

Interestingly enough I learned firsthand that not only had our own Air Force been set against the development of a reconnaissance aircraft, but so, too, had the German Luftwaffe. In my capacity as a Disarmament Officer I had, through Jo Child's intelligence contacts, physically come into possession of one Major Ulrich K. Heidelauf who was both an authority on German aerial reconnaissance and photographic technology. Heidelauf had flown recce missions from the beginning of the war and was also a brilliant scientist. As he succinctly put it: "I learned clearly that effective reconnaissance can only be done by some superior performance. You cannot just take an ordinary aircraft and have it do reconnaissance, because it will be shot down."

And while the proof of his statement lay in the fact that on both sides recce groups suffered the highest casualties, it was not until the war was far advanced and the son of the President laid it on the line, that positive action was taken.

Now, finally, in July 1946 Howard Hughes, whose company, Hughes Aircraft, had taken on the job of designing and building our first all reconnaissance aircraft, was ready to flight-test it. Designated the XF-11, the plane incorporated all the features necessary to outperform existing enemy aircraft. Even though Elliott Roosevelt had gotten Hap Arnold's go ahead in late 1943, there had been opposition on the part of Air Force Engineers who were becoming jet-minded and eventually the contract was canceled. However, two experimental models were completed, and directly after I returned from Bikini, I was ordered to Culver City, California, to witness the XF-11's initial test.

I had previously met Howard Hughes and had been impressed not only by his quiet competent manner, but also his ability as a pilot. One night he had flown me in his plane to his field at Culver City. There were no field lights, no landing lights on the plane, and he came in, using a beam just as I had done many years before at Camp Nichols in Manila.

The XF-11 was a big double-boomed plane with two 3000 horsepower radial engines, boasting twin eight bladed counter-rotating propellers. She looked impressive and revolutionary as Hughes began his preflight tests. A perfectionist, he taxied the plane up and down the full length of the runway and then made a half dozen take-off runs, rising to fifty feet or so and then setting down again. After he was satisfied with all the control adjustments, he taxied in to have the plane refueled. He apologized for taking so long, saying he wanted to make sure the elevators performed satisfactorily. When he finally took off, the XF-11 rose easily and swiftly.

After he'd been gone nearly an hour I began to feel concerned. So did his general manager, Glenn Odekirk, who took off in a company plane to try and locate him. Odekirk intercepted a message from Hughes saying he was in trouble and was going to try and make an emergency landing on the golf course of the Los Angeles Country Club.

He didn't make it, and in the spectacular crash that followed the XF-11 tore off the roof of a two-story house, careened through a line of poplars and crashed head on into another house, bursting into flames.

The actor Dennis O'Keefe, who had witnessed the crash, called the fire department and ran to help as did others in the neighborhood. One of these was Marine Sergeant William Lloyd Durking who at the risk of his life dared the flames and dragged Howard Hughes from the burning wreckage. The flames, added to by a broken gas main, consumed four houses and it was a miracle that others weren't injured or killed. The doctors gave Hughes only a fifty-fifty chance, but he recovered quickly despite third-degree burns, a punctured lung, six broken ribs, and other assorted injuries.

When I saw him several months later he apologized for cracking up the XF-11 and not giving us the opportunity to determine the true value of the plane for photoreconnaissance use.

While it had been anticipated that the XF-11 would have had a ceiling of 40,000 feet and a speed in excess of 400 miles per hour, actually the jet age had overtaken it, and we were thinking in terms of higher altitudes and greater speeds. However, it was through the combined efforts of Elliott Roosevelt and key intelligence officers that the standard for the separate production of reconnaissance aircraft was finally established. The P-80, the Lockheed *Shooting Star,* was both our first tactical jet fighter and our first jet photoreconnaissance plane. The fighters came out on one production line, the reconnaissance version on another. I considered this development on a par with the Boston University facility. Indeed, they complemented each other. New types of planes required newly designed cameras, for many of the old line cameras were not up to such high performance aircraft.

One piece of equipment that didn't require changing and only improved with the advance in airplane speed was the continuous strip camera. We proved the point, which somehow needed further proof because ignorance has a way of dying hard, with a graphic series of tests. I had put Lieutenant William Gorog, one of my most loyal supporters in our laboratory, in charge of testing the strip camera, and he had it mounted in a vertical position in a P-80 which was to fly directly west at 500 miles per hour. We took a second P-80 and had it fly east at the same speed one hundred feet below the camera plane. This gave the combined speed of 1000 miles per hour, and when the film was developed it distinctly showed the individual rivets on the wings of the lower aircraft. Next we had some of our technicians lie on their backs on the ground looking upward. The P-80 came over them at 50 feet and the film it took actually made portrait pictures of each man, showing the markings on playing cards and the headlines on newspapers they held in their hands.

Naturally tests of this nature were highly classified, but I was able to show the public the remarkable qualities of the strip camera in other ways. In both Europe and Japan we had put the camera to work photographing bomb-ravaged cities, using color film and stereo. With the use of polaroid glasses the viewer saw the film in three dimensions. I went coast to coast on the lecture circuit, giving audiences their first glimpse of this new type of "you are there" moving picture.

Sometimes unfortunately the state of the art exceeded the state of the necessary equipment, and George W. Goddard ended up the central character in a three dimensional nightmare.

At the swank Beverly Wilshire Hotel in Beverly Hills, California, a VIP crowd had been assembled, including General Ira Eaker, Howard Hughes, Gregory Peck, and Jimmy Stewart plus a flock of other Hollywood stars and assorted top military brass. After warming up the distinguished multitude to the drama it was about to witness, the lights were dimmed, the projector switch was activated and I blew out most of the fuses in the hotel. It was a matter of power, or lack of it, to supply the special projector. The show did not go on that night and I slunk away red faced and perplexed at the unkindness of fate.

Some weeks later I topped this performance by nearly setting fire to the Library of Congress. On this occasion I was to be introduced by the Chief, General Carl Spaatz. There had been much publicity and an audience of one thousand was to attend. Because of the California debacle, I took the precaution of holding a dry run on all viewings, and this time when the projector was turned on it was followed by the strong smell of smoke! There followed some frantic running about to determine what the trouble was and whether the famous building was on fire.

It was not and the trouble was again diagnosed as an overloading of the outdated electric wiring. I hastily summoned a power truck from Fort Belvoir and construction equipment was borrowed from a nearby building site on which to run extra power lines. This time the show did go on . . . barely, for while we had been racing about getting things to work the audience was filling up the hall. All through the showing I swore I could smell smoke. Maybe it came from the bombed-out cities the audience was viewing as though witnessing the scenes from a slow-moving balloon.

## 24

In the years directly following World War II, aerial reconnaissance developed in two directions—special strategic reconnaissance, the need of which was fostered primarily by our relations with the Soviet Union, and tactical reconnaissance need of which was as old as the airplane. Although the international tension gave impetus to special strategic reconnaissance, stimulating Dr. Duncan Macdonald and the Boston University facility to greater heights literally and figuratively, tactical reconnaissance was beset by three problems, two familiar and one brand new. The first was that most tactical commanders quickly reverted to pre-war concepts and generally lost interest in the use of reconnaissance. As a result they lost their specialists and technical people necessary to maintain the art and the training of new people was not pushed. On top of that, military appropriations in the years following the war were cut to the bone and TAC suffered accordingly.

The second familiar problem was that—just as it had happened at the end of World War I—many of our qualified industrial manufacturers turned to the production of civilian products. This, of course, had a direct effect on curtailing our own production, and in turn emphasized our new problem which was that jet aircraft made most of our World War II cameras obsolete. The strip camera, of course, was the exception, but a new generation of aircraft meant essentially a new generation of reconnaissance equipment.

For example, the speed of a jet made the standard use of flash bombs for night photography unusable. In 1941 with Chuck

Rulapaugh, Billy Mungal, and Al Koepfer I had started work on a flash cartridge system but could generate no interest in it. The system involved the rapid ejection from the plane of small cartridges that would explode in a brilliant flash. Now the Air Force assigned us to develop three units, one to be used in the North American Twin Jet RB-45. In operating the system the pilot would line up over the target, flip a switch, and every second or so a cartridge would be ejected. Several hundred feet from the aircraft it would explode in a one thousandth of a second flash. Then, through an updated version of my 1926 invention, a photoelectric cell in the plane's tail picked up the flash and, through a special electronic device, tripped the camera shutter. The resultant photographs revealed shadows of people and other objects on the ground so necessary to photo interpretation.

The system was developed for use at 3500 and 7000 feet and the pictures taken were comparable to those taken at the same altitude in daylight. The number of cartridges usable on a single mission ranged from two to four hundred.

It was during this time that I was reminded that I had reached the legal age limit where all commissioned officers were required by military regulations to retire. Due to the fact that I was engaged in the development of my night photographic invention, however, I would be called back to duty the following day. So I retired as a colonel at four-thirty on the afternoon of June 15, 1949, and reported back for duty the next morning at eight o'clock.

The most dramatic demonstration of the cartridge unit took place over New York City. I wanted severe conditions—the illumination and photography of people, autos, trucks on the street in the tall building areas of Wall Street, smoke, haze and reflections from the water, but I was leary of trying to get approval to conduct a test over the area because I knew nobody in the Chief's office or at Wright Field would accept the responsibility.

I decided the wisest approach would be to send Anthony D. Keogh, who handled all my lecture arrangements, to New York

City to talk to another Irishman, Mayor William O'Dwyer. As Tony wryly recalls:

You put me out as advance man, much against my better judgment. It looked to me as if this thing could be a stinker, because shortly before this a B-25 crashed into the Empire State Building in a fog, and I could see the possibility of a loud protest by the city officials. I telephoned from Mitchel Field requesting an interview with the Mayor to spread the word to the local population that they were not going to be bombed in their homes, that all we were doing was dropping harmless flash cartridges—I didn't say they amounted to 115 million candlepower, I said they were pyrotechnical flares. Fortunately, with my Irish accent, I got Mayor O'Dwyer's secretary, a fine chap by the name of Gallagher, so I felt I was in pretty good shape.

I said, "Gallagher, my lad, we're flying over your city tonight with a B-17 airplane and a cargo of specialists and we're going to drop harmless flares over the Hudson River. We're probably going to get a shot of the Statue of Liberty close up. We're ordered to stay away from the Brooklyn Navy Yard, but we'll go up the East . . ."

He said, "Wait a minute, are you crazy? You're going down the Hudson River and you're going to set off bombs?" I said, "No, just flares." He said, "Good God why . . . is this the Air Force?" I said, "Yes." He said, "I've got to see somebody about this."

Pretty soon he came back, he said, "The Mayor says for you to get down here immediately. We're going to call a conference, we're going to get the press and radio . . ." I said, "Wait a minute, we want to do this quietly." He said, "You're not going to do it quietly, we're going to relieve this office of all responsibility and the Air Force will have to accept it."

I got down to O'Dwyer's office and there were all these representatives from the various newspapers. Somebody said, "How much danger is there?" I said, "No danger whatsoever." "Do you accept all responsibility?" "No, we don't accept anything." "What can we do to talk you out of this wild adventure?" "There isn't anything you can do, you're dealing with the United States Air Force and the United States Government." O'Dwyer who had served at Wright

Field during the War as a Lieutenant Colonel, said, "Do you know what would happen if one of these things landed in the street? There would be a wild rumor of a Russian bombing and everybody in New York City would try to get out across the George Washington Bridge—you'd have the biggest panic in history." I said, "That would be unfortunate, Mr. Mayor."

On that note the discussion ended and we proceeded with plans for the flight. Colonel Al Wallace was to be the pilot, Lieutenant Cox, co-pilot, and Colonel Oscar Johnson, one of our project engineers, was to operate the camera and flash system. He had made a special setup so that every time a cartridge flashed it triggered three cameras simultaneously and formed one composite wide angle picture. Our flash cartridge expert, Master Sergeant Pete Branscom, an outstanding camera technician, was to maintain the equipment and make sure every detail was attended to.

We were over New York City ejecting our first flash cartridges at about 75th Street. Some of the events of the flight remained with Tony:

I remember you, George, were standing between Wallace and Cox. I had to promise that we'd stay above 1,300 feet. When you were at approximately 900 feet you were shouting to Wallace, "Get down lower, get down lower!" Wallace would say, "How about that promise of 1,300 feet, Colonel?" You said, "I don't care about any promises! I want detail, I've got to get maximum lines per millimeter!"

You got one picture of the face and torch of the Statue of Liberty and it doesn't appear any more than 100 feet away. Those pictures made history and I submit they were taken under terrific difficulty. We were fighting, photographically, smog, glaring lights, haze, everything you ever heard of to make it almost impossible to get a decent picture. Also, the plane was moving approximately 200–225 miles an hour. If you could possibly put together all the things that would make it impossible to get a decent picture you had them there, and all those pictures were good, the kind military commanders demand in wartime.

The details which were readily discernible in the pictures were truly outstanding; trucks, taxis and people moving along the crosstown streets between the canyons of tall skyscrapers, New York Central freight trains shunting cars in the freight yards along the west side of the island, even the tops of wooden pilings along the piers and people on the decks of ferry boats. From a military standpoint the cartridge system had unveiled a terrific potential for discovering enemy nighttime activity which wasn't long in being put to use.

The failure of our standard suppliers to produce, began to get serious when, after waiting for two years for a major company to come through, it became necessary to cancel several of its development contracts. This cancellation put me on the hot seat for not having proven equipment ready for our new jet reconnaissance planes.

General Kenneth B. Wolfe had the responsibility for seeing that both the strategic and tactical air forces were supplied with our latest efforts, and many of my pleas for help were directed to him. And one fine Sunday morning he responded by asking me to come down to his office and meet Bill Jack.

The Jack and Heinz Company had been well known and highly regarded for its development and production of aircraft parts during World War II. Bill Jack had since retired, but he was not the retiring type. A small man in his early sixties with the energy and drive of ten big men, he had stopped by to see if there was anything he might do for the Air Force. He was the answer to my prayers.

In less than a week, after looking over our R&D requirements, he presented us with a plan to erect a row of Butler Buildings at Solana Beach, California and to expand these facilities as the situation demanded. Signing up Bill Jack as a supplier was one of my better decisions. A man of proven ability, he had the knack of getting the job done and done right. During the ensuing two years, he scouted around California selecting well known scientists and engineers and his company did more research and development work and accomplished more for us than all other firms combined. This included an entirely new strip camera and controls, the all-important universal control system which controlled the operation of as many as thirteen cameras in a single aircraft. It automatically triggered the cameras, correctly spaced the intervals of each picture, controlled the aperture setting and accurately determined the film speed. Because of Bill Jack's dedication, the dependable craftsmanship of his employees, whose morale was always high, we assigned him new and more challenging assignments. And then suddenly, through decisions made at a high level in Government—which I have never understood—Bill Jack's growing facility was sharply curtailed and quickly faded away. The timing for us couldn't have been worse for the axe fell as the North Korean Army struck southward across the 38th Parallel into South Korea.

In late 1946 I had made a quick trip to Japan in connection with plans and problems incident to some large aerial mapping projects underway in the Far East. While there I called on Major General Courtney Whitney, General MacArthur's Chief of Staff. Back in the dear old days of 1920, Whitney and I had roomed together and had been first lieutenant pilots at Bolling Field. He received me royally and I asked if his boss might be free to say hello.

He was and I shook hands with him saying, "General, I was that young Air Service pilot in the photographic lab at Camp Nichols who used to make *maps!*"

MacArthur laughed heartily. "I remember very well, Colonel. You did some valuable work there. We used a lot of those photographic *maps* to good advantage. In fact we never could have won the war in the Pacific without aerial reconnaissance. You people made me a confirmed believer."

On June 25, 1950, I knew General MacArthur was going to need all the aerial reconnaissance he could get, but at the outset I was not dealing with confirmed believers like himself. General Hoyt S. Vandenberg, who had become Chief of Air Force, telephoned me: "George," he said without preamble, "we're in bad shape in Korea. I've got a list of complaints from TAC as long as your nose. They say they don't have recce equipment. They don't have trained photointerpreters. I want you to get down here and explain why."

I could explain why and I was perfectly willing to do so. I got the chance the next day, sitting on one side of a table with my trusty assistant, Colonel Art Smith, beside me. Across the table, flanked by members of his Langley Field staff, sat General Ennis C. Whitehead, Chief of the Continental Air Command, which TAC was under. The table fronted Hoyt Vandenberg's desk, and he led off by asking me to reply to the long list of complaints.

I began by giving a breakdown of the reconnaissance systems we had tested and developed for the Tactical Air Command, explaining each—the strip camera—the night photo cartridge unit—the universal control system—new processing equipment, etc.

"That's what we've done," I concluded, "but what we've done has received little interest or appreciation from TAC. It's the same old story. Most of the hardware is sitting on the shelf gathering dust. Naturally training in all phases of aerial reconnaissance has suffered accordingly."

General Whitehead and his staff did not favor me with a direct reply. They talked among themselves and made answers to General Vandenberg's brief questions. To me it began to look as though I was facing a bunch of red Indians. I deepened the color when a third assistant somebody remarked that the problem of attitude could not be overlooked.

"Exactly," I said. "I'll give you all a perfect example. Just a week ago when I was here on a visit I took the Potomac ferry from Bolling to the Pentagon. On board was a certain general." I stared at the man across the table. "I happened to overhear him talking to his friends. He said he was trying to build up an efficient command, but he had too many reconnaissance people and he was going to get rid of some of them because he needed other men for things that were more important. I couldn't agree more about attitude."

Following what can only be termed a pregnant silence, General

Vandenberg cleared his throat and said, "Well, gentlemen, it's quite apparent to me where the trouble lies. There's no use in raking over past mistakes. It's time to get cracking and correct them."

I went cracking back to the laboratory at Wright Field and soon everybody was working around the clock—writing specifications, coordinating with the supply division, and awarding letter of intent procurement contracts to various manufacturers. It was like the beginning of World War II all over again. It was hard to believe that so many million dollars could be spent so fast. This madhouse operation lasted several weeks and toward the end I was ready to have a vacation—the first in two years.

I took a month's leave and drove to the West Coast with my wife and my six-year-old daughter. They had never been to California before and we were looking forward to a pleasant leisurely time. The trip would also give me an opportunity to accept the Thurman H. Bane Award presented by the Institute of Aeronautical Sciences at their summer meeting at the Ambassador Hotel in Los Angeles. The award was presented annually to an officer or civilian of the U. S. Air Force Matériel Command, "for an outstanding achievement in aeronautical development." The award of 1950 specifically cited the work I had done in the "development of a new system of night aerial photography at low altitudes." Before the close of the presentation dinner a messenger came up to me with a telegram from General Vandenberg which read:

YOU ARE TO TERMINATE YOUR LEAVE OF ABSENCE IMMEDIATELY
AND LEAVE FOR SAN DIEGO TO BOARD A SPECIAL AIRCRAFT DEPART-
ING FOR TEMPORARY DUTY IN KOREA. COMPLETE INSTRUCTIONS AS
TO YOUR MISSION IN KOREA ARE BEING HAND-CARRIED TO YOU BY
YOUR WRIGHT FIELD ASSISTANT, COLONEL ARTHUR SMITH. BE PRE-
PARED TO BOARD THE AIRCRAFT LEAVING SAN DIEGO TOMORROW.

It was a difficult farewell, but early the next morning I flew to San Diego where my plane, a C-54 transport, was waiting for

Manhattan sky line all lit up, taken from B-17 using cartridge ejection system. The row of lights are the cartridge flashes. July 20, 1949. *U.S. Air Force*

The Battery at the tip of Manhattan as photographed on the same mission. *U.S. Air Force*

The stereo strip camera shows off its stuff at 500 feet, flying 500 mph. The railroad tracks offer to the photo interpreter a scale of measurement for all parts and equipment. *U.S. Air Force*

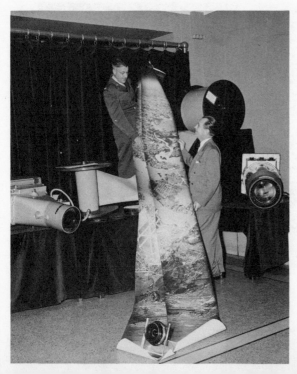

I display a little roll of film taken by the panoramic scan camera. Each roll cost $3400. *U.S. Air Force*

1925. Doc Burka and I prepare for some long range aerial photography, using an experimental camera with a 60-inch lens. *U.S. Army Air Service*

1965. The aerial camera with the 240-inch lens takes a ground shot. *NASA*

From 45,000 feet, 100 miles away, here is how New York City looks through the 240-inch lens. *U.S. Air Force*

Hail and farewell. To the sound of bugles, and flanked by General Lauris Norstad, Commander General of Allied Air Forces, NATO, I am escorted off the reservation in a send-off ceremony at Camp Guynemer, France. May 1953. *U.S. Air Force*

me. It was loaded down with aerial photographic equipment and supplies. Our first assignment was to equip a squadron of A-26 reconnaissance aircraft with my night photographic cartridge system. Our airplane carried the necessary technicians to make the installation and to train mechanics to maintain it.

The A-26 airplanes and crews arrived in Japan on an aircraft carrier and in two or three weeks Lieutenant Colonel Frank A. Sharp, an excellent officer and command pilot, took over. He and his men did a splendid job flying up and down the North Korean-held valleys and plains taking night pictures, many of which were comparable with pictures made in the daytime but from a military standpoint were much more valuable. This was because the North Koreans were generally holed up in the daytime sleeping under straw stacks, bushes, or any shady area where they could conceal themselves. The fields of central and southern Korea were full of these straw stacks and, through information gained from captured North Koreans, it was learned that soldiers were hiding in them. Each soldier would strap a pile of straw on his back which was doubly useful—providing shade from the hot sun and concealment from the view of our fighter pilots. When they saw an airplane in the distance several soldiers would fall in together and form a fair-size haystack. After many of these haystacks had been riddled with machine-gun fire from the fighters, the enemy soldiers gave up their clever scheme of concealment and daytime operations became more restricted.

One day, Colonel Bert Smiley, in command of reconnaissance in Korea, and I scouted the country flying an unarmed Beachcraft far back of the enemy lines. For over an hour we never saw a soldier or civilian anywhere on the roads or in the fields. It was hard to believe there was a war going on.

This disbelief didn't last long. Later at our aerial photographic laboratory at Tagur, South Korea, we looked at aerial photographs which had been taken by Colonel Sharp's squadron the night before. The deserted roads that I had been flying over were jammed with soldiers, tanks, artillery, supply trucks, and ambulances.

The North Korean Army were past masters at the art of concealment. To hide their tanks in a hurry they would pull off the road and ram into a nepa shack and the palm leaf roof would settle down on top of the tank and conceal it. In daytime aerial photographs it appeared as just another nepa shack. Gasoline for their military transportation was generally delivered to railroad stations along a railroad right-of-way and during the night it was concealed in hurriedly constructed nepa shacks. In moving tanks and other vehicles they naturally made many tracks in the mud, but they generally covered these by scattering straw all over the area.

Colonel Sharp did an excellent job training his night photographic personnel to operate and maintain their equipment. They were outstanding in their ability to put their planes directly over the target areas 200 or 300 miles from their home base on Kyushu.

However, the Korean War presented us with an aerial reconnaissance problem never encountered before. It was created by the high jagged mountainous terrain coupled with the fact that so much of our photography was done at night. During World War II the land our recce pilots flew over in all theaters of operations was relatively flat. In Korea it was high flung peaks without clear points of contrast. Our night cameras and illuminating systems were fine for the lower altitudes, but with mountains of seven and eight thousand feet we knew we had to get higher. That meant longer focal length lenses, greater illumination, and faster film.

General Vandenberg and General LeMay set top priority on the development of a night camera system to be used at upper altitudes by SAC's recce squadrons. It was just the kind of order the Boston University facility was geared to undertake. Because of the importance of the optics in such a large system, Jim Baker joined the effort as a consultant as did Dr. R. G. Clarke, illumination expert, who was director of Air Force Research in pyrotechnics at Wesleyan University. Assisting Duncan Macdonald in the over-all R&D were two highly competent night photographic engineers, Walter Levison and Harry Gewertz. The project which was named Red Light also included in it a shock absorbing camera mount. This last was of critical importance for the entire system was to be installed and operated in the Air Force's most powerful multi-jet reconnaissance aircraft. The six or eight jet engines driving an airplane through turbulent air creates tremendous vibration that violently shakes every item of equipment aboard. These vibrations, together with roll, pitch, and yaw of the airplane, seriously degrade the quality of the final image that is produced on the aerial film emulsion. Of great importance, too, because of the relatively slow shutter speeds that are involved in working with large optical systems, an image-motion compensation feature is required. Since the ground below is constantly moving in relation to an airplane in flight it is necessary to compensate for this by moving the film in the camera. This is a difficult problem. Also very important, the flash produced by the exploding bomb must be tremendously bright to light up the ground below from such a high altitude, and the quality of the illumination has to be matched to the sensitivity of the special night photo film. Last, but not least, the bomb must flash in the sky in the most desirable position to give the proper shadows and to place the maximum light on the area being photographed.

The end result of project Red Light marked a giant step upward in the art of night aerial photography. It was one thing to take photographs from 20 to 30,000 feet in daylight and get sharp resolution. It was quite another to take them equally high up at night over mountainous irregular terrain and get the same resolution. Korea not only presented a different kind of war for military planners and politicians, it also presented a different kind of place for aerial reconnaissance to prove itself.

While scientific and technology knowledge went forward at home, innovation was often the watchword in the field. One graphic instance of the latter involved a mission over the southern end of the Yalu River.

The Army staff wanted to know where the Chinese and the North Koreans were bringing in their supplies. We had a good surveillance of the coastal areas and along the railroads and thought the enemy was fairly well stopped as far as moving equipment was concerned. However, he still was being supplied, so our night photographic planes were deployed south of the Yalu to help find out how. One night a photographic pilot saw a row of lights below so he lined up and made a series of photographs. The first picture showed four trucks with their headlights on, the second picture showed only one truck with its lights on and in the third picture the headlights were all out.

As a result of the taking of these pictures General Earle E. Partridge and his Air Force officers at TAC headquarters in Taegu devised a system of locating and bombing truck transport by night. He equipped a large flying boxcar with a powerful antiaircraft searchlight arranged so that the crew inside the boxcar could maneuver the beam of light to illuminate the roads. Electric power was supplied by two or three extra-large gas-powered electric generators located in the front of the aircraft. The doors at the rear end of the boxcar were removed, providing sufficient room to swing the large reflector around. The operators wore heavy leather belts which were held by long straps attached to the inside of the boxcar to keep them from falling out.

The idea was for the search plane to locate the vehicles or troops on the ground then radio back to base to send the planes in to strafe and bomb the targets using the beam of light from the boxcar as a guide. The boxcar carried a radio device so that the fighter bombers could home in on it and perform their mission. It was a rather crude way of solving the problem, but it worked after a lot of practice.

General MacArthur's famous amphibious landing at Inchon in September 1950 was far more than innovation, it was military strategy at its most brilliant. And in the planning of the landing, aerial reconnaissance played a decisive preparatory role.

It was vitally necessary to know tide heights, depths of reefs, and measurements of sea walls on the selected landing beaches. To aid in gathering this information, Colonel Richard Philbrick, who had become assistant to Duncan Macdonald at Boston University, Amrom Katz, wizard, and Don Graves, mapping and charting expert of my laboratory, left for Korea to assist Mac-Arthur and his Corps of Engineers in providing accurate data on a harbor whose thirty foot tides were known to be among the swiftest and most treacherous in the world. It was a situation ready made for the strip camera.

There were two landing beaches—Red and Blue, and the rapid tidal changes presented a critical photographic and analytical problem which had to be correctly solved if the Marine assault teams were going to be able to scale the vertical sea walls. The technical team of Philbrick, Katz, and Graves went to work with Lieutenant Colonel John Dixon's 8th TAC Reconnaissance Squadron. Dixon's pilots, flying RF-80s, made their runs in daylight, coming in very low, taking both vertical and oblique shots of the beaches. To augment the accuracy of the stereo strip camera a new film technique worked out by Philbrick was utilized which measured the heights of sea walls and other ground objects. Through the calibration of shadows he and "Slide Rule" Katz were able to provide the Corps of Engineers with accurate figures that proved extremely valuable in the preparation of invasion maps.

The contributions of Philbrick, Katz, and Graves joined with the photographic missions flown by Lieutenant Colonel Dixon's pilots, were critical to the success of General MacArthur's bold strategy. The surprise landings at Inchon, that neither our friends nor our enemies conceived as possible, were a bright moment in an ugly frustrating war.

But war is always ugly and in it there is always personal loss. Upon my return from Korea I had suggested that a good many of the tactical reconnaissance bugs could be eliminated by the best operational pro we had on tap, Colonel Karl "Pop" Polifka. Pop's World War II record as a recce pilot was without parallel. My recommendation was picked up so fast Pop hardly had time to say goodbye. Shortly after the Inchon landing and our forces had moved north I received the sad news that he had been killed while flying an aerial photographic mission over enemy territory.

At the time Pop was the commanding officer of the 67th Reconnaissance Wing and, in that position, he actually should not have been flying the mission. Apparently his recce pilots had tried to get a certain picture and had failed. One of Pop's prime concerns was the morale of his men, and he was known to take on missions such as this, in large part, to maintain that morale. He was flying a single-engine propeller aircraft at low altitude when his plane was hit by enemy fire, puncturing a fuel tank and setting it afire. Pop bailed out but, tragically, his parachute became fouled in the tail of the RF-6 as it was falling.

Polifka's loss was a sad blow to me personally and to the Air Force generally. Several years prior to his assignment to Korea, he was on the staff of the Air Force Tactical School serving as an instructor and continually studying and making recommendations for advancing the tactical employment of reconnaissance in modern warfare. Pop was a great leader, had been decorated many times and was an extremely popular officer. The Air Force had important plans for his future in terms of assignments and promotions. After his death the service tried to have him made a brigadier general posthumously but could not obtain the necessary confirmation from the U. S. Senate.

As the unwinnable war in Korea dragged on, tactical reconnaissance reached new levels of performance. It was natural that it would, for the demands of conflict require not only equipment suited to the theater of operations but also the training so necessary to its full utilization. Pilots, film processing technicians, photo interpreters, all are essential to aerial reconnaissance whether tactical or strategic. Today in Vietnam they are penetrating the tangled jungles and the cleverly camouflaged supply routes of the enemy, seeking him out day and night wherever he is. As in every conflict since World War I they are the eyes of our forces and without them our losses would be far greater and our efforts far less successful.

## 25

My introduction to strategic reconnaissance came in 1923 when Howard Ramey and I secretly overflew Mexico and photographed the land beneath. Like the development of the aerial camera, aerial surveillance has come a long way since then.

Prior to World War II, from my own personal observation, and from the nature of Japanese military plans, there is no doubt that the Nippon Air Force carried out aerial photographic reconnaissance over our installations in the Pacific area as well as other nations. Conversely, though officialdom refuses to admit that Amelia Earhart's last flight was anything more than a long-distance hop, recent evidence strongly indicates she and her navigator Fred Noonan were on an aerial spying mission over Japanese-held islands.[1] In Europe in the 1930s the German *Graf Zeppelin* traveled about the world as a luxury liner of the skies. It certainly isn't farfetched to suspect that on some of her voyages there were aerial cameras on board. More conclusively it is a matter of record that in 1936 the Luftwaffe began carrying out overflights of Russia, France, and England.[2] Some months prior to the war in 1939, Sidney Cotton, a clever and adventurous Australian teamed up with an equally adventurous Canadian, Robert Nevin, and with official British sanction, fooled the Nazis, flying all about Germany with a neatly concealed camera in the belly of their twin-engine Lockheed.[3] No doubt France, Italy,

[1] Fred Goerner, *The Search for Amelia Earhart.* (New York: Doubleday & Co., 1966.)
[2] John Killen, *A History of the Luftwaffe.* (New York: Doubleday & Co., 1968.)
[3] Constance Babington-Smith, *Air Spy.* (New York: Harper & Brothers, 1957.), p. 9–12.

Russia, and other countries were similarly engaged in this new method of trying to find out what the other fellow was up to.

At war's end the international political climate gave a new meaning and importance to aerial reconnaissance. We wished a disarmament treaty; the Soviets did not. Our society was practically an open book to their agents; their society was closed to us on almost every level. As the Cold War grew colder, the problem became more acute, and the U. S. Government began to see the great necessity of using photographic reconnaissance as a means of surveillance.

Two major requirements were considered necessary for such reconnaissance: long range high altitude cameras that would supply clear sharp pictures under all atmospheric conditions, and an aerial platform that would keep the equipment out of the hands of those being photographed. The scientific and engineering intricacies of fulfilling these demands were, of course, formidable; however, like everything else concerned with aviation, high altitude long-range photography which I had begun pushing and developing at McCook Field in the twenties had progressed considerably particularly during the war years under Jim Baker and his great staff.

When I returned to the Wright Field laboratory in 1945 I had instructions to forge ahead on new equipment for the coming jets of TAC and long range, high altitude cameras for both the propellor driven and jet aircraft of the Strategic Air Command.

Jim Baker's 100-inch system, which was completed at about the time the war ended was ideal for the latter. But now with the new demands of strategic reconnaissance, I wanted to go farther, and the Boston University Air Force Optical Research Center was perfectly suited to engage in this highly classified R&D. Since it was my job to program all the Center's projects, I prepared an exhaustive study on a 240-inch system capable of taking 200 9×18 photographs in black and white or color. Its range would be more than a hundred miles and at such distance a photointerpreter would be able not only to distinguish such objects as aircraft but also recognize their make. This was but one of the systems the Center undertook, and while as always there were those in military circles who said it couldn't be done, Duncan Macdonald and his boys went ahead and did it.

In order to give Dunc added assistance in this program and many others of a similar nature, I permitted him to spirit away my assistant director, Colonel Dick Philbrick, who upon his return from Europe had joined me at the laboratory. Dunc needed Dick not only for his scientific abilities, but also to run his flight test branch. Also we added to the team Dr. Claus Aschenbrenner, a noted German physicist and authority on aerial photographic research, and Walter Levison of my laboratory, an expert photographic engineer.

One of the first important tests took place over Boston at 30,000 feet. It involved photographing one-foot square objects in alleys and on rooftops. The results were so successful I had high hopes for the longer focal length lenses to follow.

It was at this time that Dick Philbrick made a breakthrough that started the development of an entirely new line of cameras. I have always felt it was my strip camera that led the way to this new development. He took one of the latest models and equipped it with a turning crank so that it could be rotated to take a panoramic picture from horizon to horizon. He mounted the camera in the belly of a B-50 and at 36,000 feet while over Middletown, Connecticut, he shot a picture 9 inches wide and 30 inches long which showed New York City to the south and all the land between it and Portland, Maine, to the north.

This all important milestone set the pattern for most present day aerial cameras, and its application to strategic reconnaissance is obvious. It is referred to as a scanning camera, but basically it is a continuous strip camera used in a different way and with many refinements.

The Middletown picture looked so promising that I immediately started development of a 48-inch lens scanning camera. It would weigh nearly a ton, but it would eliminate the mounting of three or four large cameras in an aircraft, for the purpose of shooting both vertical and oblique pictures. Further, for the first time since 1917, there were no weight or space restrictions placed on us. This was because the aircraft slated for SAC was going to be a real big bird. The B-36 was just that, but its performance using outdated reciprocating engines was being eclipsed by new high altitude, high speed bombers equipped with the latest most powerful jet engines.

We installed the camera in a vertical position in the belly of the aircraft. The first flight test took place over Forth Worth, Texas, at 34,000 feet and the resolution was so amazing that two golf balls on a green were easily discernible with the caddy standing aside holding the flag.[4]

Since survival in strategic reconnaissance would depend on speed and altitude, I did not see how the B-36 could fit the bill, nor did it, for it was shortly replaced by SAC with the B-47 and later the B-52. These aircraft required cameras of a different design and much reduced size and weight. However, a single horizon to horizon exposure was made on a negative 9 inches wide and 16 feet long, the roll 5000 feet long, weighing 250 pounds and costing $3400 per roll.

When a Congressman on the House Subcommittee on Military Affairs saw the cost figure and learned that it had required $750,000 to develop the equipment, he turned a pale purple and declared that if he had bought a box Brownie for $3.50, that took perfectly good pictures, he didn't see why the Air Force had to spend nearly a million dollars just to take pictures!

Shortly thereafter, General Vandenberg called me, and I learned that I was going to be called on to testify before the Committee to explain our expenditure. The Subcommittee Chairman was George H. Mahon, Democrat of Texas, and I had prepared for him and the other Committee members a graphic display. In one exhibit I had a film for a Brownie camera placed next to my $3400 beauty. My theme was: if we're going to have to keep track of the world, this is what it's going to take.

When I had completed my presentation Chairman Mahon

[4] The 48 inch scanning camera was a development engineered by Perkins-Elmer Co., together with Dr. James Baker and the Boston University Laboratory.

commented: "Let me say for the record that this is one of the most interesting presentations we have ever had. It's not hard to see why you received the award for photographic achievement. It is a very splendid thing that we have Americans of your caliber positioned as you are, and I want to commend you . . . We thank you for your appearance . . . I think we are getting something for our money."

Outside in the corridor Chairman Mahon put his arm around my shoulder and said, "Colonel, we don't mind spending money for such valuable hardware. If you ever need any more and the Air Force refuses to give it to you, you come see me personally."

"Yes," I chuckled, "and I'll get my throat cut from ear to ear."

But there wasn't any need to risk it, for the Air Force as well as our top leaders recognized the value of what we were up to. As General Eisenhower put it to me in discussing the critical importance of reconnaissance: "Without it you would have only your fears on which to plan your own defense arrangements and your whole military establishment. Now if you're going to use nothing but fear and that's all you have, you're going to make us an armed camp. So this kind of knowledge is vital to us."

In the late forties and early fifties, although we had developed aerial cameras that were making great strides in high altitude photography, we had not yet perfected a manned platform to carry out such reconnaissance over hostile territory. My function was not intelligence and so I was never aware that such attempts had or had not been made, nor was I privy to the political decisions which would have approved or disapproved such flights.

During this period, however, in an entirely different pursuit and on an entirely different level, I became involved in tests which led me to make some suggestions about one method for supplying a suitable platform in which to place long-range, higher altitude reconnaissance cameras.

In 1946 the U. S. Army began testing German V-2 rockets at its Ordnance installation at White Sands, New Mexico. In these tests I saw a great opportunity to do our first aerial photographic research in space. There were many things we needed to know such as the effects of cosmic rays on film and lenses, the actions of intense cold and heat, static conditions, etc.

I obtained the necessary funds through General Spaatz and made arrangements to start working with the Ordnance Corps. Since the Air Force was still a part of the Army, this was easily arranged. What wasn't quite so easy was adjusting to the small amount of space in the V-2 allotted to us by the Ordnance specialists. I made my old compatriot, George Magnus, project engineer. He was to design a system we could fit into the rocket and to handle all other details of the operation.

Due to the limited area in the nose cone, George selected a small Fairchild gun camera. To this was added a special heater and parachute. The unit went into an aluminum container. When the rocket reached its peak altitude of around one hundred miles an explosive charge in back of the installation ejected the camera and chute, and automatically started the film running. Dr. Mees and his people at Eastman Kodak generously supplied us with experimental film and haze filters.

We believe we took the first films in space which revealed important scientific data as well as some remarkable visual effects. For the first time we photographed the operation of a parachute under vacuum conditions one hundred miles above the earth. It rotated in its folded shape until it fell into heavier atmosphere and then gradually opened. At the same time the camera was photographing earth and space. Space was black and stars could be seen, but as the camera descended the blackness transformed to the familiar blue.

From these first tests the Air Force and Kodak obtained much information which we have utilized in various aspects of our space exploration program. There were also some interesting side lights. On one test a watch had been put into the nose cone of the rocket. A chute for the cone failed to open and it came crashing back to earth.

"Where can I find a shovel?" George asked.

"What do you want a shovel for?"

"I want to dig up that nose cone."

"What's the matter, aren't you getting enough exercise?"

"You'll see," George said.

Radar had tracked the fall of the cone, and so I drove with George out into the desert and we found the point of impact without much trouble. It was a neat six-foot hole and George grimly went after it with his shovel. I sat back and observed a determined man at work. After a pretty severe struggle George unearthed the badly smashed object and when he pried it open there among the broken remains was the watch. Like a man who had found Blackbeard's treasure, George pulled it free and held it up to his ear.

"Here" he said after a moment, a big satisfied grin on his face. "Listen!"

I listened and the watch was ticking away merrily. "Well, it sure gets A for withstanding hard bumps," I said. "I can see the watch manufacturer's advertising now. 'If you fall a hundred miles through space, you may not be ticking after you land but our watches will.'"

Unfortunately, it wasn't long before we had run out of the existing supply of V-2 rockets. But I was most anxious to continue the project by any other feasible method. I knew of one and in pursuing it, I took a leaf from the book of Captain Albert Stevens in his pioneering balloon photography of the early thirties. Of course, weather balloons could not attain much more than 100,000 feet which was a long way beneath one hundred miles, but George and I realized there was a great deal to be learned and much progress to be made even at that altitude.

General Mills Corporation was the manufacturer of these balloons and with the blessing of the Chief's office I went to see them about constructing some special ones for us at their plant in Minneapolis. They were only too happy to oblige and in a short while George and I were in the balloon business. Unlike Steve we did not ascend with the cameras but placed them in a specially designed gondola. In the gondola we had a radio control by which from the ground we could automatically open the release valve and let out the gas when we wished to bring the balloon down, or use a parachute arrangement.

On one of our early tests we were both watching the ascension through powerful binoculars. Suddenly I saw the balloon take off like it was jet propelled—not upward but eastward!

"Holy cats!" I said. "What goosed that thing? Look at it go!"

"By golly, I think it hit the jet stream," George said.

And indeed it had. As we watched it speed eastward, the bells started tingling in my head. "George, old boy," I said, "What do you know about the jet stream?"

"Flows west to east and circles the earth." He gave me a speculative stare. "The altitude is constant I think."

"Where do you suppose that baby will end up?"

"Might even come back here."

"Yeah, and it might take some mighty pretty pictures on the way."

Back at Wright Field I talked to some of the Intelligence people about what I had in mind. Planting a seed was the way I thought of it.

Several years later, in February 1956, all hell hit the fan when the Soviets yelled foul and claimed that we were inundating their air space with aerial photographic balloons. To prove the point they put on a big circus-like display in Moscow, exhibiting about fifty balloon and instrument containers. The whole scene was floodlit from trucks with portable generators. In their anger the Russians offered to go on the road and exhibit their wares in the capitals of the world. They didn't say how much admission they'd charge but their spokesmen made other charges as they explained their version of how the radio-controlled vehicles "were able to traverse the entire breadth of the Soviet Union in seven to ten days and then release their apparatus by parachute into friendly hands."[5]

A Soviet military officer, Colonel Tarantsov, declared that each balloon carried nearly 1500 pounds of equipment and contained a radio-transmitting device that gave a location signal at

[5] *The New York Times,* February 10, 1956, page 1.

regular intervals. "When the balloon arrives over its point of destination," he said, "a ground radio station can give a signal that automatically explodes pyrotechnic charges and causes the equipment to be parachuted to the ground." He went on to say that if the equipment landed in the water it would float and an emergency transmitter would send out homing signals. Also that anyone finding a balloon on friendly territory could turn it in and get paid for it. Then he displayed some of the film and said the camera equipment was able to record the map coordinates of every photograph taken, and there was sufficient film to take 450 to 500 pictures.[6]

He further claimed that the balloons could be maintained at a constant altitude and that they were launched to follow well charted air currents.

In a later accusation the Soviets stated that the balloons were for aerial espionage and the purpose behind the action was to unilaterally carry out President Eisenhower's "open skies" program.[7]

The flack continued for several weeks and accordingly it was reported that President Eisenhower had given orders to suspend the launching of "weather balloons."

Either somebody didn't hear the order or some of those balloons just wouldn't come down until they were ready. Some two years later Dick Philbrick, while serving a tour of duty in Iceland, uncovered one of these packages which had spent most of its time floating around the Arctic Ocean. He had been actively involved in the program earlier and recognizing the importance of what it may contain, undertook to commandeer it and hurry it back to the Laboratories in the States. It proved to contain one of the most valuable sets of coverage. And then once again in October 1958, the Soviets were back at the old exhibit stand, hollering for us to get those damn balloons out of their piece of sky.[8]

Of course, by 1956, we had something more dependable than balloons to keep an eye on the Communist world. And, in the

[6] *Ibid.*
[7] *The New York Times,* February 18, 1958, p. 1.
[8] *The New York Times,* October 16, 1958, p. 1.

evolution of this more advanced endeavor of strategic reconnaissance, I was able to plant a seed or two.

Aside from directing my own laboratory, and cooperating with
the highly creative efforts of the Boston Center plus that of three
other Universities engaged in aerial photographic R&D, I continued to keep active on the lecture circuit. Selling the value of
aerial photography was ever a part of my business. It was for two
basic reasons. I wanted the public to understand its great merits,
to see how we were reaching out into space and beneath the seas,
and within the military, I wanted acceptance and understanding of
the art. After so many years of use and so much proof one might
think that such an effort would be unnecessary. But unfortunately
it was. Bombers and fighters and missiles were easily understood,
not so the aerial camera. Then came an opportunity to strike a
blow for the cause where it would count most. One fine day in
1952 General Vandenberg telephoned me. "George," he greeted
me. "I just received a request from Ike, wanting to know if we
can send an officer to Paris to lecture the students of the NATO
defense college on aerial photographic reconnaissance. You interested?"

"I'll be on my way in an hour!" I howled, and I almost was. I
quickly had a C-54 loaded with our camera displays and the
three dimensional strip camera projection equipment. I grabbed
Art Smith and several other technical people from the lab and
we were off and running. This to me was a lecture opportunity to
crown them all.

We set up shop in the Ecole Militaire, the main French military
headquarters in Paris. The seats had ear phones and translators
on the other end. My audience was composed mostly of generals
and admirals and air marshals. In all my years of lecturing I had
never seen so much top brass. I gave them the full treatment and
upon my return to the States, General Vandenberg sent me a
letter he had received from General Eisenhower which read:

I am grateful for your cooperation in sending Colonel George
Goddard and his experts from the Air Matériel Command to show

my officers the latest Air Force developments in photography, photographic intelligence, and camouflage detection. Colonel Goddard made a very able presentation of his subject at SHAPE, as well as at other Air and land headquarters here in Europe. He aroused considerable interest in a subject about which many of our friends here have had little opportunity to obtain first hand knowledge. The technical progress strikes me as amazing.

A few days later Hoyt Vandenberg was on the phone again. "George, Ike has requested that you be assigned to the Allied Air Forces of Central Europe as director of reconnaissance—order to take effect immediately. How does that suit you?"

"Terrific!" I replied. "It's a wonderful opportunity and a great honor, but I need something."

"What's that?"

"I don't want to feel self-conscious having to associate with all that gold draped brass. I want something to replace these eagles. I think it's time I got to be a general."

"George, hold the phone." In a few minutes he was back. "General Goddard," he said, "you're a general right now, so start packing."

While I had held the phone he had called his chief of personnel and as my good luck would have it, there was a promotion list going to the Senate Military Affairs Committee for approval; my name was added. In a few weeks, sporting my stars, my wife and daughter beside me, I was off to France on what was to be a glorious final military assignment.

We lived in a castlelike house with tower and parapet in Fontainebleau. While I was busy visiting NATO air bases helping to build the reconnaissance strength of Tactical squadrons with training lectures and new equipment, Elizabeth spent her time with the wives of the six nationalities represented in the Allied Air Forces of Central Europe. Diane was busy in dependents' school, with the British Brownie Scout Troop and playing with the French children on our street, learning to chatter in French. We were only in the "castle" for two months, then moved to the attractive new ultra-modern apartments built by the French for AAFCE families in the forêt of Fontainebleau.

There was lots of time to spend with my family on weekends. Sometimes we spent the day boating on the Seine near Samois, or driving down to the picturesque village of Barbizon. Toward the end of my tour of duty we flew to Italy where I was scheduled to give a series of lectures, and we explored Florence, Rome and Naples.

One of the high points of our leisure time was a trip to Holland in the Spring at the height of the colorful tulip festival.

In my travels I was often in contact with friends who were involved in special strategic reconnaissance. One of these was General Hal Watson, Assistant to the Chief of Intelligence for Allied Air Forces Central Europe. One day we were discussing the twin-jet B-57 Canberra which had been designed for re-connaissance. I told him that Duncan Macdonald and his staff had come out with an improved light-weight 240-inch focal length system which could be fitted into a Canberra, but I didn't see much point in it because the aircraft's performance was so disappointing.

Hal suggested I go talk to Air Marshal Fuller in London about the camera, he being in charge of RAF Intelligence. Watson thought what I had to say might be useful to the Air Marshal's plans.

The Air Marshal had started his flying career about the same time I'd started mine, and so we had much in common. I told him about the camera. He showed me his Canberra, only it didn't look like a Canberra anymore. Its wings had been extended and its power increased. I was informed that it would now fly very high and very fast. As for the new 240-inch system, the Air Marshal said he would go through regular channels to procure one.

It was in this same time period in 1953 that U. S. and British Intelligence learned that the Soviets had established a missile-testing facility north of the Caspian Sea. The place was called Kapustin Yar, and not long after I had talked to Air Marshal Fuller, a British Canberra took off from West Germany and made a very long perilous flight, overflying Kapustin Yar. The pilot was shot at, the plane was hit, but landed safely in a field in central Asia, with its aerial camera intact.[9]

A short time after my return from England and before the flight of the Canberra, I attended a big reception in Paris and found myself sitting next to none other than Hoyt Vandenberg.

"George, you devil," he said. "What have you been up to?"

I told him about my recent meeting with the Air Marshal and the new look of the B-57. Then I added, "You know that plane's a dog, and someday you're going to get hauled up before Congress and asked why you ever bought so many of the damn things. What you ought to do is just what Fuller is doing. Extend the wings. Boost the horse power. Get her up there so she can't be shot down. Then we can put that two hundred and forty inch camera in her and you'll really have yourself a hot recce aircraft."

Hoyt Vandenberg was a quiet soft spoken unexcitable officer, but as we talked this idea over he got excited. "George," he finally said, "you come on back to the States with me, and we'll discuss it with the Martin aircraft people and see what's involved. I think you've really got something here."

My tour of duty was nearly up and my send-off from Allied Air Forces of Central Europe was one I'll never forget. After the ceremony in front of headquarters building at Camp Guynemer, General Lauris Norstad and his staff of foreign Air Marshals, Admirals, and Generals marched me off the military reservation between rows of buglers and airmen of the NATO air forces. One doesn't get a farewell like that and not have it hit him where he lives. I'd lived a long time, but I was thrilled and honored to receive such recognition by such a fine group of men. NATO in those days had an *esprit de corps* that gave it snap.

In all the bases where we had provided assistance and training I had found the reconnaissance personnel to be highly competitive particularly on field maneuvers. Out of this spirit emerged a three-day series of exercises for all Allied reconnaissance units.

[9] Stewart Alsop, *The Center*. (New York: Harper & Row Publishers, Inc.), pp. 193-4.

Judges were appointed, prizes were won, and in time the competition grew so widespread that a special award, the Gruenther Trophy, was presented the winning team. The late Colonel Thomas Brown, noted peace officer, my replacement in the Allied Air Force in Central Europe should be given credit for selling the idea to General Norstad and General Gruenther. This was the kind of approach to aerial reconnaissance I had so long sought and fought for and I could not say goodbye to it without a strong sense of regret.

Upon my return home another goodbye awaited me of even greater impact: my retirement from the Air Force. It came on July 31, 1953, and it came in between the time I started pushing the Canberra project for General Vandenberg and the developments that followed.

I arrived home on June 1 and went directly to see the General. I realized when he greeted me that he was a sick man. He was also too busy to come with me to talk to the Martin Company officials who were the manufacturers of the U.S. version of the plane. I went alone and discussed with the firm's president and general manager the proposed idea. They were extremely enthusiastic, and when they learned I was soon to retire they asked me if I would come with them as a consultant to help with the aerial camera installation details. Both the cost of modification and the time it would take to accomplish the changes were very important and I agreed to sign on for a month. In the meantime I reported to the General on the results of the meeting and although he informed me that he was planning to retire shortly, he would see that his successor gave the project top priority.

In his office I said goodbye to Hoyt Vandenberg for the last time. It seemed to be a season of goodbyes. Of all with whom I had served and served under he was one of the ablest and best; a man with a brain, a heart, and a warm smile.

"Goodbye, George."

"Goodbye, Hoyt. Keep in touch."

"I'll try."

As for my own departure from the service after thirty-six

years, thirty-four of them as a pilot, General William F. McKee, the commanding general of Wright-Patterson, staged a formal parade and review of all of the airmen on duty there. During the ceremony General McKee pinned the Distinguished Service Medal on my uniform, shook hands, and, for the last time in the military service, I retired. It is difficult to describe the feeling I had when I walked away from the ceremony. To be stepping into civilian clothes and not to be a part of the military flying game left me somewhat bewildered and uneasy. Where had all the days and years gone? Everything had gone by so quickly. Time. I'd had no time for time, and after I caught hold of myself by the seat of the pants I knew I didn't have time to sit around and feel sorry for myself either. There was much to do, and there was much I could do.

Shortly thereafter I signed on with the Martin Company and began commuting between our home in Chevy Chase and Baltimore. After we had the Canberra's modification figures set and details of camera placement, a group of top operational people came up from Langley Field headed by Lieutenant General Earl W. Barnes.

The meeting was not a success because of a Colonel who did most of the talking and didn't think much of the idea. The discussion became heated. I was sitting on the other side of the fence now, but on either side it would have been the same, for the colonel appeared to be as negative as he was noisy, and I could see a good idea going down the drain. I was determined that it wouldn't so I went to see Hoyt Vandenberg's successor, General Nathan F. Twining.

I had first met Nate Twining in 1923 at Kelly Field in Texas, where I had been recruiting officers for aerial photography. I tried to get Nate who had just transferred from the infantry. I didn't get him, but over the years our paths had crossed numerous times and we had always been friendly. He knew all about the project and considered it extremely important. Nevertheless, because of the colonel who had influenced the others in the group to turn

down the offer, it was several months before the Martin Company
got the green light.

In spite of the delay, the modified Martin Canberra was engaged in strategic reconnaissance assignments well before the famous Lockheed U-2s were available for such missions.

Between 1954 and May 1, 1960, when the U-2 piloted by
Francis Gary Powers leaped into world headlines, the Soviets
were increasing their nuclear potential and refused to agree to
President Eisenhower's disarmament or "open skies" offer of June
1955.

There were several flash points in the world arena and the
flights of Canberras and U-2s were essential in our need to know.
They were weaponless aircraft. They endangered no one. The
only risk was to the pilots who took off on their long hazardous
missions, winging high across an alien sky, their cameras silently
at work. We like to celebrate our heroes, but these men go unsung
and only one is publicly known. The Russians, of course, knew the
flights were being made, but they kept furiously silent. Thus when
they captured Gary Powers they not only displayed him like a
prize goat they also brought out at his trial the remarkable quality
of the cameras in the U-2.

On August 19, 1960, Soviet "Expert" Istomin Gleb Alek-
seyevich, Doctor of Technical Sciences, testified at the trial that
"In the course of the flight the air camera was used for seven
strip photography, consecutively through seven glass-encased
windows in the skin of the plane. The lens cover was from 160 to
200 kilometers [100 to 125 miles] in width. The camera was
loaded with two films about 2000 meters long [6000 feet] . . .
The supply of film in the camera made it possible to receive
about 4000 paired aerial pictures to photograph in the course of
the flight, along a route of about thirty-five hundred kilometers
[approximately 2700 miles].

"The camera lens with a sufficiently long focus made it possible
to obtain from the high altitudes, at which the plane was flying,
relatively large scale photographs suitable for the purposes of
aerial reconnaissance. The image scale of the pictures obtained

over the territory of the USSR on May 1, 1960 was 220–230 meters in one centimeter . . . [approximately 1 inch to 1830 feet].

"Identification of the aerial pictures show that the latter contain diverse espionage information about objects located along the route of the plane's flight. The aerial photos show large inhabited places, industrial and military installations—factories, plants, electric stations, warehouses, mines, various means of communication, airfields and antiaircraft defense means. The aerial photos can be used both for espionage purposes and for specifying topographical maps . . ."[10]

Nikita Khrushchev, speaking before the Supreme Soviet of the USSR in May 1960, wise-cracked that Soviet aerial cameras produced better sharper pictures so that in shooting down Powers they had acquired very little in that respect.

As usual, he was bragging.

Later in discussing the period in question with General Eisenhower, who had then been President, he revealed the extent to which he had been willing to go to make "open skies" a two way street. "I told them [the Russians] we would do it any way they wanted to. I was willing to do anything to get them to agree with it, but they would have no part of it. After all they could come to this country and to the town library and probably find aerial photographs of every town in the United States, but we couldn't get anything from them."

To protect ourselves against surprise attack high flying reconnaissance aircraft, equipped with long range focal length cameras, seemed to be the only answer. Special strategic reconnaissance had come of age with the swift development of aerial cameras placed in a platform that kept them out of harm's reach until a day in May.

After my brief stint with the Martin Company, Arde Bulova, Chairman of the Board of the Bulova Watch Company, requested that I meet him in New York City. At this meeting he told me

[10] Court Proceedings of the Case of Francis Gary Powers, held before the Military Division of the Supreme Court of the USSR, Moscow. Translation World Publishers, Chicago, 1960.

that Bulova was going to go into the aerial camera business, and he wondered if I'd be interested in setting up their photographic research and development department.

Bulova had its laboratories in a new building near La Guardia Field, and although these facilities were a far cry from those I had taken over in the same post for Billy Mitchell at McCook, I didn't start operations with a staff any larger. At the outset, I had challenge and opportunity plus a secretary and a design engineer. In time that number swelled to nearly one hundred photographic technicians. Bulova planned to concentrate on equipment for tactical reconnaissance, especially miniature gun cameras for fighter aircraft. However, my interest in aerial photography was total, and so it was only natural that we pursued other avenues of development including strategic reconnaissance.

Later on in this regard, I had the good fortune to acquire Harry Gewertz as my Chief Engineer. Harry had distinguished himself at Harvard under Jim Baker and then at Boston with Duncan Macdonald. He was the principal designer of the highly complex mechanisms found in almost all the advanced optical systems. In fact, when I grabbed Harry, Dunc moaned, "George, you take him and you take my right arm."

Together Harry and I maintained the laboratory, completely independent and free to make our own decisions.

General Omar N. Bradley was chief of all Bulova R&D, so I didn't feel too far away from the military, but what made me feel even closer was that the Air Force requested I go annually to Europe to lecture on aerial photography to the students of the Defense College as well as other NATO groups.

In the summer of 1957, while on such a tour, I met a few of the boys from the Strategic Air Command and they gave me some extremely alarming news. I was informed that the electronic radar experts at Wright Field had been giving General LeMay a snow job on the greater value of radar over optical systems for strategic reconnaissance.

Because I had known Curtis LeMay since we flew together on the *Rex* mission in 1938, and because I knew he had always been a great booster of aerial photography, as soon as I got back home I headed for SAC headquarters at Omaha, Nebraska. I just couldn't believe his mind could be changed on the subject. But I found it had been.

"George, we've got to put our money where it will do the most good," he said. "You fellows in photography have done a splendid job all through the years, and I've supported you one hundred percent. I've backed the funding of your optical systems at Boston. But I feel new things are coming up that can do a better job for the Air Force.

"General," I said bluntly, "I don't know who sold you this pile of oatmeal, but it just ain't so."

"The electronic people at Wright Field have given me numerous briefings," he replied "and from what I've seen, I support their evaluation on the use of radar. I'm not saying we're going to cut out optics, but I'm of the mind that a lot of the money we're putting into Boston University should be diverted to radar development."

"General, don't do it," I pleaded.

"It makes sense to me, George. Radar can do reconnaissance in bad weather and in the dark, twenty-four hours a day and at a time when your photographers are grounded."

"Look, that may be so," I argued, "but there's absolutely no comparison in the resolution you get from the two systems. Isn't it better to be able to see clearly what you've photographed even if it's not on a twenty-four-hour basis, than not see much of anything over a longer period of time?"

"That will come," he smiled. "I've already seen what they can do."

"But it's practically here with optics. Radar on a comparative basis is a long way off!" I groaned.

"George," he concluded the conversation, "you know I appreciate your interest and I understand your concern. We've given it a lot of thought, and as I said, we're not phasing out optics by a long shot, but we're simply going to have to cut down on the Optical Research Laboratory at Boston."

I left Omaha pretty discouraged and my disappointment was further deepened when I paid a visit to my old laboratory at Wright Field. I found it was being directed by an electronic specialist who had had no training or experience in aerial photography or reconnaissance of any sort. I noticed, too, that most of the top jobs were curtailed and many of my former colleagues of long standing were leaving. For the moment I had the feeling that all the efforts of George W. Goddard, Air Force Retired, were being flushed down the drain.

And then a miracle happened. The wicked Russians came to the rescue. In October of 1957 they launched *Sputnik,* and did the fur ever hit the turbine at SAC and fly through every other allied agency of Government. *Sputnik* could have had cameras in it, photographing the U.S.A. When it was sadly learned that radar was not suitable or usable for satellite photography in the immediate future, the rush was on for improved optics. General LeMay and the Air Force came racing back to Boston University. But it was too late, the Optical Research Laboratory had gone! When Boston University learned its funds for the laboratory were being cut back, Dr. Harold C. Case, BU's president, was greatly disturbed about the matter and notified the Air Force that if they were not going to support the research activity he would have to close it out.

Fortunately, about this same time there were some scientists and technicians with great vision who were highly concerned. They recognized the tremendous national asset which the laboratory represented, and the discontent being generated by the temporary lack of support afforded aerial and space photography. Under the leadership of Richard Leghorn and Duncan Macdonald, these men projected this potential correctly and rounded up sufficient financial backing to insure continuation of the Boston University team and its efforts by forming a business group.

Before the laboratory was acquired from Boston University, Leghorn, Macdonald and others discussed ideas for a suitable name for the new corporation. Several were suggested and one smart researcher came up with the name of "Itek," which meant

"Information Technology." This was ideal because it actually represented the end product of the laboratory research work in optical systems, special viewers, photographic chemistry, new techniques of aerial photography, together with atmospheric and environment studies. After the name was adopted, Itek Corporation purchased the Boston University optical research laboratory.

The group was able to insure continuity to important Air Force research and development work in this area and to make giant steps forward in the state of the art.

With orbiting satellites now a reality, a host of new problems had to be solved by both of the "space" nations. They were really the old problems of speed and distance, vibration and space, updated. Instead of a platform traveling at 600 miles per hour, satellites travel near the escape velocity of 17,000 miles per hour. Instead of 60 to 70,000 feet of altitude, they orbit from 100 miles up and higher. Instead of camera space in an aircraft with room for a special mount to compensate for vibration, the available area in a satellite is relatively small. As an example of the reduction required, the first large airplane-mounted system weighed thousands of pounds, was many feet long and had hundreds of pounds of glass elements. The special optical glass window designed to withstand extreme fluctuating outside temperatures as opposed to a constant inside temperature, cost $50,000 and weighed as much as an average man. By the time of man-made satellites all of these components had been greatly reduced in size but further reduction was mandatory. The obvious answer lay in the development of lightweight reflective optics.

This was a line of research I had begun late in the fall of 1941, prior to my meeting with Jim Baker at Harvard. At that time I was frantically barging around the country seeking sources of optical and aerial camera research. At Cal Tech, I had the good fortune to meet Dr. Clark Blanchard Millikan. A professor and an aeronautical engineer, he was vitally interested in doing anything to help the Air Corps, and I discussed with him and some of his colleagues the work of our laboratory. I suggested that Cal Tech might utilize some of its know-how on reflective type optics which was then being applied to their observatory cameras. They bought the idea enthusiastically and in a few days came up with a preliminary design. It looked so promising I flew off to Washington to sell the possibility to Hap Arnold. The fact that he and Dr. Millikan were friends didn't hurt a bit, and Hap arranged to transfer the necessary funds to get the project moving. In four months I was back in Los Angeles where I conducted the flight tests of the world's first reflective type aerial camera. Excellent results were obtained. At 35,000 feet, picture resolution was sharp enough to show markings on aircraft outside the Lockheed plant at Burbank.

The camera was so successful we had a larger focal length model made for heavier aircraft. From a research point of view it was a fine beginning.

However, the camera didn't go into production during the war because its reflective mirrors tarnished under tropical conditions and also there was a serious vibration problem with propeller driven aircraft.

Following the war, the Boston University facility continued its research into reflective optics, and in 1955 it produced its first system, a system so advanced that it was used for television viewing of some of the early launchings of our Astronauts.

As Duncan Macdonald later said in an address, "We are not only in a space age; we are in an age of light. One success has been our ability to 'fold' effectively large high quality optics into small light-weight packages."[11]

If *Sputnik* galvanized our government toward the launching of satellites and entering a space race with the Soviets, one can imagine the impact on our reconnaissance people of the suspension of U-2 flights over that country in May, 1960.

The need was greater than ever, and in this instance we had permission from Nikita Khrushchev to fill it. General Eisenhower told me in a 1967 interview that Khrushchev in speaking to the abortive Summit meeting of 1960 had said: "Any pictures you can

[11] An address before the Fifteenth National Public Relation Conference, November 13, 1962.

get of the Soviet Union by satellite will be perfectly all right with us. Just take all you want."[12]

As was widely reported later, our Government must have taken him at his word, for within months U.S. satellites were known to be engaged in strategic reconnaissance.

Nearly a decade has passed since that time, and the state of the reconnaissance art has surely kept pace with space technology. Today there is probably little that moves on the surface of the earth, or little that occupies it, that aerial cameras of one kind or another cannot perceive.

The Russians entered the satellite reconnaissance business in 1962—what I call the optics race—and on July 30, 1968, they launched their 100th spy in the sky, designated by U.S. trackers as Cosmos 234. Since then they have launched others. A few years ago Soviet scientists maintained that their aerial cameras could distinguish objects on the ground about 16 inches in diameter from an altitude of a thousand miles. Although noted for their ability to hamstring the truth, their claim today is probably within the realm of possibility. But whether the Soviets wish to admit the fact or not, it seems clear that through our own efforts in advancing strategic reconnaissance, there has come into being a kind of tacit open skies reality. The Cuban missile crisis of 1962 brought home to the world not only the value of aerial photography but also the fact that an aggressor can make few covert moves without being caught in the act.

In March 1967, President Lyndon B. Johnson commented in an informal talk with a group of educators in Nashville, Tennessee, that if the American space program during the past ten years had cost ten times more than the 30 to 40 billion invested in it, it would be worth it "simply for the photography."

"Before we had the photography our guesses were way off. We were doing things we didn't need to do."

"Because of the satellites I know how many missiles the enemy has."[13]

[12] From my interview with General Dwight D. Eisenhower, July 1967.
[13] The Washington *Post*, March 18, 1968.

Recently the weekly magazine *U.S. News & World Report* reported: "Powerful spaceborn cameras have been developed that can photograph in detail objects less than a foot in diameter from an altitude of 150 miles. Ultra modern versions of World War II equipment, circling in outerspace, now penetrate cloud cover and forest vegetation to reveal objects such as hidden missile sites, trucks and even troops.

"Infrared sensors in satellites can uncover 'hot' objects—such as a submerged submarine, a missile launching, or in some cases even a running truck motor."[14]

In a pre-election speech, President Richard M. Nixon called on the Soviets once again to join with us in a pooling of reconnaissance information. This plan was "open skies" updated. The stark evidence of past performance convinces me that the Soviets will not be any more willing to accept this offer than they were General Eisenhower's original proposal. It seems clear that our reconnaissance satellites will continue in their orbits and through the use of aerial photography continue to return information of strategic value.

Ten years ago, in December 1958, some of my good friends at Itek made me an offer, that in spite of my fine association with Bulova, I felt compelled to accept. While at Bulova I had developed two patented products. One was a camera for recording nuclear tests and the other was termed a Multiple Sensor Airborn Reconnaissance System. It was designed for use by the Tactical Air Force and its function was to overlay radar and infrared on a photographic image. Thus recce aircraft flying over the dense jungles of Vietnam would be able to take pictures of objects not optically visible, such as tanks, trucks and cook stoves.

But since Itek was going into the exploration of space with the camera, I wanted to go too. As Assistant to the President, I established the firm's Washington office, which today is but one of fifty-five company installations. Itek's staff has grown from 200 to more than 6000, and besides its work for the Air Force

[14] *U.S. News & World Report,* September 9, 1968, p. 69.

and other space agencies, it is engaged in the development and production of industrial consumer optical products.

Of course, the thrust toward photography in outer space, particularly as concerns astronomy is of major national interest. Doing such work from satellites has a tremendous advantage over earth-bound telescopes. The great barriers being overcome are turbulence in the atmosphere, and the absorption by the atmosphere of ultraviolet as much as the infrared rays. We know the weightless condition of satellites will permit the operation by astronauts of greatly improved telescopes free of distortion caused by gravitational forces. That is the next goal.

Already the camera has gone to the moon and beyond, and already we take such miracles as a matter of course. But it is certain that from now on wherever man ventures, the camera will be there before him, letting him know what lies ahead.

The present state of development in aerial reconnaissance is a far cry from a long-gone day when Billy Mitchell gave me orders to improve it. In my mind's eye I have a favorite illustration of how things have changed from that day to this. I see myself in the cockpit of a DH-4 without oxygen bundled in a bulky flying suit, wearing helmet and goggles. The Liberty engine is racketing in the thin air. The altimeter's finger is jiggling icily on the 18,000 foot mark. My breath comes hard and raw. My booted feet are painfully numb; there is no feeling in my gloved fingertips. Beneath a hard blue dome of sky my plane and I are traversing an invisible track marked by my unsteady compass needle and a natural projection on the flat rim of the horizon. Behind me, Sergeant Andy Matos, similarly dressed, similarly frozen, similarly free, hunches over his aerial camera. It took us an hour to reach 18,000 feet and we have been flying for over twice that long maintaining the same altitude, inching back and forth across a square patch of sky, mapping the earth below. Soon Andy will tap me on the shoulder, his film expended, and then we shall break the monotony of level flight, and with wing braces singing, go plummeting earthward. In our mission we will have photographically mapped, approximately 200 square miles of terrain.

By comparison today an Air Force 707 jet, takes off and climbs in a few moments to 30,000 feet. On board are a crew of eight men. They will be operating in the same comfort they find in their living rooms. Automated controls will keep them on the proper course and electronically their aerial cameras will map the terrain so expertly that when the film is transcribed it will be within thirty feet of its true position on a scale map of 1:50,000. In a single mapping mission they can cover fifty thousand square miles.

From every aspect the difference is vast and between these two pictures my career of fifty years extends. I planted some seeds along the way, and if I had a wish, I'd wish for another fifty to plant some more.

# ACKNOWLEDGMENTS

I wish to express to the following my deep appreciation and thanks for kind assistance, advice and person recollections that have been so helpful to me in the presentation of this book.

Talbert Abrams
Air Attachés, American Embassy, Paris
Air Force Council of Fort Worth, Texas
Colonel Edward Aldrin
Colonel Daniel Anderson
Herman J. A. C. Arens, National Geographic Society
Robert Atwood, N.A.S.A.
Arthur Brookfield
William T. Badham
Dr. James Baker
J. J. Baudu
Colonel Clyde Barnett
Major General Lucas V. Beau
Brigadier General Russell Berg
Major General Clayton L. Bissell
Gail Borden
Lieutenant Colonel Robert Bowie
Percy "Pete" Branscom
Harry Brants
Colonel John Broderick, Library of Congress
Mrs. Samuel F. Burka
Lieutenant Colonel Sam T. Bush
General Charles P. Cabell
Miss Nelly Carico, Historical Unit, U. S. Geological Survey
Edward Cahill

Major General Franklin O. Carroll
Dr. A. K. Chapman
Roy Chapman
Josiah H. Child
Dr. Walter Clark
Dr. M. G. M. Clarke
Lieutenant Colonel Joseph Condon
Brigadier General Merian C. Cooper
Major General Richard Copeland
Major General Alden R. Crawford
Lenny Crouch
Major General John F. Curry
Major General Howard C. Davidson
James J. Deeg
Major General Frederick R. Dent
Major Alexander DeSeversky
Brigadier General Robert J. Dixon
Lieutenant General James H. Doolittle
Donald Douglas, Senior
Robert Draghi
Lieutenant General Ira C. Eaker
Dr. Harold E. Edgerton
General Dwight D. Eisenhower
Benjamin Fagan
Sherman Fairchild
Mrs. Roy G. Fitzgerald
Reuben Fleet
Major General Benjamin Foulois
General Walter Frank
Kenneth C. Fraser

Chester Fuller
Dr. Irving Gardner
Major General William Garland
Paul Garber and his Smithsonian
    Staff
Harry Gewertz
W. O. Grover Gilbert
William G. Gorog
Heinz Gruner
Louis Hagemeyer
Howard Hall
George Hallett
Dr. Arthur Hardy
Lieutenant Colonel John Hancock
Nelson Hayes
Dr. Ulrich Heidelauf
Miss Jane Hill
Mrs. A. E. Holland
Colonel John Hoover
Captain Albert J. Hoskinson
Colonel Charles F. Hoy, Jr.
Douglas J. Ingells
Benjamin Jordon
Amrom Katz
Virgil Kauffman
Colonel Oakley Kelly
General George Kenney
Tony Keogh
Miss Marguerite Kennedy and her
    Staff at the USAF Historical
    Archives, Maxwell Field
Captain Frank Klein
Major General Hugh J. Knerr
Colonel Kenneth Kerr
Murray Koch
Doctors William H. Killay and
    James P. McCarrick, Who Pre-
    sided at my Gall Bladder Outing
    during the Writing of this Book.
Major General Charles T. Lanham
Lieutenant General Sir George Lea,
    Military Attaché, The British
    Embassy, Washington, D.C.
Major General E. B. LeBailly
Richard Leghorn
Franklin A. Lindsay
Colonel David Lingle

Mr. John Loosbrock
Anthony Lloyd
Arthur C. Lundahl
Fred Lutz
Dr. Duncan C. Macdonald
Colonel John Macready
Lieutenant Colonel Andrew Matos
Major General George C. McDonald
Colonel Marvin McFarland and his
    staff, Library of Congress
Evelyn Metzger
Colonel George Northrup
Dr. Bryan O'Brian, Sr.
Colonel H. J. Odenthal
Eugene Ostroff
William Oswalt
Major Stanley Pejasek
Colonel Joe E. Pelligrini
Colonel Harold G. Peterson
Colonel Richard Philbrick
Major General James F. Phillips
Walter Pierstorff
Air Marshal Sir Thomas Pike, RAF,
    London
Captain L. A. Pope
Colonel James G. Pratt
Rear Admiral Robert S. Quacken-
    bush
"Sir Robert" Quick
Brigadier General Eugene G. Rein-
    artz
Colonel Lester Rentmeester
Hal Roach, Sr.
John Roche
"Hank" Roganti
Brigadier General Elliott Roosevelt
Max Rosenberg, Office of Air Force
    History
Colonel Richard Salome
Brigadier General Martin Scanlon
Joseph Sebantz
Mark Sloan, Wright-Patterson Mu-
    seum
Colonel Arthur E. Smith
Major General Dale Smith
Virginia Garnes Smith

Dr. Dow Smith
Everett Snyder
Colonel Gordon T. Sowers
General Carl Spaatz
Brigadier General Ralph Steakley
Captain Edward Steichen
Major General St Clair Streett
Lieutenant Colonel Donald Surles
Everett Snyder
Colonel E. R. Swanson
Colonel Clark M. Sykes
Colonel Raife Tarkington
Mrs. Polly Tate, Ogles, Austria
Jack Taylor
Colonel Harry W. Trimble
Robert Troidle
Major General Arthur W. Vanaman
Major General Leigh Wade
John Ward
Mrs. Myron Warren
Major General Harold E. Watson
Mrs. Marcella Warner

Major General John M. Weikert
Irving Weiss
General Otto P. Weyland
Lieutenant General Hewitt T. Wheless
G. C. Whitaker
Colonel Daniel White
Edwin L. Wisherd, National Geographic
Lieutenant General K. B. Wolfe
R. B. Wood, Air & Space Library, Smithsonian
Brigadier General Walter W. Wood
Edward Woodford
Mrs. Burdette Wright
Colonel Roscoe Wriston
Lieutenant Colonel Fred Yochim
Hon. Eugene M. Zuckert
Dorothy Miklas, Ann Barnes and Mary Santangelo of the Itek Office in Arlington, Virginia.

Special credit should be given to Mrs. Patricia Erickson who gave valuable assistance to the preparation of the background material for this book.

Excerpts from the October 7, 1925 Editorial of *The Chicago Tribune*, reprinted by permission.

Excerpts from the May 6, 1927 Editorial of *The Manila Times*, reprinted by permission.

# INDEX